The Ride Down Mount Morgan

THE
RIDE DOWN
MOUNT MORGAN

By
Arthur Miller

STAGE
&SCREEN

The Book Club for the Performing Arts

GARDEN CITY, NEW YORK

Arthur Miller's THE RIDE DOWN MOUNT MORGAN opened April 9, 2000, at the Ambassador Theatre. It was produced by The Shubert Organization, Scott Rudin, Roger Berlind, Spring Sirkin, ABC Inc., in association with The Public Theater/New York Shakespeare Festival and George C. Wolfe, Producer. It was directed by David Esbjornson. Scenic design was by John Arnone, costume design was by Elizabeth Hope Clancy, lighting design was by Brian MacDevitt, original music and sound by Dan Moses Schreier. Production stage manager was Erica Schwartz. Casting was by Pat McCorkle, Jordan Thaler and Heidi Griffiths. Production supervisor was Fred Gallo, Jr. General management by Niko Associates, Inc./Marvin A. Krauss Associates, Inc. and Carl Pasbjerg. Director of marketing was David B. Steffen. Press representative was Barlow Hartman Public Relationships.

THE CAST
(*In Order of Appearance*)

Lyman	Patrick Stewart
Nurse Logan	Oni Faida Lampley
Theo	Frances Conroy
Bessie	Shannon Burkett
Leah	Katy Selverstone
Tom	John C. Vennema
Pianist	Glen Pearson
Hospital Staff/Dream Figures	Portia Johnson, Terry Layman, Jennifer Piech and Sherry Skinker

TIME
The Present

PLACE
Clearhaven Memorial Hospital, Elmira, New York

PRODUCTION NOTE

The play moves from scene to scene without pause.

Lyman need have no bandages on him. He can lie in bed with his clothes on or in a hospital gown, as appropriate.

The bed, chairs, etc. can be openly moved by stagehands dressed as hospital orderlies.

ACT I

ACT I

Scene One

Snow is falling. A bed hovers in mid-air. A crash splits it apart and it flies away. Light rises on Lyman Felt asleep in a hospital bed. Nurse Logan is reading a magazine a few feet away. She is black. He is deeply asleep, snoring now and then.

LYMAN (*his eyes still shut*): Thank you, thank you all very much. Please be seated. (*Nurse turns, looks towards him*) We have a lot of . . . not material . . . yes, material . . . to cover this afternoon, so please take your seats and cross you . . . No-no . . . (*Laughs weakly*) . . . Not cross your legs, just take your seats . . .

NURSE: That was a lot of surgery, Mr. Felt. You're supposed to be resting . . . Or you out?

(*For a moment he sleeps, snores, than . . .*)

LYMAN: Today I would like you to consider life insurance from a different perspective. I want you to look at the whole economic system as one enormous tit. (*Nurse chuckles quietly*) So the job of the individual is to get a good place in line for a suck. (*She laughs louder*) Which gives us the word "suck-cess." Or . . . or not.

NURSE: You know, you better settle down after all that surgery.

3

LYMAN (*focusing on her*): You black?

NURSE: That's what they keep telling me.

LYMAN: Good for you. I've got the biggest training program of any company for you guys. And the first one that ever put them in sales. There's no election now, is there? Eisenhower or something?

NURSE: It's December. And he's been dead since I don't know when.

LYMAN: Eisenhower *dead*? (*Peers in confusion*) Oh, right, right! Why can't I move, do you mind?

NURSE (*returns to her chair*): You're all in a cast, you broke a lot of bones.

LYMAN: Who?

NURSE: You. You smashed your car. They say you went skiing down that Mount Morgan in a Porsche.

(*She chuckles. He squints, trying to orient himself*)

LYMAN: Where . . . where . . . I'm where?

NURSE: Clearhaven Memorial Hospital.

LYMAN: That Earl Hines?

NURSE: Who

(*A piano moves across the stage behind him*)

LYMAN: That piano. Sounds like Earl Hines, (*Sings*) "You made me happy sometimes. You made me sad; and there were times, dear . . ." (*Laughs apprecia- tively. Piano disappears*) Listen to that, will you? That beautiful? Jimmy Baldwin . . . long, long ago when I was still a writer . . . used to say, "Lyman, you're a nigger underneath." (*Chuckles; it fades. Now with some anxiety . . .*) Where?

NURSE: Clearhaven Memorial Hospital.

LYMAN (*it is slowly penetrating*): *Clearhaven?*

NURSE: Your wife and daughter just arrived up from New York. They're out in the visitor's room.

LYMAN (*canniness attempt, but still confused*): From *New York?* Why? Who called them?

NURSE: What do you mean? Why not?

LYMAN: And where is this?

NURSE: Clearhaven. I'm from Canada myself, I only just started here. We've still got railroads in Canada.

LYMAN (*a moment of silent confusion*): Listen. I'm not feeling well . . . why are we talking about Cana- dian railroads?

NURSE: No, I just mentioned it as there is a storm.

LYMAN: Now what . . . what . . . what was that about my wife . . . New York?

NURSE: She's here in the waiting room . . .

LYMAN: Here in the waiting . . .

NURSE: . . . And your daughter.

LYMAN (*tension rising with clearing of mind, he looks at his hands, turns them over*): Would you mind? Just . . . touch me? (*She touches his face; he angers with the fully dawning fact*) Who the hell called them, for God's sake? Why didn't somebody ask me?

NURSE: I'm new here! I'm sorry if I'm not satisfactory.

LYMAN (*high anxiety*): Who said you're not satisfactory? What is this . . . endless . . . *verbiage?*—not verbiage, for Christ's sake, I meant . . . (*Panting*) Listen, I absolutely can't see anyone and they have to go back to New York right away.

NURSE: But as long as you're awake . . .

LYMAN: Immediately! Go—get them out of here! (*A jab of pain*) Ow! Please, quickly, go! Wait! There's no . . . like another . . . you know, woman out there?

NURSE: Not while I was out there.

LYMAN: Please . . . quickly, huh? I can't see anybody. (*Bewildered, Nurse exits*) Oh, poor Theo—here! My God, what have I done! How could I have gone out on that road in a storm! (*Terrified of self-betrayal*) Have you lost your fucking mind?! (*Frozen in an-*

guish, he stares straight ahead as music is heard. His mood changes as he is caught by his catastrophic vision) Oh, dear God this mustn't happen. *(His wife, Theo, and daughter Bessie are discovered seated on a waiting room settee. A burst of weeping from Bessie. He is not looking directly at them but imagining them)* No-no-no, it mustn't happen! Think of something else! Oh, Bessie, my poor Bessie!

(Covers his eyes, as Bessie weeps. His bed is moved upstage but with the women still in view. Music fades out)

THEO *(Touching Bessie's hand)*: Darling, try not to.

BESSIE: I can't help it.

THEO: Of course you can. Be brave now, dear.

LYMAN: Oh yes! My Theo! That's exactly what she'd say! What a woman!

THEO: Try to think of all the happiness; think of his laughter; Daddy loves life, he'll fight for it.

BESSIE: I guess I've just never had anything really bad happen.

LYMAN: Oh, my dear child . . . !

THEO: But you'll see as you get older—everything ultimately fits together . . . and for the good.

LYMAN: Oh yes . . . good old Episcopal Theo!

THEO: Now come, Bessie. Remember what a wonderful time we had in Africa? Think of Africa.

BESSIE: What an amazing woman you are, Mother.

(*Nurse Logan enters*)

NURSE: It'll still be a while before he can see anybody. Would you like me to call a motel? It's ski season, but my husband can probably get you in, he plows their driveway.

BESSIE: Do you know if he's out of danger?

NURSE: I'm sure the doctors will let you know. (*Obviously changing the subject*) I can't believe you made it up from New York in this sleet.

THEO: One does what one has to. Actually . . . would you mind calling the motel? It was a terrible drive . . .

NURSE: Sometimes I feel like going back to Canada—at least we had a railroad.

THEO: We'll have them again; things take time in this country but in the end we get them done.

NURSE: Don't hesitate if you want more tea.

(*Nurse exits*)

THEO (*turns to Bessie, smiling painfully*): Why'd you start to laugh?

BESSIE (*touching Theo's hand*): It's nothing . . .

THEO: Well, what is it?

BESSIE: Well . . . I mean things really don't always get done in this country.

THEO (*hurt*): I think they do, ultimately. I've lived through changes that were inconceivable thirty years ago. (*Straining to laugh*) Really, dear, I'm not *that* naive.

BESSIE: Well, don't be upset! They certainly are very nice people around here, aren't they?

THEO: I'm sorry you never knew small town life— there is a goodness.

BESSIE: I'm wondering if we should call Grandma Esther.

THEO: If you like. (*Slight pause*) She gets so impressively emotional, that's all. But call . . . she *is* his mother.

BESSIE: I know she's a superficial woman, but I can't help it, I . . .

THEO: But you *should* like her, she adores you; she simply never liked me and I've always known it, that's all. (*She looks away*)

BESSIE: I mean she can be awfully funny sometimes. And she is warm.

THEO: Warm? Yes, I suppose—provided it doesn't commit her to anything or anyone. I've never hidden it, dear—I think she's the center of his psychological problem . . .

LYMAN: Perfect!

THEO: . . . But I suppose I'm prejudiced. (*Lyman laughs silently with a head shake of joyful recognition*) I used to think it was because he didn't marry Jewish, but . . .

BESSIE: But she didn't either.

THEO: Darling, she'd have disliked any woman he married . . . except an heiress or a sexpot. But go ahead, I do think you should call her. (*Bessie stands*) And give her my love, will you?

(*Lyman issues a cackling laugh of appreciation of her nature. Leah enters. She is in her thirties; in an open raccoon coat, high heels. Nurse enters with her*)

LYMAN (*on the instant she enters, claps his hands over his eyes*): No, she mustn't! It can't happen! She mustn't!

LEAH: After all the money we've put into this hospital it seems to me I ought to be able to speak to the Chief Nurse, for Christ's sake!

NURSE: I'm doing my best to get her for you . . . !

LEAH: Well hurry, will you? (*Nurse starts to exit*) I'm

only asking for a little information, dear! (*Nurse exits. Pause*)

LYMAN (*imploring himself, his eyes clamped shut*): Think of something else. Let's see now—the new Mercedes convertible . . . that actress, what's her name . . . ?

(*But he fails to escape; and scared, slowly turns his head toward Leah, who sits, but quickly stands again and moves restlessly. Theo and Bessie observe her indirectly, with polite curiosity. Now their eyes meet. Leah throws up her hands*)

LEAH: The same thing when I had my baby here, it was like pulling teeth to get them to tell me if it was a boy or a girl.

BESSIE: Is it an emergency?

LEAH: Yes, my husband; he cracked up the car on Mount Morgan. You?

BESSIE: My father. It was a car, too.

LYMAN (*eyes heavenward, hands clasped*): Oh please, please!

THEO: The roads are impossible.

LEAH: I can't imagine what got into him, driving down Mount Morgan on ice . . . and at night yet! It's incomprehensible! (*A sudden explosion*) Damn

11

them, I have a right to know what's happening! (*She charges out*)

BESSIE: Poor thing.

THEO: But she *knows* how busy they are ... (*Silence now; Theo leans back, closing her eyes. Another sobbing fit threatens Bessie, who downs it, covers her eyes. Then suddenly she breaks down and weeps*) Oh Bessie, dear, try not to.

BESSIE (*shaking her head helplessly*): ... I just love him so!

(*Leah returns, more subdued now. She sits tiredly, closes her eyes. Pause. She gets up, goes to a window, looks out*)

LEAH: *Now* the moon comes out! Everybody smashes up in the dark and now you could read a paper out there.

BESSIE: You live around here?

LEAH: Not far. We're out near the lake.

BESSIE: It looks like beautiful country.

LEAH: Oh, it is. But I'll take New York anytime. (*A great sob suddenly bursts from her; she chokes it back*) I'm sorry. (*But she weeps again, helplessly into her handkerchief. Bessie is affected and begins weeping, too*)

THEO: Now really! (*Shakes Bessie's arm*) Stop this!

(*She sees Leah's indignant look*) You still don't know how serious it is, why do you carry on like this?

LEAH (*rather unwillingly*): You're probably right.

THEO: Of course! I mean there's always time to despair, why should . . . ?

LEAH (*sharply*): I *said* you were right, I was agreeing with you! (*Theo turns away stiffly*) I'm sorry.

(*Now the women go into stop-motion*)

LYMAN (*marveling*): What strong, admirable women they are! What definite characters! Thank God I'm only imagining this to torture myself . . . But it's enough! (*Caught by his tempting vision*) Now what would they say next?

(*The women reanimate*)

BESSIE: You raise things on your place?

LEAH: We grow most of what we eat. And we're starting to raise a few thoroughbreds now, in a small way.

BESSIE: Oh, I'd love that . . .

LEAH: I envy your composure—both of you. Really, you make me feel better. What part of New York are you in?

BESSIE: East 74th Street.

LYMAN: Oh no! No no!

LEAH: Really! We often stay at the Carlyle . . .

BESSIE: Oh, it's practically around the corner.

THEO: You sound like a New Yorker.

LEAH: I went to NYU School of Business for three years; I loved it but I was raised up here in Elmira . . . and my business is here, so . . . (*She shrugs and goes to the window again*)

THEO: What sort of business do you have?

LEAH: Insurance.

BESSIE: That's what Daddy does!

LYMAN (*knocking his knuckles against his head*): No-no-no-no-no!

LEAH: Well, there's a million of us. You in it, too?

BESSIE: No, I'm at home . . . take care of my husband.

LEAH: I'm hoping to sell out in a couple of years, get a place in Manhattan somewhere, and just paint morning to night the rest of my life.

BESSIE: Really! My husband's a painter.

LEAH: Professional, or . . . ?

BESSIE: Oh yes. He's Harold Lamb.

(*Lyman pulls the covers over his head*)

LEAH: Harold Lamb? (*Leah ceases all movement, staring at Bessie. She turns to stare at Theo*)

THEO: What is it?

LEAH: Your husband is really Harold Lamb?

BESSIE (*very pleased and proud*): You've heard of him?

LEAH: You're not Mrs. Felt, are you?

THEO: Why yes.

LEAH (*her puzzled look*): Then you . . . (*Breaks off, then . . .*) You're not here for Lyman, are you?

BESSIE: You know Daddy?

LEAH: But . . . (*Turning from one to the other*) . . . how'd they come to notify *you*?

LYMAN (*sits up in bed and raises a devout, monitory hand to heaven, whispering loudly*): Stop it, stop it, stop it . . . !

THEO (*uncomprehending, but beginning to take affront*): Why shouldn't they notify me?

LEAH: Well . . . after so many years.

THEO: What do you mean?

LEAH: But it's over nine . . .

THEO: What is?

LEAH: Your divorce. (*Theo and Bessie are struck dumb. A silence*) You're Theodora Felt, right?

THEO: Who *are* you?

LEAH: I'm Leah. Leah Felt.

THEO (*a haughtiness begins*): Felt!

LEAH: Lyman is my husband.

THEO: Who *are* you? What are you talking about!

BESSIE (*intensely curious about Leah, she angers at Theo*): Well don't get *angry*, for heaven's sake!

THEO: Be quiet!

LEAH (*seeing Theo's genuineness*): Well, you're divorced, aren't you?

THEO: Divorced! Who the hell *are* you!

LEAH: I'm Lyman's wife.

(*Theo sees she is a serious woman; it silences her*)

BESSIE: When . . . when did you . . . ? I mean . . .

THEO (*in motion again*): She's insane! She's some kind of a nut!

LEAH (*to Bessie*): It was nine years this past July.

THEO: Really. And who performed this . . . this *event*?

LEAH: The Reno City Hall Clerk, later a Rabbi here in Elmira. My son's name is Benjamin, for Lyman's father, and Alexander for his great-grandmother— Benjamin Alexander Felt.

THEO (*with a weak attempt to sustain mockery*): Really!

LEAH: Yes, I'm terribly sorry if you didn't know.

THEO: Didn't know *what*? What are you *talking* about?

LEAH: We have been married a little over nine years, Mrs. Felt.

THEO: Have you? And I suppose you have some document . . . ?

LEAH: I have our marriage certificate, I guess . . .

THEO: You guess!

LEAH (*angrily*): Well I'm sure I do! And I know I have Lyman's will in our safe deposit box . . .

THEO (*helplessly mocking*): And it names you as his wife!

17

LEAH: And Benjamin as his son. (*Theo is halted by her factuality*) . . . But I guess you have more or less the same . . . is that right? (*Theo is still as a stone*) They really was no divorce?

BESSIE (*with a glance at her stricken mother—softly, almost apologetically*): . . . No.

LEAH: Well, I guess we'd better . . . meet, or something. And talk. (*Theo is staring into space*) Mrs. Felt? I understand your feelings, but you'll just have to believe it, I guess—we have a terrible problem. Mrs. Felt?

THEO: It's impossible, nine years ago . . . (*To Bessie*) That's when we all went to Africa.

BESSIE: Oh, right!—the safari!

THEO (*to Leah, with a victorious, if nearly demented laugh*): We were never closer in our lives! We traveled through Kenya, Nigeria . . . (*As though this clinched everything*) . . . we even flew to Egypt!

(*Nurse enters. It instantly galvanizes all of them. She glances from one to the other*)

NURSE: Doctor Lowry would like to see Mrs. Felt now.

(*For one instant no one moves—then both Theo and Leah rise simultaneously. This actualization of Leah's claim stiffens Theo, forcing her to start assertively towards the nurse—and she sways and starts to fall to the floor*)

LEAH: Catch her!

BESSIE: Mother!

(*Nurse and Bessie catch Theo, then lower her to the floor*)

LEAH (*over her shoulder*): Help here, someone's fainted! Where the hell is a doctor, goddamnit! (*To the air*) Is there a doctor in this fucking hospital?!?

Scene Two

Another room in the hospital. Leah is seated facing Tom Wilson, a middle-aged but very fit lawyer who is reading a will and sipping coffee. After a moment she gets up and moves to a point and stares, eyes filled with fear. Then dialing a phone, turns to him)

TOM (*immersed*): I'm just about done here.

LEAH (*dialing*): God, I dread it—my boy'll be home any minute . . . (*In phone*) Put my brother on, Tina. . . . Lou? I don't know, they won't let me see him yet. What'd Uniroyal say? *What?* Well get on it, will you, call L.A. this minute! I mean for God's sake, Lou, I want that business! (*Hangs up*) How much do you have to pay relatives to get them to do any work? (*Tom closes the file, turns to her, silent*)—I know you're her lawyer, but I'm not really asking advice, am I?

TOM: I can discuss this. (*Returns her file*) This will

does recognize the boy as his son, but you are not his wife.

LEAH (*lifting the file*): Even if this refers to me as his wife?

TOM: I'm afraid that's legally meaningless, since he never divorced. However . . . (*Breaks off, pressing his eyes*) I'm just stunned, I simply can't absorb it.

LEAH: I'm still in midair someplace.

TOM: What'd you ask me? Oh yes—provided the legal wife gets a minimum of one third of the estate he can leave you as much as he likes. So you're very well taken care of. (*Sighs, leaning forward gripping his head*) He actually flies a plane, you say?

LEAH: Oh yes, soaring planes, too.

TOM: You know, for years he'd never get off the ground unless it was unavoidable.

LEAH: Oh, he's wonderful in the air. (*Pause*) I'm not here. I'm simply . . . not here. Can he be two people? Is that possible?

TOM: . . . May I ask you . . . ?

LEAH: Please. . . . Incidentally, have you known him long?

TOM: Sixteen, seventeen years. When you decided to marry, I assume he told you he'd gotten a divorce . . .

LEAH: Of course. We went to Reno together.

TOM: No kidding! And what happened?

LEAH: God, I'd forgotten all about this . . . (*Breaks off*) How could I be so *stupid*! You see, it was July, streets were boiling hot, so he had me stay in the hotel while he went to pick up his divorce decree . . . (*She goes silent*)

TOM: Yes?

LEAH (*shaking her head*): God! My gullibility! I was curious to see what a decree looked like, so . . . (*Lyman enters, wearing a short-sleeved summer shirt*) No particular reason, but I'd never seen one . . .

LYMAN: I threw it away.

LEAH (*with a surprised laugh*): Why!

LYMAN: I don't want to look back, I feel twenty-five! (*Laughs*) You looked stunned!

LEAH: I guess I never believed you'd marry me, darling.

LYMAN (*he draws her to him*): Feeling is all I really believe in, Leah—you made me see that. Feeling is chaos, but any decent thing I've ever done was out of feeling, and every lousy thing I'm ashamed of came from careful thinking. I simply can't lose you, Leah, you're precious to me. You look scared . . . what is it?

LEAH: I don't want to say it.

LYMAN: Go ahead. Please!

LEAH: Every relationship I've known gets to where it needs a lie to keep it going.

LYMAN: But does that always have to be!

LEAH (*hesitates*): Can I say something? I wish we could make a different wedding vow; like "Dearly beloved, I promise everything good, but I might have to lie to you sometimes." (*He is taken aback, but grins*) I wanted to say that, okay? You're shocked, aren't you.

LYMAN: What balls you have to say that! Come here. (*Takes her hand, closes his eyes*) I'm going to learn to fly a plane.

LEAH: What are you talking about?

LYMAN: Because flying terrifies me. I'm going to wrestle down one fear at a time till I've dumped them all and I am a free man! (*Gripping her hands, nose to nose*) I have a car and driver downstairs. (*Holds out his beckoning arm*) Come to your wedding, Leah, my darling! (*Lyman exits without lowering his arm*)

LEAH: . . . And it was all lies! How is it possible?! Why did he do it? What did he want?

TOM: Actually, though . . . (*Tries to recall*) Yes, I think it was about nine years ago, we did have a discussion about a divorce . . . although at the time I didn't take it all that seriously. He suddenly popped in one day with this "research" he said he'd done . . .

(*Lyman enters in a business suit. Tom has moved out of Leah's area*)

LYMAN: . . . I've been looking into bigamy, Tom.

TOM (*Laughs, surprised*): Bigamy! What are you talking about?

LYMAN: You know there's an enormous amount of it in the United States now.

TOM: Really? But what's the point . . . ?

LYMAN: . . . And not just among blacks or the poor. I've been wondering about a desertion insurance policy. Might call it the Bigamy Protection Plan. (*Tom laughs*) I'm serious. We could set the premiums really low. Be great, especially for minority women.

TOM (*admiringly*): Say now! Where the hell do you get these ideas?

LYMAN: Just put myself in other people's places. Incidentally, how frequently do they prosecute for bigamy anymore, you have any idea?

TOM: None whatsoever. But it's a victimless crime so it can't be often.

LYMAN: That's my impression, too. Get somebody to research it, will you, I want to be sure . . . I'll be in Elmira till Friday. (*Lyman starts to leave but dawdles*)

TOM: Why do I think you're depressed?

LYMAN: I guess I am—slightly. (*He grins*) I'm turning fifty-four this July.

TOM: Fifty's much tougher, I think.

LYMAN: My father died at fifty-three.

TOM: Well, you're over the hump. Anyway, you're in better shape than anybody I know.

LYMAN: Famous last words.

TOM: Something wrong, Lyman?

LYMAN: I don't think I have the balls. (*A laugh. Moves into high tension; then, facing his challenge, turns rather abruptly to Tom*) There's no man I trust like you, Tom. (*A grin*) I guess you know I've cheated on Theodora.

TOM: Well, I've had my suspicions, yes—ever since I walked in on you humping that Pakistani typist on your desk.

LYMAN (*laughs*): "Humping!"—I love that Presbyterian jive of yours, haven't heard that in years.

TOM: Quaker.

LYMAN (*confessionally, quietly*): There've been more than that one, Tommy.

TOM (*laughs*): God, where do you get the time?

LYMAN: Disgust you?

TOM: Not catastrophically.

LYMAN (*pause; he composes himself, then . . . again with the grin*): I think I've fallen in love.

TOM: Oh Lyman . . . don't tell me!

LYMAN (*pointing at him and laughing nervously*): Look at you! God, you really love Theodora, don't you!

TOM: Of course I do!—you're not thinking of divorce, are you?

LYMAN: I don't know. Maybe I just wanted to say it aloud to somebody.

TOM: But how sure are you about your feelings for this woman?

LYMAN: I'm sure. A new woman has always been an undiscovered shore, but I'd really like to go straight now, Tom. I want one woman for the rest of my life. And I can't quite see it being Theodora.

TOM: You know she loves you deeply, Lyman.

LYMAN: Tom, I love her, too. But after thirty-two

years we bore each other, we just do. And boredom is a form of deception, isn't it. And deception has become like my Nazi, my worst horror—I want nothing now but to wear my own face on my face every day till the day I die. Or do you think that kind of honesty is possible?

TOM: I don't have to tell you, the problem is not honesty but how much you hurt others with it.

LYMAN: Right. What about your religion. But there's no solution there either, I guess.

TOM: I somehow can't imagine you praying, Lyman.

(*Short pause*)

LYMAN: Is there any answer?

TOM: I don't know, maybe all one can do is hope to end up with the right regrets.

LYMAN (*silent a moment*): You ever cheated, Tom?

TOM: No.

LYMAN: Honest to God? I've seen you eye the girls around here.

TOM: It's the truth.

LYMAN: Is that the regret you end up with? (*Tom laughs bashfully, then Lyman joins him. And sud-*

denly, Lyman's embarrassment and suffering is on his face). . . . Shit, that was cruel, Tom, forgive me, will you? Damnit, why do I let myself get depressed? It's all pointless guilt, that's all! Here I start from nothing, create forty-two hundred jobs for people and raise over sixty ghetto blacks to office positions when that was not easy to do—I should be proud of myself, son of a bitch! I am! I am! (*He bangs on the desk, then subsides, looks front and downward*) I love your view. That red river of taillights gliding down Park Avenue on a winter's night—and all those silky white thighs crossing inside those heated limousines . . . Christ, can there be a sexier vision in the world? (*Turning back to Tom*) I keep thinking of my father—how connected he was to his life; couldn't wait to open the store every morning and happily count the pickles, rearrange the olive barrels. People like that knew the main thing. Which is what? What is the main thing, do you know? (*Tom is silent*) Look, don't worry, I really can't imagine myself without Theodora, she's a great, great wife! . . . I love that woman! It's always good talking to you, Tom. (*Starts to go, halts*) Maybe it's simply that if you try to live according to your real desires, you have to end up looking like a shit.

(*Lyman exits. Leah covers her face and there is a pause and Tom observes her*)

TOM: I'm sorry.

LEAH: He had it all carefully worked out from the very beginning.

TOM: I'd say it was more like . . . a continuous improvisation.

LEAH: It was the baby, you see—once I was pregnant he simply wouldn't listen to reason . . .

(*Lyman hurries on in a winter overcoat, claps a hand over her mouth*)

LYMAN: Don't tell me it's too late. (*Kisses her*) Did you do it?

LEAH: I was just walking out the door for the hospital.

LYMAN: Oh, thank God. (*Draws her to a seat, and pulls her down*) Please dear, give me one full minute and then you can do as you like.

LEAH: Don't Lyme, it's impossible.

LEAH: You know if you do this it's going to change it between us.

LEAH: Darling, it comes down to being a single parent and I just don't want that.

LYMAN: I've already named him.

LEAH (*amused, touching his face*): How do you know it's a him?

LYMAN: I'm never wrong. I have a very intimate relationship with ladies' bellies. His name is Benjamin after my father and Alexander after my mother's mother who I loved a lot. (*Grins at his own egoism*) You can put in a middle name.

LEAH (*with an unhappy laugh*): Well thanks so much! (*She tries to stand up but he holds her*) He asked me not to be late.

LYMAN: The Russians—this is an ancient custom—before an important parting, they sit for a moment in silence. Give Benjamin this moment.

LEAH: He's not Benjamin, now stop it!

LYMAN: Believe in your feelings, Leah, the rest is nonsense. What do you really and truly want? (*Silence for a moment*) I would drive him to school in the mornings and take him to ballgames.

LEAH: Twice a month?

LYMAN: With the new office set up here, I could easily be with you more than half the time.

LEAH: And Theodora?

LYMAN: It's difficult to talk about her.

LEAH: With me, you mean?

LYMAN: I can't lie to myself, darling, she's been a tremendous wife. It would be too unjust.

LEAH: But keeping it a secret—where does that leave

me? It's hard enough to identify myself as it is. And I can't believe she won't find out sooner or later, and then what?

LYMAN: If I actually have to choose it'll be you. But she doesn't know a soul in this whole area, it'd be a million-to-one shot for her to ever find out. I'm practically with you half the time now, and it's been pretty good, hasn't it?

LEAH (*touching her belly*): . . . But what do we tell . . . ?

LYMAN: . . . Benjamin.

LEAH: Oh stop calling him Benjamin! It's not even three weeks!

LYMAN: That's long enough to be Benjamin—he has a horoscope, stars and planets; he has a *future*!

LEAH: . . . Why do I feel we're circling around something? There's something I don't believe here—what is it?

LYMAN: Maybe that I'm this desperate. (*Kisses her belly*)

LEAH: Are you?—I can't express it—there's just something about this baby that doesn't seem . . . I don't know—inevitable.

LYMAN: Leah, I haven't wanted anything this much since my twenties, when I was struggling to be a poet and make something of my own that would last.

LEAH: Really.

LYMAN: It's the truth.

LEAH: That's touching, Lyman, I'm very moved. (*So it is up in the air for a moment*) But I can't, I won't, it's the story of my life, I always end up with all the responsibility; I'd have to be in total charge of your child and I know I'd resent it finally—and maybe even you as well. You're putting me back to being twelve or thirteen and my parents asking *me* where to go on vacation, or what kind of car to buy or what color drapes. I hate that position! One of the most sensuous things about you was that I could lie back and let you drive, and now you're putting me behind the wheel again. It's just all wrong.

LYMAN: I thought if we lived together let's say ten years, you'd still be in the prime, and pretty rich, and I'd . . .

LEAH: . . . Walk away into the sunset.

LYMAN: I'm trying to be as cruelly realistic as life, darling. Have you ever loved a man the way you love me?

LEAH: No.

LYMAN: Well? That's the only reality.

LEAH: You can drive me to the hospital, if you like realism so much. (*She stands, he does too*) You look so

31

sad! You poor man. (*She kisses him; a silent farewell is in the kiss; she gets her coat and turns to him*) I won't weaken on this, dear, so make up your mind.

LYMAN: We're going to lose each other if you do this. I feel it.

LEAH: Well, there's a very simple way not to lose me, dear, I guess that's why they invented it. Come, wait in the hospital if you want to. If not, I'll be back tomorrow. (*She draws him on, but he halts*)

LYMAN: Will you give me a week to tell her? It's still early for you, isn't it?

LEAH: Tell her what?

LYMAN: . . . That I'm going to marry you.

TOM: I see.

(*Lyman moves into darkness*)

LEAH: I don't understand it; he'd had dozens of women, why did he pick me to be irreplaceable? (*She looks down at her watch, stares in silence*) God! How do I tell my boy?

TOM: He's nine now?

LEAH: And worships Lyman. Worships him.

TOM: I should go see him. (*He moves to go, halts hes-*

itantly) Don't answer this if you'd rather not, but you think you could ever take him back?

LEAH (*thinks for a moment*): How could you ask me that? It's outrageous! Would Theodora? She struck me as a rather judgmental sort of woman.

TOM: Oh she has a tender side, too—I guess she hasn't had time to think of the future, any more than you have.

LEAH: All this reminds me of an idea I used to have about him that . . . well, it'll sound mystical and silly . . .

TOM: Please. I'd love to understand him.

LEAH: Well, it's just that he wants so much; like a kid at a fair; a jelly apple here, a cotton candy there, and then a ride on a loop-the-loop . . . and it never lets up in him; it's what's so attractive about him—to women, I mean—Lyman's mind is up your skirt but it's such a rare thing to be wanted like that— indifference is what most men feel now—I mean they have an appetite but not hunger—and here is such a splendidly hungry man and it's simply . . . well . . . precious once you're past twenty-five. I tell you the truth, somewhere deep down I think I sensed something about him wasn't on the level, but . . . I guess I must have loved him so much that I . . . (*Breaks off*) but I mustn't talk this way; he's unforgivable! It's the rottenest thing I've ever heard of! The answer is no, absolutely not!

TOM (*nods, thinks, then . . .*): Well, I'll be off. I hope it's not too difficult for you with the little boy. (*He exits*)

(*Lyman is softly snoring; a deep troubled sleep, however; bad dreams, muttering, an arm raised in a gesture. . . . Tom enters with Nurse. She raises Lyman's eyelid*)

NURSE: He still goes in and out but you can try him.

TOM: Lyman? Can you hear me? (*Lyman stops snoring but eyes remain shut*) It's Tom Wilson.

NURSE: Keep going, he shouldn't be staying under this much by now.

TOM: Lyman, it's Tom.

LYMAN (*opens his eyes*): *You* in the store?

TOM: It's the hospital.

LYMAN: Hospital? Oh right, right . . . Jesus, I was dreaming of my father's store; everytime he looked at me he'd shake his head and say, "Hopeless case." (*Laughs tiredly, trying to focus*) Give me a second; little mixed up. How'd you get here?

TOM: Theodora called me.

LYMAN: Theodora?

TOM: Your car is registered in the city so the state police called her.

LYMAN: I had some weird dream that she and Bessie.... (*Breaks off*) They're not here, are they?

NURSE: I told you your wife came . . .

TOM (*to Nurse*): Excuse us, please?

NURSE: But I told him. (*She exits*)

TOM: They've met, Lyman.

LYMAN (*pause. He struggles to orient himself*): Theo . . . didn't collapse, did she?

TOM: Yes, but she's come around, she'll be alright.

LYMAN: I don't understand it, I think I dreamed the whole thing . . .

TOM: Well, that wouldn't be too difficult, it's all pretty inevitable.

LYMAN: Why're you being so brutal?

TOM: There's no time to fool around, you've got things to decide. It's all over television . . .

LYMAN: Oh.—Have you met her?—Leah? I'm finished.

TOM: We've had a talk. She's a considerable woman.

LYMAN (*gratefully*): Isn't she? She's furious, too, huh?

TOM: Well, what do you expect?

LYMAN: . . . See . . . I thought I'd somehow divorce Theo later . . . but it sort of settled in where I had both of them. And after a while it didn't seem so godawful . . . What about Bessie?

TOM: It's hit her pretty bad, I guess.

LYMAN: God, and poor little Benny! Jesus, if I could go through the ceiling and just disappear.

TOM: The television is flogging it. I think you ought to issue a press statement to cut the whole thing short. As to your intentions.

LYMAN: What intentions? Just give each of them whatever they want. I'll probably go and live somewhere . . . maybe like Brazil or something . . .

TOM: You won't try to hold onto either of them?

LYMAN: Are you mad? They wouldn't have anything to do with me. My God . . . (*He turns away, tears in his eyes*) How could I have destroyed everything like this! My character! (*Higher intensity*) Why did I drive into that storm? I can't understand it! I had the room in the Howard Johnson's, I think I was even in bed . . . figured I'd wait out the storm there . . . Why'd I go out into it again?

TOM: Can you give Theo a few minutes? She wants to say goodbye.

LYMAN: How can I face her? Ask her to wait till tomorrow, maybe I'll feel a little better and . . .

(*Theodora and Bessie enter; Lyman does not see them as they are above him*)

TOM: They're here, Lyman.

(*Lyman closes his eyes, breathing fast. Bessie, holding Theodora by the elbow, accompanies her to the bedside*)

BESSIE (*whispering with some shock*): Look at his bandages! (*Turning away*) Oh, Mother!

THEO: Stop that. (*Bending to Lyman*): Lyman? (*He can't get himself to speak*) It's Theodora.

LYMAN (*opening his eyes*): Hi.

THEO: How are you feeling?

LYMAN: Not too bad now. I hope I make sense with all this painkiller. . . . Is that you Bessie?

BESSIE: I'm only here because of Mother.

LYMAN: Oh. Okay. I'm sorry Bess—I mean that my character's so bad. But I'm proud that you have enough strength to despise me.

BESSIE: But who wouldn't?

LYMAN: Good! (*His voice starts to break but he controls himself*): That was well-spoken, sweetie.

BESSIE (*with quick anger*): Don't call me that . . .

THEO (*to Bessie*): Shhh! Lyman—is it true? (*Lyman closes his eyes*) I have to hear it from you. Did you marry that woman? (*Deep snores emerge*) (*More urgently*) Lyman?

BESSIE: He's not really sleeping!

THEO: Did you have a child with that woman? Lyman? I insist!!! I insist!!!

LYMAN (*Sitting up*): I hear you!

(*He leaps out of bed and crosses back and forth across the stage. Theo and Bessie continue addressing the pillow as though he were still on it. They are formalized, part of his vision*)

THEO: What in God's name have you done!

(*Almost writhing in conflict, Lyman clears his throat. He remains a distance upstage of the bed*)

BESSIE (*bent over the pillow*): Shh! He's saying something!

LYMAN: I realize . . . how crazy it sounds, Theodora . . . (*Breaks off*)

THEO: Yes?

LYMAN: . . . I'm not really sure, but . . . I wonder if this crash . . . was maybe to sort of subconsciously . . . get you both to . . . meet one another, finally.

THEO (*with disgust*): Meet *her?*

LYMAN: I know it sounds absurd but . . .

THEO: Absurd! It's disgusting! She's exactly the type who forgets to wash out her panties.

LYMAN (*wincing, but with a certain pleasurable recognition*): I *knew* you'd say that! I admit it, though, there is a sloppy side to her . . .

THEO: She's the worst generation in our history— screw anybody in pants, then drop their litters like cats, and spout mystic credos on cosmic responsibility, ecology, and human rights!

LYMAN: To my dying day I will stand amazed at your ability to speak in complete paragraphs!

THEO: I insist you explain this to me yourself. Lyman? Lyman! (*Leah enters. Theo reacts instantly*) There'll be no one in here but family! (*To Bessie*) Get the nurse!

LEAH (*despite Theo, approaches the cast, but with uncertainty about his reaction to her*): Lyman?

THEO (*to Tom*): Get her out of here! (*Tom is immobile, and she goes to him furiously*): She does not belong here!

LEAH (*to the pillow, with a certain warmth*): It's me, Lyme. Can you hear me? Lyman?

THEO (*rushing threateningly towards Leah*): Get out, get out, get out . . . !

(*Just as she is about to lay hands on Leah, Lyman stands behind the bed head and throws his arms up and cries imploringly*)

LYMAN: I want everybody to lie down!

(*The three women instantly deanimate as though suddenly falling under the urgency of his control. Lyman gestures, without actually touching them, and causes Theo and Leah to lie on the bed*)

LEAH (*as she lies down; voice soft, remote*): What am I going to tell Benny? Oh gee whiz, Lyman, why did you . . . ?

THEO (*lying down beside Leah*): You have a bitter smell, you should use something.

LEAH: I have, but he likes it.

THEO: Blah. (*To Lyman*): And what would you say if one of us took another man to bed and asked you to lie next to him?

LYMAN (*lifting off her glasses*): Oh, I'd kill him, dear; but you're a lady, Theodora; the delicate sculpture of your noble eye, your girlish faith in me and your disillusion; your idealism and your unadmitted greed for wealth; the awkward tenderness of your wooden fingers, your incurably Protestant cooking; your savoir-faire and your sexual inexperience; your sensible shoes and devoted motherhood, your tolerant former radicalism and stalwart love of country now—your Theodorism! Who can ever take your place!

LEAH (*laughing*): Why am I laughing!!

LYMAN: Because you're an anarchist, my darling! (*He stretches out between both of them*) Oh, what pleasure, what intensity! Your countercurrents are like bare live wires! (*Kisses each in turn*) I'd have no problem defending both of you to the death! Oh the double heat of two blessed wives—this is heaven! (*Rests his head on Leah while holding Theo's hand to his cheek*)

LEAH (*undressing*): Listen, you've got to make up your mind about something.

LYMAN: I'm only delaying as long as possible, let's delay it till we all die! Delay, delay, how delicious, my loving Leah, is delay!

THEO (*sits up*): How you can still go on talking about love is beyond my understanding.

LYMAN: And still I love you, Theodora, although certain parts of your body fill me with *rage!*

THEO: So you simply got yourself some other parts instead.

(*Leah, still lying on her back, raises one leg in the air, and her skirt slides down, exposing her thigh*)

LYMAN (*replying to Theo, kissing Leah's thigh*): That's the truth, yes—at least it was all flesh at first. (*Leah mounts him*) Oh, Glory!

LEAH (*stretching out her arms and her body*): Oh, how good that was! I'm still pulsing to the tips of my toes.

LYMAN (*begins dressing*): I have a plane to catch.

LEAH: You're really healthy, aren't you.

(*Theo helps him on with his shirt. He kisses her and she walks into darkness*)

LYMAN (*dressing*): You mean for my age? Yes.

LEAH: I did not mean that!

LYMAN: My health is terrific. In fact, it keeps threatening my dignity.

LEAH: Why!

LYMAN: Well, how do I come to be in a girl's bedroom in the afternoon, and on a working day! I really hadn't planned to do that this afternoon. Did you know I was going to?

LEAH: No . . . but I never do.

LYMAN: But you seem so organized.

LEAH: In business; but not in pleasure. (*They kiss*) (*Loud knocking. A man's angry voice to which both react*)

LYMAN: You okay?

LEAH: It's nothing. Do you have time for a walk before you go?

LYMAN: All the way to the moon. (*They stroll toward a park bench*) What surprised me was the openness of your laughter with those heavy executives at the table.

LEAH: Well, your presentation was so funny, I'd heard you were a real brain, not a comic.

LYMAN: Well, insurance is basically comical, isn't it—at least pathetic.

LEAH: Why?

LYMAN: You're buying immortality, aren't you? Reaching out of your grave to pay the bills and remind people of your life? It's poetry. The soul was once immortal, now we've got an insurance policy.

LEAH: You sound pretty cynical about it.

LYMAN: Not at all—I started as a writer, nobody lusts after the immortal like a writer.

LEAH: How'd you get into insurance?

LYMAN: Pure accident. How'd you?

LEAH: My mother had died, my dad had his stroke,

and insurance was something I could do from home. Dad knew a lot of people, being a doctor, so the thing just took off.

LYMAN: Don't take this wrong—but you know what I find terrifically sexy about you?

LEAH: What?

LYMAN: Your financial independence. Horrible, huh?

LEAH: Why? (*Wryly*) Whatever helps, helps.

LYMAN: You don't sound married, are you?

LEAH: It's a hell of a time to ask! (*They laugh, come closer*) I can't see myself getting married . . . not yet anyway. Incidentally are you listening to me?

LYMAN: Yes, but my attention keeps wandering toward a warm and furry place . . . (*She laughs, delighted*) It's funny, my generation got married to show its maturity, yours stays single for the same reason.

LEAH: That's good!

LYMAN: How happy I am! (*Sniffs his hands*) Here in the park, in Elmira, in the sun with you, and your scent still on my hands! God!—all the different ways there are to try to be real!—I don't know the connection, but when I turned twenty I sold three poems to *The New Yorker* and a story to *Harper's*, and the first thing I bought was a successful blue suit to impress my father how real I was even

though a writer. He ran an appetizer store on Forti-
eth Street and Ninth Avenue. (*Grinning, near laughter*) And he sees the suit and says, "How much you
pay?" And I said, "Twenty-nine fifty," thinking I'd
got a terrific bargain. An he says, "Pray God keep
an eye on you the rest of your life."

LEAH (*laughs*): That's awful!

LYMAN: No! It spurred me on! (*Laughs*) He had two
pieces of wisdom—never trust anybody, and never
forgive. Funny, it's like magic, I simply can't trace
how we got into bed.

LEAH (*a glance at her watch*): I really have to get back
to the office—but is Lyman an Albanian name?

LYMAN: Lyman's the judge's name in Worcester,
Massachusetts, who gave my father his citizenship.
Felt is short for Feltman, my mother's name because my father's was unpronounceable and they
wanted a successful American for a son.

LEAH: Then your mother was Jewish.

LYMAN: And the source of all my conflicts. In the
Jewish heart is a lawyer and a judge, in the Albanian
a bandit defying the government with a knife.

LEAH: What a surprise you are! (*She stands, and he
does*)

LYMAN: Being so silly?

LEAH: Being so interesting, and in the insurance business.

LYMAN (*taking her hand*): When was the moment?— I'm just curious.

LEAH: I don't know . . . I guess at the conference table I suddenly thought, "He's basically talking to me." But then I figured, this is probably why he's such a great salesman, because everybody he talks to feels loved.

LYMAN: You know—I've never before with a Jewish girl.

LEAH: Well, you're my first Albanian.

LYMAN: There's something venerable in your eyes. Not old—ancient. Like our peoples.

LEAH (*touching his cheek*): Take care, dear.

LYMAN (*as she passes before him to leave, he takes her hand*): Why do I feel I know nothing about you?

LEAH (*shrugs, smiles*): Maybe you weren't listening . . . which I don't mind if it's in a good cause.

LYMAN (*letting go of her hand*): I walk in the valley of your thighs. (*She laughs, gives him a quick kiss*) When you move away now, would you turn back to me for a moment?

LEAH (*amused*): Why?

LYMAN (*half kidding in his romanticism*): I have to take a small commuter plane and if I die I want that vision as I go down—

LEAH (*backing away with a wave*): 'Bye, Lyman . . .

LYMAN: Can I ask who that fellow was banging on your apartment door?

LEAH (*caught off guard*): Somebody I used to go with . . . he was angry, that's all.

LYMAN: Are you afraid of him?

LEAH (*shrugs in an accepted uncertainty*): See you, dear. (*She turns and walks a few yards, then halts and turns her head to look back at him over her shoulder*)

LYMAN: Beautiful. (*Leah exits. Alone*) Miraculous. (*Thinks for a moment*) Still . . . was it really all *that* great? (*A phone is lit up, he goes to it, picks it up, troubled*) Theo?—Hi darling, I'm just about to take off. Oh, definitely, it has the makings of a much bigger operation; had a talk with Aetna's chief rep up here, and she's agreed to take us on, so I'll probably be spending more time here. Yes, a woman; she's got a great agency, I might try to buy into her. Listen, dear, how about you flying up here and we rent a car and drive through Cherry Valley—it's bursting into bloom now! Oh, I forgot; no-no you'd better go to your meeting then; it's okay; no, it just suddenly hit me how quickly it's all going by and . . . You ever have the feeling that you never *really* got to know anybody? (*She never has; he resents it, and a sharpness enters his voice. He is alone in a spotlight surrounded by near-darkness*) Well, yes, I do feel that sometimes, very much; sometimes I feel I'm going to vanish without a trace, Theo! (*Unhappily now, with hidden anger, the romance gone*) Theo, dear, it's nothing against you, I only meant that with all the analysis and the novels and the Freuds we're still as opaque and unknowable as some line of statues in a church wall. (*He hangs up. Now a light strikes the bed. He moves to it and looks down at himself. Bessie, Theo, and Leah are standing motionless around the bed and Tom is off to one side, observing. Lyman slowly lifts his arms and raises his face like a suppliant*) We're all in a cave . . . (*The three women now begin to move, ever so slightly at first; their heads turning as they appear to be searching for the sight of something far away or overhead or on the floor*) . . . where we entered to make love or money or fame. It's dark in here, as dark as sleep, and each one moves blindly, searching for another; to touch, hoping to touch and afraid; and hoping, and afraid. (*As he speaks, the women and Tom move in criss-crossing, serpentine paths, just missing one another, spreading further and further across the stage until one by one they disappear. Lyman has returned to the bed and pulls up the covers*) So now that we're here . . . what are we going to say?

(*Blackout.*)

ACT II

ACT II

Scene One

The hospital waiting room. Tom is seated with Theo.

TOM: Really, Theo, I wish you'd let Bessie take you back to the city.

THEO: Please stop repeating that! (*Slight pause*) I need to talk to him . . . I'll never see him again. I can't simply walk away. Is my head trembling?

TOM: A little, maybe. Should you let one of the doctors look at you?

THEO: I'll be all right, my family has a tendency to tremors, I've had it for years when I'm tense. What time is it?

TOM: Give them a few minutes more—you seem pale.

THEO (*pressing fingers against her temples to steady herself*): When you spoke with this woman . . . was there any feeling about . . . what she has in mind?

TOM: She's as much in shock as you. The child was her main concern.

THEO: Really? I wouldn't have thought so.

TOM: Oh, I think he means everything to her.

THEO (*begrudgingly*): Well, that's nice. Messes like this are basically comical, aren't they—until you come to the children. I'm very worried about Bessie. She lies there staring at the ceiling. She can hardly talk without starting to weep. He's been her . . . her world. (*She begins to fill up*) You're right, I think I'll go. It just seemed unfinished, somehow . . . but maybe it's better to leave it this way . . . (*Starts for her bag, stops*) I don't know what to do. One minute I could kill him, the next I wonder if some . . . aberration got into him . . .

(*Leah enters. They did not expect to see each other. A momentary pause. Leah sits*)

LEAH: Good afternoon.

TOM: Good afternoon.

(*Awkward silence*)

LEAH (*asking*): He's not in his room.

THEO (*as it is difficult for her to address Leah, she turns to her slowly*): They're treating his eye.

LEAH: His eye?

TOM: It's nothing serious, he tried to climb out his window. Probably in his sleep. His eyelid was slightly scratched by a rhododendron.

THEO (*making a stab at communication*): He must not have realized he's on the ground floor.

(*Short pause*)

LEAH: Hm! That's interesting, because a friend of ours, Ted Colby, called this morning—he's a Commander of the State Police here. They'd put up a wooden barrier across the Mount Morgan road when it got so icy; and he thinks Lyman moved the barrier aside.

TOM: How could they know it was him?

LEAH: There was only one set of tire tracks.

THEO: Oh my God.

LEAH: He's worried about him. They're good friends, they go hunting together.

THEO: Lyman hunts?

LEAH: Oh sure. (*Theo shakes her head incredulously*) But I can't imagine him in that kind of depression, can you?

TOM: Actually . . . yes, I think I can.

LEAH: Really. He's always seemed so . . . up with me, and happy. (*Theo glances from her, irked, then away. Leah glances at her watch*) I just have to settle some business with him for a few minutes, I won't be in your way.

THEO: *My* way? You're free to do anything you like, as far as I'm concerned.

LEAH (*slightly taken aback*): Yes . . . the same with me
. . . in your case. (*Beat*) I mean as far as I'm concerned. (*The hostility turns her to look at her watch
again*) I want to tell you . . . I almost feel worse for
you, somehow, than for myself.

THEO (*gives a hard laugh*): Why! Do I seem *that* old?
(*The second rebuff stiffens Leah*) I shouldn't have
said that. I apologize. I'm exhausted.

LEAH (*letting it pass*): How is your daughter? She still
here?

THEO (*a hostile color despite everything*): In the
motel. She's devastated.

TOM: Your boy taking it all right?

LEAH: No, it's wracked him, it's terrible. (*To Theo*) I
thought Lyman might have some idea how to deal
with him, the kid's always idolized him so. I'm really
at my wits end.

THEO (*bitterly angry, but contained*): We are his dust;
we billow up behind his steps and settle again when
he passes by. Billie Holliday . . . (*She touches her
forehead*) I can't recall when she died, it's quite a
while, isn't it.

TOM: Billie Holliday? Why?

(*Tom and Leah observe, puzzled, as Theo stares in silence. Then . . .*)

LEAH: Why don't I come back in a couple of hours—
I've got a two o'clock conference call and it's getting
a bit late . . . (*She stands, goes to Theo, and, extending
her hand . . .*) Well, if we don't meet again . . .

THEO (*touching her hand briefly, hostility momentarily
overcome*): . . . Do you understand this?

LEAH: It's baffling. He's raced the Mount Morgan
road, he knows what it's like, even in summer.

THEO: Raced? You mean cars?

LEAH: Sure. He has a Lotus and a Z. He had a Fer-
rari, but he totalled it. (*Theo turns and stares into
space, stunned*) I was thinking before . . .

THEO: He's always been terrified of speed; he never
drives over sixty . . .

LEAH: He reminds me of a frog . . .

THEO: A frog?

LEAH: I mean you never know when you look at a
frog whether it's the same one you just saw or a different one. (*To Tom*) When you talk to him—he really has to make a definite statement to stop all this
stupid speculation.

THEO: What speculation?

LEAH: You've seen the *Daily News* haven't you?

THEO: What!

LEAH: We're both on the front page with a headline . . .

TOM (*to Theo, placating*): It's unimportant . . .

THEO (*to Leah*): What's the headline?

LEAH: "Who gets Lyman?"

THEO: How dare they!

TOM: Don't be upset. (*To Leah*) I'll get a statement from him this afternoon . . .

LEAH: Goodbye, Mrs. . . . (*Stops herself, a short laugh*) I was going to call you Mrs. Felt, but . . . (*Correcting again*) . . . well you are, aren't you—I guess I'm the one who's not! I'll come by about three or so. (*Leah exits*)

THEO: She wants him back, doesn't she.

TOM: Why?

THEO (*gives her little laugh*): Didn't you hear it? She's the one he was happy with!

TOM: Oh, I don't think she meant . . .

THEO: That's *all* she meant. I pity her, though, with such a young child. (*She fumes in silence*) *Can* it have been suicide?

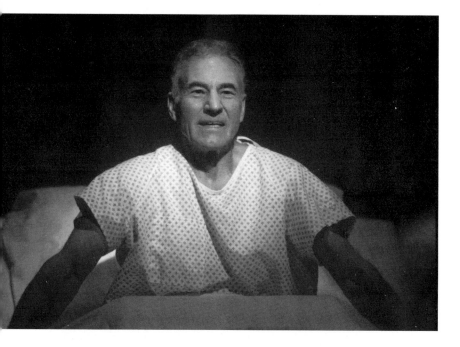

Patrick Stewart as Lyman Felt in the Broadway production of Arthur Miller's The Ride Down Mt. Morgan.
All photos by Joan Marcus.

Katy Selverstone as Leah and Patrick Stewart as Lyman in the Broadway production of The Ride Down Mt. Morgan.

John C. Vennema as Tom and Frances Conroy as
Theo in the Broadway production of The Ride Down
Mt. Morgan.

Katy Selverstone (left), Patrick Stewart and Frances Conroy in the 2000 Broadway production of The Ride Down Mt. Morgan.

TOM: Frankly, I'd almost hope so, in a way.

THEO: You mean it would indicate a moral conscience.

TOM: Yes. But I'm wondering . . . maybe he just wanted to change his life; become a completely different person.

THEO (*stares for a moment*): . . . Maybe not so different.

TOM: How do you mean?

THEO (*a long hesitation*): I don't know why I'm still trying to protect him—he tried to kill me once.

TOM: You're not serious.

(*Lyman appears in sunlight in swim trunks, inhaling deeply on a boat deck. She begins walking towards him*)

THEO: Oh yes! I didn't know this woman existed then, but I see now it was just about the time they had either married or were on the verge. (*As she moves towards Lyman, her coat slides off, revealing her in a swimsuit*) He seemed very strange, unreal. We'd gone for a two-day sail off Montauk . . .

(*Lyman is doing breathing exercises*)

LYMAN: The morning mist rising from the sea is always like the first day of the world—the "oystery-gods and the visigods . . ."

(*Theo enters into his acting area*)

THEO: Finnegan's Wake.

LYMAN: I'll get the weather. (*Kneels, tunes a radio; static*) Is that a new suit? It's sexy as hell.

THEO: Two years ago. You bought it for me in San Diego.

LYMAN (*mimes a pistol to his head*): Bang.

ANNOUNCER (*voice over*): . . . Due to the unusually warm spring tides there've been several shark sightings off Montauk . . . one is reported to be twelve to fourteen feet long . . .

(*Heavy static intervenes; Lyman mimes switching the radio off*)

LYMAN: Jesus.

THEO: Oh that's ridiculous, it's only May! I'm going in for a dip . . . (*She looks over into the ocean*)

LYMAN: But the radio said . . .

THEO: Nonsense. I've sailed around here since my childhood, and so did my grandparents—there are never sharks until July if at all, the water's much too cold. Come in with me?

LYMAN: I'm the Mediterranean type—we're unreliable and hate cold water. I know I shouldn't say this, Theo, but how you can hang onto your convictions in the face of a report like that . . . just seems . . . I don't know—fanatical.

THEO (*with a hard, determined laugh*): Now that is really uncalled for! You're just as stubborn as I am when you're committed to something.

LYMAN: Goddamnit, you're right! And I love your convictions! Go ahead, I'll keep an eye out.

THEO (*with loving laughter*): You simply can't stand me contradicting you, darling, but it's the best exercise for your character.

LYMAN: Right! And a miserable character it is. Into the ocean! (*He leaves her side, scans the ocean*)

THEO (*bends for a dive*): On the mark . . . get set . . .

LYMAN (*pointing leftward*): What's that out there!

THEO: No, sharks always move, that's a log.

LYMAN: Oh right. Okay, jump in.

THEO: I'll run in! Wait, let me warm up. (*Backs up to make a run for it*) Join me! Come on.

LYMAN: I can't, dear, I fear death.

(*She is behind him, running in place. His back is to her*

and his eye catches sight of something towards the right front; his mouth opens, eyes staring in horror following the moving shark. She bends to start her run)

THEO: Okay, one . . . and a two . . . and a . . . three!

(She runs and as she comes abreast of him he suddenly, at the last moment, reaches out and stops her at the edge)

LYMAN: Stop!

(He points front; she looks, horror rising on her face as their eyes follow the fish)

THEO: My God, the *size* of him! Ahhh . . . ! *(She bursts into tears of released terror; he takes her in his arms)*

LYMAN: Honey, when are you going to trust something I say!

THEO: Oh, I'm going to be sick . . . !

(About to vomit, she bends and rushes into darkness. Lights go out on Lyman and up on Tom in the waiting room; he is staring straight ahead, listening. The light widens and finds Theo standing in her fur coat)

TOM: That sounds like he saved you.

THEO: I've always tried to think of it that way, too, but I have to face everything, now—*(Coming downstage; newly distressed by the memory)*—it was not quite at the top of his voice. I mean, it wasn't . . .

(*Light flares up on Lyman in his trunks. At top voice and in horror he shouts . . .*)

LYMAN: Stop!

(*He stands mesmerized looking at the shark below. Blackout on Lyman*)

THEO: It was more like . . .

(*Lights flare up again on Lyman, and he merely semi-urgently—as he did in the scene—shouts . . .*)

LYMAN: Stop.

(*Blackout on Lyman*)

THEO: I tell you he was on the verge of letting me go.

TOM: Come on, Theo, you can't really believe that. I mean, how could you have gone on living with him?

THEO: How I've gone on? (*A bitter and embarrassed smile*) Well, we did have two serious breakups and . . . months have gone by without . . . relations. (*Gradually becomes furious*) No, dammit, I'm not going to evade this anymore. Maybe I've gone on because I'm corrupt, Tom. I certainly wasn't once, but who knows, now? He's rich, isn't he? And vastly respected, and what would I do with myself alone? Why does anybody stay together, once they realize who they're with? (*Suddenly livid*) What the hell am I hanging around here for? This is the stupidest thing I've ever done in my life! (*Indignantly grabs her bag*)

TOM: You love him, Theo. (*Physically stops her*) Please go home, will you? And give it a few weeks before you decide anything? (*She stifles a sob as he embraces her*) I know how crazy this sounds, but part of him worships you. I'm sure of it.

THEO (*suddenly screams in his face*): I hate him! I hate him! (*She is rigid, pale, and he grips her shoulders to steady her. A pause*) I must lie down. We'll probably go back to the city tonight. But call me if he wakes up. It's so hard to just walk away without knowing what happened. Or maybe I should just leave ... (*She passes her hand across her brow*) Do I look strange?

TOM: Just tired. Come, I'll find you a cab.

THEO: It's only a few blocks, I need the air. (*Starting off, turns back*) Amazing how beautiful the country still is up here. Like nothing bad had ever happened in the world. (*Theo exits*)

(*Alone, Tom stands staring into space, arms folded, trying to figure out an approach. He exits*)

(*Lyman's room. He is deeply asleep, snoring placidly at first. Now he starts muttering*)

NURSE: Whyn't you take some time off? You do more work asleep than most of us awake. You ought to come up ice fishing with us sometime, that'll slow you down.

(*Nurse goes out. Now there is a tensing up, he is groaning in his sleep. Leah and Theo appear on either side of him, but on elevated platforms, like two stone deities; they are in kitchen aprons, wifely ribbons tying up their hair. But something menacing about their deathly stillness as the sepulchral dream-light finds them, motionless in this tableau. After a long moment they reanimate. Their manner of speaking is godlike, deathly and cute*)

THEO: I wouldn't mind it at all if you did some of the cooking, I'm not all that super.

LEAH (*generously*): I hear you make good desserts, though.

THEO: Apple cobbler, yes; gingerbread with whipped cream. (*Gaining confidence*) And exceptional waffles for breakfast, with real maple syrup, although he's had to cut out the sausages.

LEAH: I can do potato pancakes and segadina goulash.

THEO (*disapproving*): And all that paprika?

LEAH: It has to be blended in, of course.

THEO (*at a loss, sensing defeat*): Ah, blended in! I'm afraid I couldn't do something like that.

LEAH (*smiling, brutally pressing her advantage, grinding her hips*): Oh yes, blended in and really blended *in!* And my gefilte fish is feather-light. (*Clapping her cupped palms together*) I wet my hands and keep patting it till it shapes up just perfect!

THEO (*struggling, at a loss*): He does love my glazed ham. Yes! And my boiled tongue. (*A sudden bright idea*) Custard!

LEAH (*generously*): You can do all the custard and glazed ham and I'll do all the gefilte fish and goulash ... *and* the blending in.

THEO: But may I do *some*? Once or twice a month, perhaps?

LEAH: Let's leave it up to him—some months you can do more ...

THEO: Yes! And some months you.

LEAH: 'Kay! Would you wash out my panties?

THEO: Certainly. As long as he tells me my lies.

LEAH: Good! Then you'll have your lies and I'll have mine! (*Filled with admiration*) You certainly have class!

THEO and LEAH: Hurrah for the menu!

(*Lyman's joy turns to horror as the women come down off the pedestals threatening him with kitchen knives; enormous birds have descended on Lyman and are eating him hungrily. He changes now ... begins to pant in anxiety. He writhes in terror, trying to free himself, gasping for breath and shouting incoherently. The nightmare ends and the women go into darkness.*

Nurse hurries in, finds him yelling, thrashing around blindly)

NURSE: All right now, let's come back, dear, come on back . . .

(*He stops struggling and opens his eyes*)

LYMAN: Wah. Oh. What dreams. God, how I'd like to be dead.

NURSE: Don't start feeling sorry for yourself; you know what they say—come down off the cross, they need the wood.

LYMAN: I'm suffocating, can't you open a window?

NURSE: Not anymore, I can't.

LYMAN: Huh? Oh listen, that's ridiculous, I wasn't really trying to climb out . . .

NURSE: Well, you did a pretty good imitation. Your lawyer's asking can he come in . . .

LYMAN: I thought he'd gone back to New York. I look terrible?

NURSE (*swabbing his face and hands*): You takin' it too hard. Be different if you deserted those women, but anybody can see how well taken care of they are . . .

LYMAN: Go on, you don't kid me, Logan—underneath all this cool you know you're as shocked as hell.

NURSE: Go on, brush your teeth. (*As he does*) The last shock I had come off a short in my vacuum cleaner . . . (*He laughs, then groans in pain*) One thing I *have* been wondering, though.

LYMAN: What've you been wondering?

NURSE: Whatever got into you to actually marry that woman? Man as smart as you?

LYMAN: Were you talking about ice before?

NURSE: Ice? Oh, you mean . . . ya, we go ice fishing on the lake, me, my husband, and my boy—you're remembering a lot better now.

LYMAN (*staring*): Not being married is going to feel very strange—like suddenly your case has been dismissed and you don't have to be in court anymore.

NURSE: Don't you talk bad about those women; they don't look mean to me.

LYMAN: Why I married her? I'm very attracted to women who smell like fruit; Leah smelled like a pink, ripe cantaloupe. And when she smiled, her clothes seemed to drop off. I'd never been so jealous. I swear, if a hundred women walked past me on a sidewalk I could pick out the clack of Leah's heels. I even loved lying in bed listening to the quiet splash of her bath water. And of course slipping into her pink cathedral . . .

NURSE: You have the dirtiest mind I ever seen on an educated man.

LYMAN: I couldn't lose her, Logan, and that's the best reason to marry anybody, unless you're married already.

NURSE: I'll get your lawyer, okay? (*He seems suddenly overcome; weeps*) Now don't you start that cryin' again . . .

LYMAN: It's just my children . . . you can't imagine how they respected me . . . (*Bracing himself*) But nobody's any better, goddamnit!

(*Tom enters*)

TOM: May I come in?

LYMAN (*uncertainly, trying to read Tom*): Hi! I thought you'd gone back—something happen?

TOM: Can we talk?

(*Nurse exits*)

LYMAN: If you can bear it. (*Grins*) You despise me Tom?

TOM: I'm still staggering. I don't know what to think.

LYMAN: Sure you do, but that's okay. (*His charming grin*) So, what's up?

TOM: I've been discussing things with the women . . .

LYMAN: I thought I told you—or did I?—just give them what they want. Within reason, I mean.

TOM: I really believe Theo'd like to find a way to forgive you.

LYMAN: Impossible!

TOM: She's a great spirit, Lyman.

LYMAN: . . . Not that great; I'd have to live on my knees for the rest of my life.

TOM: Maybe not—if you were clear about yourselves . . .

LYMAN: I'm pretty clear now—I'm a selfish son of a bitch. But I have loved the truth.

TOM: And what's the truth?

LYMAN: A man can be faithful to himself or to other people—but not to both. At least not happily. We all know this, but it's immoral to admit that the first law of life is betrayal; why else did those rabbis pick Cain and Abel to open the bible? Cain felt betrayed by god so he betrayed him and killed his brother.

TOM: But the bible doesn't end there, does it.

LYMAN: Jesus Christ? I can't worship self denial; it's just not true for me. We're all ego, kid, ego plus an occasional heartfelt prayer.

TOM: Then why'd you bother building one of the most socially responsible companies in America?

LYMAN: The truth? I did that twenty-five years ago, when I was a righteous young man; but I am an unrighteous middle-aged man now, so all I have left is to try not to live with too many lies. (*Suddenly collapsing within*) Why must I see them? What can I say to them? Christ, if I could only lose consciousness! (*Rocking side to side in anguish*) Advise me, Tom, tell me something.

TOM: Maybe you ought to give up trying to seem so strong.

(*Slight pause*)

LYMAN: What do you want me to say, I'm a loser?

TOM: Well, right now, aren't you?

LYMAN: No, goddamnit! A loser has lived somebody else's life, I've lived my own; crappy as it may seem, it's mine. And I'm no worse than anybody else! Now answer that, and don't kid me.

TOM: All right, I won't kid you; I think you've done these women terrible harm.

LYMAN: You do.

TOM: If you want to get off this dime you're on I'd begin by confronting the damage I'd done—I think you've raked Theo's soul.

LYMAN: I've also given her an interesting life, a terrific daughter, and made her very rich. I mean, exactly what harm are you talking about?

TOM: Lyman, you deceived her . . .

LYMAN (*fury overtaking him*): But she couldn't have had all that if I hadn't deceived her! You know as well as I that nobody could live with Theo for more than a month without some relief! I've suffered at least as much as she has in this marriage!

TOM (*demurring*): Well . . .

LYMAN: Now listen, you want the rock bottom truth? I curse the day I ever laid eyes on her and I don't *want* her forgiveness!

TOM: For Pete's sake . . .

LYMAN: I ever tell you how we met? Let's stop pretending this marriage was made in heaven, for Christ's sake! I was hitchhiking back from Cornell; nineteen innocent years of age; I'm standing beside the road with my suitcase and I go behind a bush. This minister sees the suitcase and stops, gives me a ride and I end up at an Audubon Society picnic, where lo and behold, I meet his daughter Theodora. Had I taken that suitcase with me behind the bush

I'd never have met her! And serious people are still talking about the moral purpose of the universe!

TOM: Give or take a bad patch or two, you've had the best marriage of anyone I've ever met.

LYMAN (*with a sigh*): I know—look, we're all the same; a man is a fourteen-room house; in the bedroom he's asleep with his intelligent wife, in his living room he's rolling around with some bare-assed girl, in the library he's paying his taxes, in the yard he's raising tomatoes, and in the cellar he's making a bomb to blow it all up. And nobody's different . . . Except you, maybe. Are you?

TOM: I don't raise tomatoes . . . Listen, the TV is not letting up on this and it's humiliating for the women; let's settle on a statement and be done with it. What do you want?

LYMAN: What I always wanted; both of them.

TOM: Be serious . . .

LYMAN: I know these women and they still love me! It's only what they think they're *supposed* to feel that's confusing them.

TOM: Listen, I forgot to tell you—Jeff Huddleston called me this morning; heard it on the radio; he insists you resign from the board.

LYMAN: Not on your life! I started that company and

I'm keeping it. That fat fraud—Jeff Huddleston's got a woman stashed in Trump Tower and two in L.A.

TOM: *Huddleston!*

LYMAN: He offered to loan me one once! Huddleston has more outside ass than a Nevada whorehouse!

TOM: But he doesn't marry them.

LYMAN: Right! In other words, what I really violated was the law of hypocrisy.

TOM: Unfortunately that's the one that operates.

LYMAN: Not with me, baby! I may be a bastard but I am not a hypocrite! I am not quitting my company! What's Leah saying . . . anything?

TOM: She's stunned. But frankly, I'm not sure she's out of the question either . . . if that's the move you wanted to make.

LYMAN (*deeply touched*): What size these women have! I wish I was struck dead! (*Weeping threatens again*) Oh Tom, I'm lost!

(*Bessie and Theo enter. Theo stands beside his bed staring at him without expression. Bessie doesn't so much as look at him. After a long moment . . .*)

LYMAN (*downing fear*): My God, Theo—thank you—

I mean for coming. I didn't expect you . . . (*She sits down in a potent silence. Bessie stands, fiercely aloof. He is openly and awkwardly ashamed*) Hi, Bessie.

BESSIE: I'm here for her sake, she wanted to say something to you. (*Hurrying her along*) Mother?

(*But Theo takes no notice, staring at Lyman with a fixed, unreadable smile. After a long awkward moment . . .*)

LYMAN (*to fill the void*): How are you feeling today? I hear you were . . .

THEO (*dead flat, cutting him off*): I won't be seeing you again, Lyman.

LYMAN (*despite everything, a bit of a blow—slight pause*): Yes. Well . . . I guess there's no use in apologizing, you know my character . . . But I am sorry, Theo.

THEO: I can't leave my life lying all over the floor like this.

LYMAN: I'll talk about anything you like.

THEO: I seem confused but I'm not; there's just so much that I . . . that I don't want bottled up in me anymore.

LYMAN: Sure, I understand.

THEO: Do you remember that young English instructor whose wife walked out on him—his advice to you about sex?

LYMAN: An English instructor? At Cornell, you mean?

THEO: "Bend it in half," he said, "and tie a rubber band around it."

LYMAN (*laughing a little alarmed*): Oh, sure, Jim Donaldson!

THEO: Everyone used to laugh at that.

LYMAN (*her smile is empty, his charm desperate*): Right! "Bend it in half and . . ." (*Continues a strained chuckling*)

THEO (*Cutting him off*): I *hated* you laughing at that; it showed a vulgar and disgusting side of you. I was ashamed . . . for you and for myself.

LYMAN (*brought up short*): I see. But that's so long ago, Theo . . .

THEO: I want to tell you that I nearly ended it right then and there, but I thought I was too inexperienced to make a judgment. But I was right—you *were* a vulgar, unfeeling man, and you are still.

(*Anxiously, Lyman glances over to Bessie for help or explanation of this weirdness*)

LYMAN: I see. Well, I guess our whole life was a mistake then. (*Angered but attempting charm*) But I made a good living.

BESSIE: Please Mother, let's go, he's mocking you, can't you hear it?

LYMAN (*flaring up*): Must I not defend myself? Please go ahead, Theo, I'm listening, I understand what you're saying, and it's okay, it's what you feel.

THEO (*seemingly relaxed*): What was the name of the river, about half an hour's walk past the Chemistry building?

LYMAN (*puzzled, is she mad?*): What river?

THEO: Where we went skinny dipping with those geologists and their girls?

LYMAN (*at a loss for a moment*): Oh, you mean graduation night!

THEO: . . . The whole crowd swimming naked at the falls . . . and the girls all laughing in the darkness . . . ?

LYMAN (*starting to smile but still uncomprehending*): Oh sure . . . that was a great night!

THEO: I straddled you, and over your shoulder . . . did I dream this? I recall a white wall of limestone, rising straight out of the river . . . ?

LYMAN: That's right, Devonian. It was full of fossils.

THEO: Yes! Beetle imprints, worm tracks, crustacea fifty million years old going straight up like a white temple wall . . . and we floated around below, like two frogs attached in the darkness . . . our wet eyelashes touching.

LYMAN: Yes. It was beautiful. I'm glad you remember it that way.

THEO: Of course I do; I was never a Puritan, Lyman, it is simply a question of taste—that night was inspiring.

LYMAN: Well, I never had taste, we both know that. But I won't lie to you, Theo—taste to me is what's left of life after people can't screw anymore.

THEO: You should have told me that thirty years ago.

LYMAN: I didn't know it thirty years ago.

THEO: And do you remember what you said as we floated there?

LYMAN (*hesitates*): Yes.

THEO: You couldn't.

LYMAN: I said, "What could ever come between us?" Correct?

THEO (*surprised, derailed*): But did you mean that then? Please tell me the truth, its important to me.

LYMAN (*affected*): Yes, I meant it.

THEO: Then ... when did you begin to fool me?

LYMAN: Please don't go on anymore ...

THEO: I am trying to pinpoint when my life died. That's not unreasonable, is it?

LYMAN: From my heart, Theo, I ask your pardon.

THEO: When did Billie Holliday die?

LYMAN (*perplexed*): Billie Holliday? Oh I don't know, ten, twelve years ago? Why? (*Theo goes silent, staring into space. He is suddenly weeping at the sight of her suffering*) Why do you want to know about Billie?

BESSIE: All right, Mother, let's go, huh?

LYMAN: I think it might be better if she talked it out ...

BESSIE: No one is interested in what you think. (*To Theo*) I want you to come now!

LYMAN: Have mercy!

BESSIE: You talking mercy?!

LYMAN: For her, not me! Don't you hear what she's trying to say? She loved me!

BESSIE: How can you listen to this shit!

77

LYMAN: How dare you! Bessie, I gave you a damned fine life!

BESSIE: You have nothing to say anymore, you are nonsense!

THEO: Please dear! Wait outside for a few minutes. (*Bessie, seeing her adamance, strides out*) You've torn out her heart. (*Lyman turns away trying not to weep*) Was there some pleasure in making a fool of me? Why couldn't you have told me about this woman?

LYMAN: I did try, many times, but . . . I guess it sounds crazy, but . . . I just couldn't bear to lose you.

THEO: But—(*With sudden intensity*) you were lying to me every day all these nine or ten years—what could you possibly lose?

LYMAN (*determined not to flinch*): Your happiness.

THEO: *My* happiness! In God's name what are you talking about!

LYMAN: Only the truth can help us, Theo—I think you were happier in those years than ever in our marriage—you feel that, don't you? (*She doesn't contradict*) May I tell you why? Because I was never bored being with you.

THEO: You'd been bored with me?

LYMAN: Same as you'd been bored with me, dear . . .

I'm talking about—you know—just normal marital boredom. (*She seems obtuse to this, so he tries to explain*) You know, like at dinner—when I'd repeat some inane story you'd heard a thousand times . . . ? Like my grandfather losing three fingers under the Ninth Avenue trolley . . . ?

THEO: But I loved that story! I was *never* bored with you . . . stupid as that was.

LYMAN (*now she just seems perverse*): Theo, you were bored—it's no sin! Same as I was when, for instance, you'd start telling people for the ten thousandth time that—(*His charming laugh*) as a minister's daughter you were not permitted to climb a tree and show off your panties?

THEO (*sternly resisting his charm*): But I think that story describes a kind of society that has completely disappeared! That story has historical importance!

LYMAN (*the full agony*): That story is engraved in my flesh! . . . And I beg you, don't make this a moral dilemma. It is just common domestic tedium, dear, it is life, and there's no other woman I know who has the honesty and strength to accept it as life—if you wanted to!

THEO (*a pause; above her confusion, she is striving desperately to understand*): And why do you say I was happier in these last years?

LYMAN: Because you could see my contentment, and I was content . . .

THEO: Because she . . . ?

LYMAN: Because whenever you started with your panties again I could still find you lovable, knowing that story was not going to be my entire and total fate till the day I died.

THEO: Because she was waiting for you.

LYMAN: Right.

THEO: You were never bored with *her*?

LYMAN: Oh God yes! Sometimes even more than with you.

THEO (*with quick intense hopeful curiosity*): Really! And what then?

LYMAN: Then I would thank my luck that I had you to come back to. I know how hard this is to understand, Theo.

THEO: No-no . . . I guess I've always known it.

LYMAN: What.

THEO: You are some kind of . . . of giant clam.

LYMAN: Clam?

THEO: Waiting on the bottom for whatever happens to fall from the ocean into your mouth; you are simply a craving, and that craving you call love. You are a kind of monster, and I think you even know it, don't you. I can almost pity you, Lyman. (*She turns to leave*) I hope you make a good recovery. It's all very clear now, I'm glad I stayed.

LYMAN: It's amazing—the minute the mystery of life appears, you think everything's cleared up.

THEO: There's no mystery to me, you have never loved anyone!

LYMAN: Then explain to yourself how this worthless, loveless, treacherous clam could have singlehandedly made two such different women happier than they'd ever been in their lives!

THEO: Really! (*Laughs ending in a near-scream*) Really and truly *happy*?!

LYMAN: In fact, if I dared admit the whole idiotic truth, the only one who suffered these past nine years— was *me!* (*He leaps out of bed as an enormous echoing roar fills the theater—the roar of a lion. Light rises on Bessie looking front through field glasses; she is wearing shorts and pith helmet and khaki safari jacket*)

THEO: *You suffering?* Oh dear God save us!

(*She is trying to sustain her bitter laughing and moves toward Bessie, and as she enters Bessie's area her laughter dies off and she takes a pith helmet out of a picnic basket and puts it on. There is no dialogue break*)

LYMAN: What would you call it, then—having to look into your innocent, loving faces, when I knew the hollowness your happiness was based on? That isn't suffering?

(*He takes his place beside the two women, looking in the same direction out front, shading his eyes*)

BESSIE (*looking through field glasses*): Good heavens, is he going to mount her *again?*

LYMAN: They don't call him the king of the beasts for nothing, honey.

BESSIE: Poor thing, how patient she is.

THEO (*taking the glasses from her*): Oh come, dear, she's not *only* patient.

BESSIE (*spreading a tablecloth and picnic things on the ground*): But it's only once every half a year, isn't it?

LYMAN: Once that we *know* about.

THEO (*helping to spread the picnic*): Oh no, they're marvelously loyal couples.

LYMAN: No, dear, lions have harems—you're thinking of storks.

BESSIE (*offering an egg*): Daddy?

LYMAN (*sitting—happily eating*): I love you in those helmets, you look like two noble ladies on safari.

THEO (*stretching out on the ground*): The air here! The silence. These hills.

BESSIE: Thanks for bringing me, Daddy. I wish Harold could have been here. Why do you look sad?

LYMAN: Just thinking. (*To Theo*) About monogamy—why do you suppose we think of it as a higher form of life? (*She turns up to him . . . defensively*) . . . I mean I was just wondering.

THEO: Well, it implies an intensification of love.

LYMAN: How about that, Bess? You had a lot of boyfriends before Harold, didn't you?

BESSIE: Well . . . yes, I guess it is more intense with one.

LYMAN: But how does that make it a higher form?

THEO: Monogamy strengthens the family; random screwing undermines it.

LYMAN: But as one neurotic to another, what's so good about strengthening the family?

THEO: Well, for one thing it enhances liberty.

BESSIE: Liberty? Really?

THEO: The family disciplines its members; when the family is weak the state has to move in; so the stronger the family the fewer the police. And that is why monogamy is a higher form.

LYMAN: Jesus, did you just make that up? (*To Bessie*) Isn't she marvelous? I'm giving her an A-plus!

THEO (*happily hurt*): Oh shut up.

LYMAN: But what about those Muslims? They're very big on stable families but a lot of them have two or three wives.

THEO: But only one is really the *wife*.

LYMAN: Not according to my father—they often had two main women in Albania, one to run the house and the other for the bed. But they were both serious wives.

THEO: Your father's sociology was on a par with his morals. A wife to your father was a walking dish towel.

LYMAN (*laughs, to Bessie*): Your mother is a classical woman, you know why?

BESSIE (*laughing delightedly*): Why?

LYMAN: Because she is always clear and consistent and . . .

THEO: . . . Rather boring.

(*Lyman guffaws, warmly, clapping his hands over his head in appreciation*)

BESSIE: You are not boring! (*Rushing to embrace Theo*) Tell her she is not boring!

LYMAN (*Embracing Theo with Bessie*): Theo, please . . . I swear I didn't mean boring!

THEO (*tearfully hurt*): Well I'd rather be boring and clear than cute and stupid!

LYMAN: Who asked you to be cute! Now please don't go on about it.

THEO: I wish I knew how to amuse you! Your eyes have been glazed over since we stepped onto this wretched continent!

LYMAN (*guiltily stretching an awkward embrace toward her*): I *love* this trip, and being with both of you . . . ! I love it! Theo, please! Now you are making me guilty!

(*The lion's roar interrupts and they all look front in shock*)

BESSIE: Is he heading here . . . ? Daddy! He's trotting!

GUIDE'S VOICE (*off, on bullhorn*): You will have to come back to the car, everyone! At once!

LYMAN: Quick!

(*He pushes both women; a man rolls on a potted palm and they hide behind it*)

BESSIE (*on exiting*): Daddy, come . . . !

THEO (*sensing he is remaining behind*): Lyman . . . ?

LYMAN: Go! (*He pushes her off, but turns back himself*)

GUIDE'S VOICE: Come back to the car at once, Mr. Felt! (*Lion's roar—but closer now. Lyman facing front and the lion, prepared to run for it but holding his ground*) Mr. Felt, get back to the car! (*Another roar*)

LYMAN (*Eyes on the lion, shouting toward it with fear's exhilaration*): I *am* happy, yes! That I'm married to Theodora and have Bessie . . . yes, *and Leah, too!* (*Another roar*)

BESSIE (*from a distance*): Daddy, please come here!

LYMAN: And that I've made a mountain of money . . . yes, and have no impending lawsuits!

BESSIE (*from a distance*): Daddy . . . !

LYMAN (*Flinging his words toward the approaching beast, but crouched and ready to flee*): . . . And that I don't sacrifice one day to things I don't believe in— including monogamy, yes! (*Arms thrown out, terror-inspired*) I love my life, I am not guilty! I dare you to eat me, son of a bitch!

(*Immense roar! Wide-eyed, crouched now and on the very verge of fleeing, he is watching the approaching lion—whose roar, as we now hear, has changed to a rather more relaxed guttural growling, much diminished; and Lyman cautiously straightens up, and now turns triumphantly toward the women offstage. And Bessie flies out and throws her arms around him in ecstatic relief, kissing him*)

BESSIE (*looking front*): Daddy, he turned back! What did you do that for!

(*Theo enters from behind the plant*)

THEO: He turned back! (*To Lyman*) How did you do that! (*To Bessie*) Did you see how he stopped and turned around? (*To Lyman*) What happened?

LYMAN: I think I've lost my guilt! I think he sensed it! (*Half-laughing*) Maybe lions don't eat happy people!

THEO: What are you talking about?

LYMAN (*staring in wonder*): I tell you his roar hit my teeth like voltage and suddenly it was so clear that . . . (*Turns to her*) I've always been happy with you, Theo! I just somehow couldn't accept it! But I am never going to apologize for my happiness again! It's a miracle!

THEO (*with tears of gratitude, clasping her hands together prayerfully*): Oh, Lyman! (*Rushing to kiss him*) Oh, darling!

87

LYMAN (*still riding his wave, holding out his hand to her*): What old good friends we are, Theo! Put her there! (*She laughs and manfully shakes hands*) What a *person* you are, what a grave and beautiful face you have!

BESSIE: Oh, Daddy, that's so lovely! You're just marvellous! (*She weeps*)

LYMAN: I worship this woman, Bessie! (*To Theo*) How the hell are we still together? (*To Bessie*) Do you realize how she must love me to stand for my character?

THEO: Oh, this is what I always saw happening someday! (*A sophisticated laugh*) Not with a lion, of course, but exactly this sudden flash of light . . . !

LYMAN: The whole future is clear to me now! We are going to march happily into our late middle age, proudly, heads up! I'm going to build a totally selfish little cottage in the Carribean and we'll fill it up with all the thick English novels we never got to finish . . . plus Proust! And I'll buy two mopeds with little baskets on the handlebars for the shopping trips . . .

THEO: I knew it, I knew it!

LYMAN: . . . And I'll spend every day with you—except maybe a week or so a month in the Elmira office!

BESSIE: How fantastic, Mother!

THEO: Thank you, lion! Thank you, Africa! (*Turning to him*) Lyman?

LYMAN (*already mentally departing the scene*): . . .
Huh? Yes!

THEO: I am all new!

(*She throws her arms around him, burying her face in
his neck. He looks front with an expression of deepening
agony*)

BESSIE: This has been the most fantastic two weeks
of my life! I love you, Daddy! (*She rushes to him and
with one arm he embraces her, the other around Theo.
Tears are starting in his eyes*) Are you weeping?

LYMAN: Just amazement, honey . . . at my luck, I
guess. Come, we'd better go back.

(*Somberly he turns them upstage; lights are changing,
growing dimmer, and they walk into the darkness
while he remains behind. Alone he slowly turns front;
light spreads and reveals the Nurse sitting near the
bed*)

NURSE (*to the pillow, as earlier*): The only thing I
don't understand is why you married that woman, a
smart man like you.

(*Lyman stares ahead as Leah appears, isolated in light;
she is in her fur coat, exactly as in Act I when she was
about to go for an abortion. The Nurse remains in periphery, immobile*)

LEAH: Yes, I suppose it could wait a week or so, but

. . . really, Lyman, you know you're never going to leave her.

LYMAN: You cancel the operation, okay? And I'm telling her tomorrow.

LEAH: You're telling her what?

LYMAN (*almost holding his breath*): I will not rationalize you away. I have one life! I'm going to ask her for a divorce.

LEAH: My God, Lyman! But listen, I know your attachment to her . . .

LYMAN (*he kisses her hand*): Please keep this baby. Will you? And stay home and cross your legs, you hear?

LEAH: Would you stop worrying about another man, okay? This is serious?

LYMAN: This is serious. I'm asking her for a divorce.

LEAH: Suddenly . . . why am I not sure I want to be a mother! Do I, do you think?

LYMAN: Yes you do, we think! (*Kisses her. They laugh together. He turns to leave; she grasps his hands and presses them together between hers in a prayerful gesture; and facing heaven . . .*)

LEAH: Please! Some good luck! (*To Lyman directly*)

Why is everything so dangerous! (*She gives him a violent kiss*)

(*Theo appears walking; she is hiding something behind her back and smiling lovingly. Lyman appears. He looks solemn, prepared for the showdown*)

LYMAN: Theo, dear . . . there's something I have to tell you . . .

THEO (*holding out a cashmere sweater*): Happy birthday!

LYMAN (*startled*): Hah? But it's not July, is it!

THEO: But it was so sinfully expensive I needed an excuse. (*Putting him into the sweater*) It's Italian. Here . . . straighten it. It's not too big, is it? (*Stepping back to admire*) It's gorgeous, look in the mirror!

LYMAN: It's beautiful, thank you, dear. But listen, I really have something to . . .

THEO: My God, Lyman, you are simply magnificent! (*Linking arms with him and walking in her cumbersome way*) I have another surprise—I got tickets for the Balanchine! And a table at Luigi's afterwards!

LYMAN (*grimly screwing up his courage—and beginning to resent her domination*) I have something to tell you, Theo, why do you make it so hard for me!

THEO: What. (*He is paralyzed*) What is it? Has some-

thing happened? (*Alarmed now*) Lyman! (*Asking*)—
you went for your checkup!

LYMAN (*about to explode*): God's sake, no, it's not that!

THEO: Why is your face so grey? Please, what is it,
you look terrified! (*He moves away from her and her
awful caring, and halts facing front. She remains behind and calls to him from the distance*)—My cousin
Wilbur's still at Mass. General, we can go up there
together . . . ! Please, darling, don't worry about
anything . . . ! What is it, can't you tell me?

(*In total blockage—both in the past and in the present—
he inhales deeply and lets out a gigantic long howl, arms
raised, imploring heaven for relief. In effect, it blasts her
out of his mind—she deanimates and goes dark, and he
is alone again*)

LYMAN (*to himself, facing front*): No guts. That's the
whole story. Courage! If I'd been honest for three
consecutive minutes . . . No! I know what's wrong
with me—I could never stand still for death! Which
you've got to do by a certain age, or be ridiculous—
you've got to stand there nobly and serene . . . (*Leah
is gone now, he's alone*) . . . and let death run his tape
out your arms and around your belly and up your
crotch until he's got you fitted for that last black suit.
And I can't, I won't! . . . So I'm left wrestling with this
anachronistic energy which . . . (*As he leaps onto bed,
crying out to the world*) . . . God has charged me with
and I will use it till the dirt is shovelled into my
mouth! Life! Life! Fuck death and dying!

(*Pulls up covers. Light widens, finding Leah in the present, dressed differently than previously—in her fur coat—standing near the bed with the Nurse, listening to his shouts*)

NURSE: Don't be afraid, just wait a minute, he comes out of it. I'm sure he wants to see you.

LEAH (*moving tentatively to the cast*): Lyman? (*He looks at her with cloudy recognition*) It's me, Leah.

(*Nurse exits. Lyman now fully aware of Leah*)

LYMAN: Leah! (*Turning away from her*) Jesus, what have I done to you! Wait . . . (*A moment. He looks around*) Was Theo here?

LEAH: I think she's gone, I just got here.

LYMAN: Oh, Leah, it's sitting on my chest like a bag of cement.

LEAH: What is?

LYMAN: My character.

LEAH: Yes, well . . . it's pretty bad. Listen . . .

LYMAN (*moved*): Thanks for coming. You're a friend.

LEAH: I only came about Benny.

LYMAN (*about to weep again*): What's he saying?

LEAH (*frustrated, turns away*): He's excited that he has a sister.

LYMAN (*painful admiration*): Oh that dear boy!

LEAH: He's very badly mixed up, Lyman; he's seen us all on TV and the other kids tell him he has two mothers. He keeps asking me are you coming home again. It's twisting my heart. I'm terrified if this isn't settled right it could screw up the rest of his life. (*Tears start*) You're his idol, his god, Lyman!

LYMAN: Oh, the wreckage, the wreckage . . .

LEAH: Tell me the truth; whichever it is is okay but I just want to know—do you feel a responsibility or not?

LYMAN (*flaring up, scared as much as indignant*): How can you ask such a thing?

LEAH: Why! That's a reasonable question!

LYMAN: Now listen to me—I know I'm wrong and I'm wrong and I'm wrong but I did not throw you both across my saddle to rape you in my tent! You knew I was married, and you tried to make me love you, so I'm not entirely . . .

LEAH: Lyman, if you're blaming me I'm going to sink through this floor!

LYMAN: I'm talking about truth not blame—this is not entirely a one man disaster!

LEAH: It's amazing, the minute you talk about truth

you always come out looking better than anyone else!

LYMAN: Now that's unfair!

LEAH (*slight pause*): I want to talk about Benny.

LYMAN: You could bring him tomorrow if you like. But go ahead, we can talk now.

LEAH (*A pause as she settles down*): I'm thinking.

LYMAN: Well stop thinking and bring him!

LEAH (*with a flushed grin*): Incidentally . . . they tell me you spent over an hour with your wife. Are you settling in there again?

LYMAN: All she did was sit there telling me I'm a monster who never loved anybody.

LEAH (*with a hard grin*): And you reassured her otherwise, of course.

LYMAN: Well, I did love her. And you know that better than anybody.

LEAH: What a piece of work you are, Lyman, really— you go falling off a mountain and you still don't understand your hatred for that woman. It's monumental. It's . . . it's *oceanic.*

LYMAN: What the hell is this now!

LEAH: My dear man, in case it slipped your mind, when we'd been married for two months we went to New York and you picked the Carlyle Hotel to stay at—four blocks from your house! "Loved her" . . . good God! (*A window begins to appear upstage with Theo seated in profile, reading a book. He is staring as he emerges from the bed, turning to look up at the window. Leah goes on with no pause*) What was all that about if it wasn't hatred! And walking me past your front window with her sitting there . . . ? You had murder in you and you still do! Probably for me too!

LYMAN (*glancing up at Theo in the window*): But it didn't feel like murder at all. I was dancing the high wire on the edge of the world . . . finally risking everything to find myself! Strolling with you past my house, the autumn breeze, the lingerie in the Madison Avenue shop windows, the swish of . . . wasn't it a taffeta skirt you wore? (*She is moving toward him, part of his recall*) . . . And how languorous you were, glowing in your new motherhood. I'd beaten guilt forever. (*She takes on the ease of that long-ago stroll, and . . .*)

LEAH: Is that her? (*Lyman looks up at Theo then at Leah, inspired, alive*)

LYMAN: Oh Leah darling, how sexy you look against tall buildings.

LEAH (*with a warm smile, taking his arm*): You're tense, aren't you.

LYMAN: Well, I lived here with her for so many years
. . . You know? I'd love to go in and say hello . . . But
I don't have the guts . . .

LEAH: Was she very upset when you told her?

LYMAN (*tragically, but hesitates*): Very, yes.

LEAH: Well, maybe she'll think of marrying again.

LYMAN: Marrying again? (*With a glance to the window; loosening her grip on his arm*) I doubt it,
somehow.

LEAH (*with an intrigued smile*): Mustn't we touch?

LYMAN (*quickly regaining her arm*): Of course! (*They
start walking away*)

LEAH: I'd love to meet her sometime . . . just as
friends.

LYMAN: You might. (*Lyman halts. A strange determi-
nation suddenly*) Listen, I'd like to see if I can go in
and say hello.

LEAH: Why not? You don't want me to come, do you?

LYMAN: Not just yet. Would you mind a lot?

LEAH: Why! I'm glad that you still have feeling for her.

LYMAN: God, you have balls! I'll see you back at the
hotel in twenty minutes, okay?

LEAH: Take your time! I'll play with all that gorgeous underwear you bought. (*Touching her belly*) I'm so contented, Lyman!

(*She turns and walks toward the cast, which lights up. He remains below the window, staring at her departing figure*)

LYMAN (*alone*): Why is it the happier she is the sadder I get? Guilt, burn in hell! (*Now he again hurries toward the window . . . which disappears, as she rises, startled*)

THEO: Lyman! You said Tuesday, didn't you?

(*He takes her in his arms, kisses her frantically. She is surprised and happy*)

LYMAN: What a handsome lady! Theo, you are God's handwriting.

THEO: Ralph Waldo Emerson.

LYMAN: Someday I'm going to swipe an image you never heard of! (*Laughing, in a comradely style, embraces her closely as he takes her to a seat—stoking up a certain excited intimacy here*) Listen, I just hitched a ride down with this pilot in his new Cessna—I have meetings up there starting seven-thirty tomorrow but I just had to astonish you.

THEO: You flew in a small plane *at night?*

LYMAN: That whole fear was guilt, Theo—I thought

I *deserved* to crash. But I deserve to live because I am not a bad guy and I love you.

THEO: Well, I'm floating away! When must you go back?

LYMAN: Now.

THEO (*near laughter at the absurdity*): Can't we even chat?

LYMAN: Let me call that I'm on my way. (*Dials a phone*)

THEO: I'll drive you to the airport.

LYMAN: No, he's picking me up at the Carlyle . . . Hello?

(*Lights up on Leah in negligee, holding a phone*)

LEAH: Darling!

LYMAN: Be there in ten minutes.

LEAH (*puzzled*): Oh? Okay. Why are you calling?

LYMAN: Just to make sure you didn't forget me and took off.

LEAH: Your jealousy is so comforting! You know, she made a very dignified picture, reading in the window—it was like an Edward Hopper, kind of haunted.

LYMAN: Yes. Well, I'm leaving right now.

(*He hangs up, kisses the phone. Theo, misunderstanding, kisses the air in his direction*)

THEO: You won't forget about dinner Thursday with Leona and Gilbert . . . he's gotten his hearing aid so it won't be so bad.

LYMAN (*with a certain solemnity, taking her hands*): I just had to steal this extra look at you . . . life's so stupidly short, Theo.

THEO (*happily*): Why must death always sit on your shoulder when you've got more life in you than anybody! (*Ruffling his hair*) In fact, you're kind of sparkly tonight.

LYMAN (*responding to her acceptance*): Listen, we have time to make love.

THEO (*with a surprised, delighted laugh*): I wish I knew what's come over you!

LYMAN: The realization of what a sweet piece of ass my wife is. (*He starts to lead her*)

THEO: I bet its the new office in Elmira—new beginnings are always so exciting! There's such power in you, Lyman.

LYMAN (*turning her to him, he kisses her mouth*): Yes, we're going to do great business up there! Tell me something—has there ever been a god who was guilty?

THEO: Gods are never guilty, that's why they're gods.

LYMAN: It feels like the moon's in my belly and the sun's in my mouth and I'm shining down on the world. (*Laughs with a self-mocking charm*) . . . A regular planetary flashlight! Come! (*And laughing in high tension takes her hand and moves her into darkness . . .*)

THEO: Oh, Lyman—how wonderfully, endlessly changing you are!

(*Lights up on Leah in hospital room; Lyman is returning to the bed*)

LEAH: So you bopped her that night.

LYMAN: What can I say?

LEAH: And when you came back to the hotel, didn't we . . . ?

LYMAN: I couldn't help myself, you both looked absolutely gorgeous! How can that be evil?

LEAH (*with a sigh*): There's just no end to you, is there. Listen, I came to talk business; I want the house transferred to my name . . .

LYMAN: *What?*

LEAH: . . . Immediately. I know how much feeling you put into it but I want the security for Benny's sake.

LYMAN: Leah, I beg you to wait with that . . .

LEAH: I will not wait with that! And I want my business returned to me.

LYMAN: That'll be complicated—it's many times bigger than when I took it over . . .

LEAH: I want it back! I would have expanded without you! I'm not going to be a *total* fool! I will sue you!

LYMAN (*with a very uncertain grin*): You'd really sue me?

LEAH (*searching in hr pocketbook*): I'm not fooling around, Lyman. You've hurt me very deeply . . . (*Breaks off, holding back tears. She takes out a sheet of paper*)

LYMAN (*forced to turn from her*): Jesus, how I hate to see you cry.

LEAH: I have something I want you to sign.

LYMAN: To *sign?*

LEAH: It's a quit-claim on the house and my business. Will you read it?

LYMAN: You're not serious.

LEAH: I had Ted Lester draw it up. Here, read it.

LYMAN: I know what a quit-claim is, don't tell me to read a quit-claim. How can you do this?

LEAH: We aren't married and I don't want you making claims on me.

LYMAN: And . . . and what about Benny. You don't mean you're taking Benny from me . . .

LEAH: I . . .

LYMAN: I want you to bring him here tomorrow morning so I can talk to him.

LEAH: Just a minute . . .

LYMAN: No! You're going to bring him, Leah . . .

LEAH: Now you listen to me! I will not allow you to see him until I know what you intend to say to him about all this. I've also been through it with my father's old lawyer and you haven't a legal leg to stand on.

LYMAN: I'll tell him the truth—I love him.

LEAH: You mean it's all right to lie and deceive people you love? He's all I have now, Lyman, I am not going to see him go crazy!

LYMAN: Now you stop that! I did a helluva lot more than lie to him . . .

LEAH (*outpouring*): You lied to him! Why don't you seem to register this? . . . To buy him the pony, and teach him to ski, and take him up in the glider . . . you made him worship you . . . when you knew what you knew! That was cruelty!

LYMAN: All right, what do you think I should tell him?

LEAH: That you beg his pardon and say he mustn't follow your example because lying to people injures them.

LYMAN: I am not turning myself into a pile of shit in front of my son's face! If I can teach him anything now it's to have the guts to be true to himself! That's all that matters!

LEAH: Even if he has to betray the whole world to do it?

LYMAN (*in an agony*): Only the truth is sacred, Leah!—to hold back nothing!

LEAH: You must be crazy—you held back everything! You really don't know right from wrong, do you!

LYMAN: Jesus Christ, you sound like Theo!

LEAH: Well maybe it's what happens to people who marry you! Look—I don't think it's a good idea at the moment . . .

LYMAN: I have a right to see my son!

LEAH: I won't have him copying you, Lyman, it will destroy his life! I'm leaving! (*She starts to leave*)

LYMAN: You bring me Benny or I'll . . . I'll sue you, goddamit!

(*Enter Bessie alone. She is extremely tense and anxious*)

BESSIE: Oh, good, I was hoping you'd still be here. Listen . . .

LEAH: I was just going . . .

BESSIE: Oh please wait! My mother's had an attack of some kind . . .

LYMAN: My god, what is it?

BESSIE: They're looking at her in a room down the hall. She's a little delusionary and talks about taking him home with her, and I think it would help for her to see you're still together.

LEAH: But we're not at all together . . .

LYMAN: Wait! Why must it be delusional—maybe she really wants me back!

BESSIE (*with a frustrated stamp of her foot*): I want her out of here and home!

LYMAN: I am not a monster, Bessie! My God, where did all this cruelty come from!

LEAH: He wants her, you see . . .

LYMAN: I want you both!

BESSIE (*an hysterical overtone, screaming*): Will you once in your life think of another human being!

(*Tom and Theo enter with the Nurse; he has her by the arm. She has a heightened, seeing air about her, but a fixed, dead smile, and her head trembles*)

LYMAN: Theo! Come, sit her down, Tom!

LEAH (*to Bessie, fearfully*): I really feel I ought to go . . .

THEO: Oh, I wish you could stay for a few minutes! (*To Nurse*) Please get a chair for Mrs. Felt.

(*The reference surprises Bessie. Leah looks quickly to Bessie, perplexed because this is the opposite of what Bessie and Theo wished. Lyman is immensely encouraged. The Nurse, as she goes out for the chair, glances about, perplexed*)

THEO (*pleasantly*): Well! Here we are all together. (*Slight pause*)

TOM: She's had a little . . . incident, Lyman. (*To Bessie*) I've arranged for a plane; the three of us can fly down together.

BESSIE: Oh good. We're ready to leave whenever you say, Mother.

LYMAN: Thanks, Theo . . . for coming.

THEO (*turns to him, smiling blankly*): Socialism is dead.

LYMAN: Beg your pardon?

THEO: And Christianity is finished, so . . . (*Searches*) . . . there really is nothing left to . . . to . . . to defend—except simplicity? (*She crosses her legs, and her coat falls partially open revealing a bare thigh*)

BESSIE: Mother! Where's your skirt?

THEO: I'm comfortable, it's all right . . .

(*Nurse enters with a chair*)

BESSIE: She must have left her skirt in that room she was just in—would you get it, please?

(*Nurse, perplexed again, exits*)

THEO (*to Leah*): I wish I hadn't carried on that way . . . I'm sorry. I've really nothing against you personally, I just never cared for your *type*. The surprise is what threw me, I mean that you were actually married. But I think you are rather an interesting person. I was just unprepared, but I'm seeing things much clearer now. Yes. (*Breaks off*) Do you see the *Village Voice* up here?

LEAH: Yes, occasionally.

THEO: There was a strange interview some years back with Isaac Bashevis Singer, the novelist? The interviewer was a woman whose husband had left her for another woman, and she couldn't understand why. And Singer said, "Maybe he liked her hole better." I was shocked at the time, really outraged—you know, that he'd gotten a Nobel; but now I think it was courageous to have said that, because it's probably true. Courage . . . courage and directness are always the main thing!

(*Nurse enters, offers Theo the skirt*)

NURSE: Can I help you on with it?

THEO (*takes the skirt, looks at it without recognition, and drops it on the floor*): I can't remember if I called you Leah or Mrs. Felt.

LEAH: I'm not really Mrs. Felt.

THEO (*with a pleasant social smile*): Well, you are *a* Mrs. Felt; perhaps that's all one can hope for when we are so interchangeable—who knows anymore which Mrs. Felt will be coming down for breakfast! (*Short pause*) Your boy needs his father, I imagine.

LEAH: Well . . . yes, but . . .

THEO: Then he should be here with you, shouldn't he. We must all be realistic now. (*To Lyman*) You can come up here whenever you want to . . . if that's what you'd really like.

BESSIE (*to Tom*): She's really too ill for this. Come, Mother, we're going.

THEO: I'm not at all ill; (*to Lyman*) I can say "fuck" you know. I never cared for the word but I'm sure she has her limitations too. I can say "fuck me, Lyman," "fuck you, Lyman," whatever.

(*Lyman is silent in guilty anguish*)

BESSIE (*to Lyman, furiously*): Will you tell her to leave? Just out of respect, out of friendship!

LYMAN: Yes. (*Delicately*) She's right, Theo, I think that would be the best . . .

THEO (*to Bessie*): But I can take better care of him at home. (*To Leah*) I really have nothing to do, and you're busy, I imagine . . .

BESSIE: Tom, will you . . .

TOM: Why don't we let her say what's on her mind?

THEO (*to Bessie*): I want to start being real—he had every right to resent me. What did I ever do but correct him? (*To Leah*) You don't correct him, do you. You like him as he is, even now, don't you. And that's the secret, isn't it. (*To Lyman*) Well I can do that. I don't need to correct you . . . or pretend to . . .

BESSIE: I can't bear this, Mother!

THEO: But this is our *life,* Bessie dear; you must bear it. I think I've always pretty well known what he was doing. Somewhere inside we all really know everything, don't we? But one has to live, darling—one has to live—in the same house, the same bed. And so one learns to tolerate . . . it's a good thing to tolerate . . . (*a furious shout*) and tolerate, and tolerate!

BESSIE (*terrified for her mother*): Daddy, please . . . tell her to go!

LYMAN: But she's telling the truth!

LEAH (*suddenly filling up*): You poor woman! (*To him*) What a bastard you are; one honest sentence from you and none of this would have happened, it's despicable! (*Appealing to Theo*) I'm so sorry about it, Mrs. Felt . . .

THEO: No-no . . . he's absolutely right—he's always said it—it's life I can't trust! But you—you trust it, and that's why you *should* win out.

LEAH: But it's not true—I never really trusted him! Not really! I always knew there was something dreadful wriggling around underneath! (*In full revolt now*) I'll tell you the goddamned truth, I never really wanted to marry anybody! I've never known one happy couple! Listen, you mustn't blame yourself, the whole damned thing doesn't work, it never works . . . which I knew and went ahead and did it anyway and I'll never understand why!

LYMAN: Because if you hadn't married me you wouldn't have kept Benny, that's why. (*She can't find words*) You wouldn't have had Benny or this last nine years of your happiness. Shit that I am, I helped you become the woman you always wanted to be, instead of . . . (*Catches himself*) Well, what's the difference?

LEAH: No, don't stop—instead of what? What did you save me from?

LYMAN (*accepting her challenge*): All right . . . from all those lonely postcoital showerbaths, and the pointless pillow talk and the boxes of heartless condoms beside your bed . . . !

LEAH (*speechless*): Well now!

LYMAN: I'm sick of this crap, Leah! You got a little something out of this despicable treachery!

THEO: That's a terrible thing to say to the woman.

LYMAN: But the truth is terrible, what else have you just been saying? It's terrible because it's embarrassing, but the truth is always embarrassing or it isn't the truth! You tolerated me because you loved me, dear, but wasn't it also the good life that I gave you? Well, what's wrong with that? Aren't women people? Don't people love comfort and power? I don't understand the disgrace here!

BESSIE (*to both women*): Why are you still sitting

111

here, don't you have any pride! (*To Leah*) This is disgusting!

LEAH: Will you please stop this high moral tone? I have business with him, so I have to talk to him! I'll go out of my mind here! Am I being accused of something?

(*Off to the side, Tom bends his head over clasped hands, eyes shut*)

BESSIE: You shouldn't be in the same room with him!

LEAH (*rattled*): I just explained that, didn't I? *What the hell do you want?*

LYMAN (*crying out, voice cracking with a sob*): She wants her father back!

BESSIE: You son of a bitch! (*Raises her fists, then weeps helplessly*)

LYMAN: I love you—Bessie!—all of you!

BESSIE: You ought to be killed!

LYMAN: You are all magnificent!

(*Bessie bursts into tears. A helpless river of grief which now overflows to sweep up Lyman; then Leah is carried away by the wave of weeping. All strategies collapse as finally Theo is infected. The four of them are helplessly*

covering their faces. It is a veritable mass keening, a fu-
nerary explosion of grief, each for his or her own condi-
tion, for love's frustration, and for the end of all their
capacity to reason. Tom has turned from them, head
bent in prayer, hands clasped, eyes shut)

LYMAN (*his eye falls on Theo's bare leg*): Tom, please!
Get her to put some clothes on ... (*Breaks off*) Are
you praying, for Christ's sake?

TOM (*staring ahead*): There is no way to go forward.
You must all stop loving him. You must or he will destroy you. He is an endless string attached to nothing.

LYMAN: Who is not an endless string? Who is sworn
to some high golden purpose now—lawyers? Why
are you all talking nonsense?

TOM: Theo needs help now, Lyman, and I don't want
a conflict, so I don't see how I can go on representing you.

LYMAN: Of course not, I am not worthy. (*A shout, but*
with the strain of his loss, his inability to connect) But
I *am* human, and proud of it!—yes, of the glory and
the shit! The truth, the truth is holy!

TOM: Is it. Well! Then you'll admit that you moved
that barrier aside yourself, and drove onto that
sheet of ice? That's the truth, isn't it?

LYMAN (*instant's hesitation*): That was not suicide—
I am not a cop-out!

113

TOM: Why is it a cop-out? Your shame finally caught up with you—

LYMAN: Wait.

TOM: Or is that too true for comfort? Your shame is the best part of you, for God's sake, why do you pretend you're beyond it?

LYMAN: Wait!

TOM (*breaks off, giving it up*): I'm ready to go, Theo.

LYMAN (*nearly breathless, staring*): Wait. Wait. Wait! I'd like to tell you something.

BESSIE (*quietly relentless*): Mother? (*She raises Theo to her feet. Her head is trembling. She turns to Lyman*)

LYMAN (*a new desperation now*): Theo.

THEO: I have nothing left in me anymore, Lyman.

(*Bessie takes her by the arm to go. Leah stands, as though to leave*)

LYMAN: I beg you, Leah, stay two minutes.

LEAH (*an evasive color*): I have work in the office . . .

LYMAN (*losing control, open desperation*): Two minutes, Leah. I need to tell you . . . how I got on the Mount Morgan road! (*Everything stops*) I kept calling you, Leah, from the Howard Johnson's to tell you I'd be staying over because of the storm . . . but the line was busy. So I went to bed, but it was busy . . . over an hour . . . more! And I started to ask the operator to cut in as an emergency when . . .

LEAH: I was talking to my *brother!*

LYMAN: In Japan, for over an hour?

LEAH: He just got back on Monday.

LYMAN: It doesn't matter.

LEAH: It certainly does matter.

LYMAN: Please let me finish Leah. Remember what you once said to me—Leah; remember you said—"I might lie to you," remember that? Way at the beginning? It seemed so wonderful then . . . that you could be so honest; but now, remember that—all feeling seeped out of me, Leah—for myself and anybody else. I felt like a corpse. (*Something visionary and genuine in his voice holds them*) On my back in that room, snow piling up outside, the wind howling at my window, this whole ten-year commute seemed ludicrous, laughable. I didn't know why I'd done it. And I saw something so simple . . . and terrible. That I'd spent my life trying to stop the clock, trying never to die—every morning to be reborn, all fresh and wonderful and brand new, and that I'd sacrificed everyone I loved to that boy's dream. And there I lay, one o'clock in

115

the morning and your busy signal snarling in my ear, again and again and . . . I simply had to get out of that room! And I drove back into the storm and what I really thought—silly as it sounds now—was that if I walked in, two, three in the morning out of a roaring blizzard like that, you'd believe how desperately I needed you . . . *and I would believe it too!* I would believe in my love, Leah, and life would come back to me again! Tom, I don't remember wanting to crash, but I did and I needn't have. (*To the women*) I know I have harmed you; I know it is finished, but I swear I have never felt the pure love for all of you that I feel right now. But we mustn't part with even a small lie between us; it is also true that in some barbaric corner of my soul I still don't understand why I am condemned.

THEO: . . . Say goodbye to him, dear.

BESSIE (*dry-eyed now; her feeling clearer, she has a close to impersonal sound*): I hope you're better soon, Daddy. Goodbye.

(*Bessie leaves. Lyman turns to Leah*)

LYMAN: Oh Leah, say something tough and honest . . . the way you can.

LEAH: I don't know if I'll every believe anything . . . or anybody, again.

LYMAN: Oh no. No!—I haven't done that! (*A great weeping sweeps her and she rushes out*) Leah! Leah! Don't say I've done that! (*But she, too, is gone*) Theo.

(*Theo stands, looks long at Lyman, exits*)

TOM: Talk to you soon.

(*He sees that Lyman is lost in space, and he goes out. The Nurse comes from her corner to Lyman*)

NURSE: You got pain? (*He doesn't reply*) I'll get you something to smooth you out.

LYMAN: Wait, will you, don't leave me alone. Come sit over here. Come, don't be afraid. (*She comes and remains standing by the bed. He takes her hand*) I want to thank you for all your help, Logan. I won't forget your warmth especially. A woman's warmth is the last magic, you're a piece of the sun. Tell me something . . . when you're out there on the ice with your husband and your boy . . . what do you talk about?

NURSE: Well, let's see . . . this last time we all bought us some shoes at that big Knapp Shoe Outlet up there?—they're seconds, but you can't tell them from new.

LYMAN: So you talked about your new shoes?

NURSE: Well, they're great buys.

LYMAN: Right. That . . . that's just wonderful to do that. I don't know why, but it just is.

NURSE: I'll be right back (*She starts away*)

LYMAN: Hate me?

NURSE (*halts, with an embarrassed shrug*): I don't know. I got to think about it.

LYMAN: Come right back, huh? I'm still a little . . . shaky. (*She returns, leans down and kisses his cheek*) Why'd you do that?

NURSE: No reason. (*She exits*)

LYMAN (*painful wonder and longing in his face, his eyes wide, alive*): What a miracle everything is! Absolutely everything! . . . Imagine . . . three of them sitting out there together on that lake, talking about their shoes!

(*Blackout*)

MECHANICS' INSTITUTE
❦ MECHANICS' ❧
MERCANTILE LIBRARY

CLEOPATRA DISMOUNTS

Also by Carmen Boullosa from Grove Press:

They're Cows, We're Pigs

Leaving Tabasco

CLEOPATRA DISMOUNTS

A NOVEL BY
CARMEN BOULLOSA

Translated from the Spanish by

Geoff Hargreaves

Grove Press / New York

Originally published in Spanish by Editorial Debate, S.A., Madrid, under the title
De un salto descabalga la reina.

Published by arrangement with Julie Popkin, Popkin Literary Agency

Published simultaneously in Canada
Printed in the United States of America

FIRST EDITION

Library of Congress Cataloging-in-Publication Data
Boullosa, Carmen.
     [De un salto descabalga la reina. English]
     Cleopatra dismounts : a novel / by Carmen Boullosa ; translated from the Spanish
by Geoff Hargreaves.
          p. cm.
     ISBN 0-8021-1753-8
     1. Cleopatra, Queen of Egypt, d. 30 B.C.—Fiction.   I. Hargreaves, Geoff.
     II. Title.
PQ7298.12.O76D4313 2003
863'.64—dc21

                                                                    2003047018

Grove Press
841 Broadway
New York, NY 10003

03 04 05 06 07   10 9 8 7 6 5 4 3 2 1

To Roberto Bolaño, Francisco Goldman, and Paul Berman,
to whom,
in one way or another, I owe this book.

"My heart, my heart, be whole and free:
Love is thine only enemy."

—George Bernard Shaw, *Caesar and Cleopatra*

CLEOPATRA
DISMOUNTS

Prologue

Diomedes, the funny old fart, left behind a pile of documents, written in his own hand, but he gave me no clear idea what to do with them. "I'm leaving you things I want preserved and copied," he said. "My eternal rest depends on them."

With that, he lay down to sleep, for good. Without a word of goodbye! He breathed his last as if it were a matter of indifference.

His life went out like the flame of an exhausted oil lamp. Easier, because there was no guttering, no nervous flicker, no nothing. He gave up the ghost without a murmur. Imperturbably. Like a creature turned to stone. Exactly the way he'd lived, at least for as long as I'd known him. A man of stone, is precisely what he was. You know, I had never even heard the sound of his breathing.

"My eternal rest," I ask you! Did he want more of the same, in death as in life? Wasn't he sick of his stone-like state? Always perched there, motionless, immovable, petrified. Day and night, bent over his writing tablet, like he was nailed to the thing, like an old bone drying out in that cell of his, forever shut in, forever silent, doing nothing that amounted to anything, just scratch, scratch, scratch on his wax tablet, scribbling away all hours of the day and night. What did he want more peace for? Hadn't he had more than his fill of it already?

Since the day I started as his assistant, he didn't open his mouth to me. And what a mouth! Plagued by open sores. He didn't seem to be aware how revolting his dying flesh was. He was so blind to his own condition and everything else he didn't even notice the difference between day and night. The only thing he attended to was the rapid scribbling of his stylus on the wax. Mr. Scratch-his-wax! What a disgusting, dreary, old bore!

Three years I spent at his place, right up to his death. I never heard him utter a word of complaint. And I was there the whole time, listening, waiting for orders. He never gave me a single one. My job turned out to be the same as his, to wait for his death. Finally he let his life slip away, the same way he'd lived it, as if nothing were happening.

The total absence of drama, his desire not to rouse any desire, the will to reduce himself to absolute zero made him, I can tell you, as boring as hell! What could I have found interesting about him? That he was a record-breaking monument of dullness, maybe? Yes, they'd told me that he and Cleopatra, etc., etc. . . . . But I wasn't going to fall for that crap. No way. A sucker I am not.

Yet, when I thought about Cleopatra, the last words to come to mind were "boring, stupid, and decrepit." The mere mention of her name was enough to set bells ringing, shadows dancing, and handsome lips seeking out a handsome body. The name Cleopatra wakens the world to life.

I never figured out why Diomedes had hired me. Why the hell did he need a scribe at his side? What was the point of it? Nothing that I could see. Nothing at all. But I was a poor student and needed the cash. So I kept my mouth shut, pocketed the money, and got on with my job, which, to the best of my understanding, consisted of doing nothing.

I got dreadfully bored while he scribbled away like a man possessed. At the end, on that last day, he did give me an order, if you can call it that. I mean the few words he muttered before he died. Or burned out, as would be the truer description. Some people die, others just run out of fuel. Diomedes did the latter.

Thus, to fulfil my contract, now that he is gone, I read what he'd been writing on those tablets during his last years. I read every single word. Then I started to copy them in my own hand, which is a lot firmer than the old man's was, and a lot more legible, too, for that is the nature and beauty of ink. So far I've made two copies of his tablets. Once I've finished chatting with you, I'll start on the third copy. After that, I'll do the fourth, the fifth, and so on, till the end of my days. To my eyes, they are not well organized, but that's the order in which he left the tablets. So of necessity, I've made my own choices, and they are as follows: first, Cleopatra does the talking. Then Diomedes. In his rambling fashion he explains who he is and why he is transcribing the words of Cleopatra. Then come two more times the voice of Cleopatra, plus three short interventions from the old boy.

I've referred to Diomedes as an old fart, who did nothing but scratch wax tablets instead of his fat belly and who really disgusted me. It took me a positive effort even to look at him, while he died there bit by bit, in silence, from his revolting disease. It was beyond my comprehension what I was doing there. But now I've seen another side to him. I'm not unsaying anything I've said. I'll never rid my memory of his repulsive figure, but there is another way of seeing him. If I were to write his biography, I'd have to make two versions. In the first, he would be this boring, motionless bulk, with disease eating away at his face. In the second, there would be a young man trapped inside that rotting carcass. What sort of man? Well, a lively, sparky character, with burning appetites and smothering regrets, alert and vital, eager to get the best out of life. How do I reconcile him with that silent hulk? How do I decide which was the real Diomedes? Do I need to decide?

In those texts, Diomedes was trying to recapture Cleopatra's voice, trying to get her to speak through him. Isn't recapturing a sort of assimilating, eating, digesting? I'm reminded of the horses of the hero Diomedes, which Euripides talks about. They devoured human flesh. Maybe the old boy was devouring Cleopatra in his way, while I thought he was doing nothing whatsoever. And motionless as he was, working on his too difficult digestion, for she's not an easy dish!

The old boy turned into a lively youngster. Now, look, he's turned into a flesh-eating stallion. You can see why he ended up with three different portraits of the same Cleopatra. Each one appears at a different period of her life. I placed them in the order I personally liked best. First, Diomedes presents her talking, while she awaits death at the hands of the Romans, a Cleopatra in defeat. Then comes the girl Cleopatra, escaping from her father at the age of twelve and seeking out the alliances that will elevate her to the Egyptian throne. In the third version appears the young queen. Once again, she has momentarily lost the throne and once again she goes in search of military allies to restore what properly belongs to her. Why did I adopt this order? Because, as I read them, I began to see Cleopatra through the eyes of Diomedes. These texts are both hers and his. He shows us his Cleopatra, filtered through his feelings for her, her starry night sky glimpsed through his humble, squinting eyes. Between one voice of Cleopatra and another, I let Diomedes interject his views. Here and there, I must confess, I have even added silently an observation or two of my own. Why not? I have valid opinions, too, you know.

I am still unsettled by the difference between the Diomedes who so scrupulously reflected Cleopatra in his writings, and the blindly indifferent figure, careless of his own welfare, whom I myself saw each day. I believe he caught the genuine accents of some of Cleopatra's voice in these texts, as surely as if he again heard her speaking before him. But speaking in his own voice, the old boy revealed just how lost he had become.

That's all I have to say. I am going to copy out one more version of these words that you can now read for yourselves.

The Corpse

Your love has buried everything.
—Propertius

"I am dead, my king," I wrote to you, meaning that defeat had overtaken me, even before the battle at Actium. "I am dead, my king. The word will not scorch your mouth because I have been dead to you for some time now. Follow the steps of Dionysus. Your god has abandoned Alexandria. Attended by an ostentatious procession, he left by the eastern gate late at night, awash with music, bearing our laughter with him."

I can imagine how lost you must have felt, Mark Antony, on reading in that first sentence, penned by the living hand of Cleopatra: the details of my death. Around you, played your musicians, interpreting your sadness at the undeniable departure of your dear Dionysus. You read only the start of my letter, rashly jumping to erroneous conclusions and delivering yourself into the hands of your evil genius.

"I am a dead woman," I should have told you in my message. "I have been a corpse from even before the time I bore you twins, while you were celebrating your marriage to the sister of the man who wishes to turn himself into our torturer. From that moment on, I have been a dead woman. From that moment on, I suffocate, and I return to life only in your presence, rolling like a barren sphere toward the grave, or soaring like a golden

5

orange from the Garden of the Hesperides, tossed from the hand of the handsome hero—all as your caprices dictate. My willpower is stolen from me by yours, enslaved by your destiny since the time we conceived a woman and a man, a sun and a moon, when first you lived with me in Alexandria. You, Mark Antony, my guide and my destroyer, once again you have lost me and this time for ever."

Defeat, Marcus Antonius Dionysus Osiris, befell us long before the events in the Gulf of Ambracia, south of Epirus, facing the promontory of Actium. There we planned to make our move as soon as the enemy fleet gave us an opening. To provoke this, we sent out Publicola, pretending to be a rowdy boor, to attack them. But then I released to the winds the sails of my squadron's sixty ships and, loaded with the treasures of the Lagids, I fled the Peloponnesus to avoid a pointless sacrifice. With abrupt swiftness you followed me, chasing me in a quinquireme. You ordered the other 180 ships in your fleet to do the same. On board your ship you had Alexander of Syria and Artavasde, king of Armenia, the last of the Arsacids, son and heir of the great Tigranes.

When you and your men came aboard my vessel, the "Antony"—its purple sails aloft, swollen by a favorable wind—Artavasde witnessed your foolish outburst of rage at not having won the victory. You blamed the advice I gave you—to wage war at sea and not on land. It was wrong, I admit, but you could have ignored it, General, and relied on your own strategists.

After your show of fury came silence. For the three days it took us to reach Tenarus, you refused to speak. You broke silence only to answer (and then merely in the form of a question) the shouts of a cocky, strutting youth who wagged his spear at you. His chest bare, his sinews bronzed by the sun, he humiliated you, saved from our rage by our bad luck. In his light Liburnian ship he had overtaken us, his hair and beard unornamented but for sea-salt and sand. Seeing you hunched up and motionless, your face hidden in your hands, elbows on your knees, he plucked up enough courage to shout at you, all bravado, befouling you with ugly epithets.

"Who are you to be pursuing Antony?" was all you said. With a few astute commands you could have captured him and, if your frame of mind had not been so enfeebled, you would have had him strung up for far less an impertinence.

"I'm Eurycles, son of Lacares, blessed with the luck you so badly need. I am here to avenge the death of my father."

You did not explain to me that Lacares had been convicted of theft and then beheaded on your orders. You were still refusing to speak a word to me. Somebody else had to explain things to me before I understood that outrageous scene.

With these words Eurycles, the son of a thief, turned his ship around and attacked another of our contingent, carrying off its load of silver, more out of greed than a sense of honor. It was typical of a man who dared no more than shout that he wanted to avenge the insult to his family's name; his squalid inherited character proved how just had been the death sentence passed on his father. On the periphery of the battle, under the pretext of vengeance, the rascal stole from us; he sullied his hands with theft, like the vile devourers of carrion that stalk their prey in cowardly style only after the battle is over.

While the coward behaved this way, you did not stir an inch. You remained seated near the ship's keel, elbows on knees, your face in the palms of your hands. I could not take the reins and avenge this humiliation because the shame you were inflicting on us had shattered my will to act.

As for those who witnessed your reproaches, your anger, your stony silence, I hereby give the order for their decapitation. I had been planning this ever since we disembarked at Tenerus. There I visited the shrines of Demeter and Aphrodite. Jupiter's temple I avoided, for they say it contains the entrance to Hell. I want no record to remain of that degrading scene, where you were the *acrostolium* on the prow of my ship, the "Antony," exposing us in your weakness to so much humiliation that even a common thief, without brains, honor, or money ventured to attack us.

Those witnesses have been silent for one year, but what guarantee is there that they will be so for two? Hence, I order their execution. From that order I except you, Diomedes, for your eyes are not eyes; you are the hand with which I write these words: Behead the witnesses! I especially want Artavasde dead.

And yes, it's true, Mark Antony, you didn't want to take me to the confrontation with Octavius. You wanted me to stay in Alexandria. But I bribed your general, Canidius, to convince you of the advantages of taking me to the battleground. I allowed him to export, tax-free, 10,000 sacks of wheat and to import 5,000 ceramic jars. Hence he found the means to make you see how much you needed to take your Cleopatra to the scene of the battle.

If Diomedes does not know this—and I can see by your eyes you don't—it's because it was his own secretary who presented Canidius with the terms I sealed with my own signature. I wasn't thinking about war; I just couldn't bear, Antony, for you to be far away from me, to see you stolen again from your Cleopatra by the charms of a Roman wife.

I came back to the "Antony" to make that notorious return crossing. All the while, you, Antony, bent over, almost kneeling, sunk deep inside yourself, you were humiliating us both, all because of that sickly, second-rate weakling who had pursued us. Meanwhile that nobody, Octavius, was crowing over a victory that neither he nor his clever Agrippa deserved credit for. Standing high on the stern, he relished the thought of the praises his poets would lavish on him in the near future.

And you, Antony, did nothing but freeze into a stone. Mark my words, you were committing the worst of disgraces, the foulest of your crimes. There you were, transformed into a stone copy of a thinker, a bad-luck symbol aboard my ship, when you should have been acting the astute strategist, combining intelligence with daring, taking risks, giving the lie to everything your enemy wanted from you: that you had accepted defeat, that you had admitted his triumph, that you had accepted your overthrow and finally your departure from this life.

It was you who gave him the one thing he was seeking, a victory he did not deserve. You let your personal anguish deny access to you, to me, to Egypt, to our men, to my people, to our children.

With your head in your hands, motionless, stony in your rage against me, you made a gift to that ignoble creature of the entire Nile and its seven mouths—the Nile, "the Father of Life, the secret god who rises from secret shadows, the deity who floods the fields, who quenches the thirst of the flocks, who gives drink to the soil, who allows seeds to grow, the pasture to green, who provides delicious victuals. Along the Nile the wheat flows regularly to the granaries. Through it everything comes to new birth, everything receives nourishment, and the land tingles with joy." You surrendered to Octavius the date palm and the sycamore, the crocodile, the birds, the papyrus, the lotus flower, Upper and Lower Egypt, the red crown and the white crown, and the *psen* that unites them both. You handed over the dark soil, *keme,* that generates life on the banks of the river, and the reddish sands, *dasre.* You gave away the dark country, with all its fertility, and the golden country of the desert, dense with the memories of Hatseput, of Prince Sebeki, of the Theban king, Ahmes, of Tutankhamen in his war chariot. You bestowed on a despicable soul all the baggage of our dead, the pyramids gilded by the sun. You gave him our floods, our winters and summers. And worst of all, along with yourself, you handed him the surrender of our gods, Atum-Ra, the father of all the gods, and after him, Su,

Tefnut, Geb, Nut, Osiris, Set, Isis, Neftis, and Toth, the god of wisdom. Along with you there died everything we hold beautiful, *nefer* like the goddess Hator, kind as well as beautiful, *tut, menej,* and *tehen.*

You have permitted the man who schemed our overthrow to ready himself for writing his name on our temples, glory superimposed on glory, usurping what is rightly ours. You made him a gift of total control over Judaea, a control you so often denied to me. You surrendered Nabatea, Cyprus, and Ascalon. You bestowed on him our sages, astronomers, philosophers, poets, the library of Alexandria, the automata that Architas built in the shape of a wooden cock pigeon that flew. You showered him with our treasures, not only those that hands can touch and eyes can see, but those that only the soul can appreciate. You made him a present of the power of Greece, the power that we Lagids claim as our rightful inheritance. Enough!

You sowed the seeds of a conflagration, total and definitive, upon our two bodies interlocked in love's battles, and upon the indomitable Eros, the only god by whom you and I can be enslaved.

Defeat overtook me early. Even before the swallows nesting on the poop of my galley were attacked by others, late arrivals with savage beaks. On seeing the abandoned nests of their predecessors, they vented their fury on them as well, ripping them apart—a frightful omen. Before, the morale of our army declined at the first victory of Agrippa. Before, at our camp on the peninsula of Actium, you had Iamblicus, king of Arabia, put to the torture for his disloyalty. Before that, you had a Roman senator executed and embittered the spirits of our men even more. Before the fall of Corfu, before losing dozens of ships at Leucadia, before the disasters of Patras and Corinth.

With all that happening, what did it matter that we had already detected the treason of Domitius Enobarbus, though you had appointed him governor of Bythinia? We had also guessed at the treason of King Amintas, even after you had given him the throne of Bactria and Kabul. I paid him my respects by issuing a coin to commemorate his coronation. It bore the legend "Of the great, victorious King Amintas," though his only victory consisted of being named king by Mark Antony, and then only because he fascinated me with his description of the frontiers of Bactria, to the northeast, where on a chain of hills there stands a line of artificial prominences built in unsettling shapes out of huge, unbaked bricks and whose walls have a thickness equivalent to the height of ten men. Then followed the treason of King Deiotarus of Armenia, then that of Danidius, who was to be commander of the legions.

What did it matter that the cavalry and our fleet had surrendered to the crude seductions of Octavius? That your generals had scurried like lambs seeking the refuge of the farmyard, the minute they heard the name of Rome? That there were enough deserters to make up an army against us? What difference did it make that, thwarting our last chance of success, the quadriremes and quinquiremes I had had transported overland to the Red Sea were put to the torch by the treacherous King Malchus of Nabatea, by whose side you had only recently fought against Octavius?

You and I would have recovered everything, if we had still possessed our old vigor—if we had not allowed ourselves to be beaten by our greatest enemy. Worse for us than all the desertions was the scandal that befell Publius Ventidius, your master general, the sole Roman ever to bring the Parthians to their knees—it robbed you of him forever. With Publius Ventidius at our side, we could have crushed Agrippa to dust! And Agrippa is the only real strength that Octavius possesses.

While these betrayals were working against us, one thing did even more damage—a recurrent dream that haunted me in the small hours of the night, just before the sun rose. In it, my father Auletes, usually so kindly, turned solemn and cold, rebuking me and fixing on me an angry stare. My Caesar was seated with him at the same table and he, too, rebuked me with uncharacteristic wildness. Reclining by Caesar's side, as though he were his equal, was Apollodorus, my trusty Apollodorus, and he turned on me as well, glaring fiercely. He was the only one of the three I dared address.

"What makes you all so angry with me?" I asked.

"I am more than just angry with you," he replied. "Once too often you have spoken like an imbecile. An imbecile. An imbecile."

Then I would wake up.

This nightmare had a more powerful effect on me than all the betrayals that followed the battle of Actium. Now even in the depths of my mind, those who had once loved me most were deserting me.

Before you misunderstood my words, Antony, the words I dispatched from this mausoleum, before you snatched up your sword and with tears in your eyes implored one last favor of your faithful slave Eros: "Put me to death. Pierce my heart with this point, rip it out of my chest with its sharp edge, tear me asunder till I am only an unrecognizable lump of flesh"—before all that, you were already the incarnation of darkness. You were the blood that formed the slippery mud on which the sphere I mentioned to you went sliding toward the grave. You were the breath of life to me. You were also my death. Something welded us two into a third being that was neither you nor I, and I do not mean the notorious beast with two backs, the fleshy animal of desire.

You read the opening of my letter: "I am dead, my king." Without understanding my meaning, you shouted: "Do it, Antony. Do not delay one instant. Fate has robbed you of the only reason you had for wanting to live any longer!" You entered your bedroom and, opening your breastplate, handed a sword to faithful Eros, saying: "Stab me here. I follow Cleopatra, the greatest of the Lagids, monarch of the world's oldest kingdom and my beloved! More than the pain of her loss is the shame of knowing myself a greater coward than she!"

Eros, handsome, noble-hearted youth with his clear gaze, bravely brandished the sword but then, without shedding a tear, he plunged it into himself.

"What have you done, my loyal Eros?" you asked, as if unable to believe the fearful sight.

Eros made no answer. With fixed, wild eyes, he stared at you, struggling to reach the land of the dead with all possible speed.

"Well done, Eros. You have shown your master how to do what you did not have the heart to do."

Then you, Antony, sighing and grieving, took a dagger and stabbed yourself twice in the lower stomach. Your words turned to screams as Diomedes, my secretary, entered the room to tell you that Cleopatra was summoning you, that I needed to see you. I have told you, Mark Antony, that I cannot breathe outside your presence. When did I ever fail to call your name? Even today, when your lungs contain no air, I speak to you, I call upon you: "Come, breathe through me. Give me what the water gives to the lotus flower!"

Diomedes, who is both wise and practical but turns pale at the sight of blood, put to good use what little of the Seleucid inheritance he received from his mother. They stripped you naked and carefully loosened the dagger held tight in your frozen fist. With the serene calm of a Syrian, a calm we Lagids find so irritating, he ordered you to be bandaged immediately so that your intestines would not obtrude through your wounds. He had them cover your body with blankets and fasten you to a stretcher.

"And if you're lying, Diomedes, what then? Without my queen, I will thrust that dagger a thousand times into my body until not one recognizable piece remains." You had stopped screaming and weeping, but your lips were now babbling.

The industrious Diomedes must now have had to bend over you, to understand the words of a brass-voiced man who so many times had inspired armies to invincibility. Your voice was the first thing that left you as you went to join your ancestors. Alone, it crossed the Lethe, shaking the leaves of the poplars, startling the birds of the riverbanks into flight, and silencing the barking of dogs. Who else but yourself had the power to rob you of your voice on the road to the land of the dead? Your voice, so strong and attractive, should reside today among the living, and he who stole it away would be here to restore me to power. But it has gone. And at this very moment your voice is listening to the words of Nu, the triumphal palace overseer, chancellor in chief of the dead: "I am the deathless inheritor, the exalted one, the powerful one, he who brings rest. I made my name bear fruit, I will set it free, and you will live with me, day after day."

Inside your body, my king, your destruction stalked its slow and silent way to its end. The great warrior could now enunciate no strategy for his defence. Where the interwoven tissues of your body should have maintained an unseen order, senseless floodgates opened and let out sluices of murderous blood. Partitions cracked asunder. The tense warp and woof was reduced to sheerest linen, spindly and textureless. Over your lungs an assault was gathering to burst them apart. Your inner enemies learned of your speechless-ness and abused your frailties, and took your defenses by surprise.

They brought you to me. I am shut up tight in the Temple of Isis. While my defeat was gaining ground, I had them build a mausoleum worthy of Cleopatra. Surrounded by my treasures, I am safe here.

Sooner or later the Romans will be able to capture it and think that in doing so they possess the immortality of Egypt. But they will never exhibit me alive, chained like a slave to the chariot of the man who will delight in parading his victory through the streets of Rome. They will publish a false account of Cleopatra, manipulating her image to disguise the truth about a civil war Octavius waged solely to settle a score with his fellow-triumvir Antony. They will not trap me. The Roman mob will not make me an occasion for mockery and contempt. I know the truth of what I say. Did I not see Arsinoe, my sister and enemy, paraded through Rome in chains of gold in the procession to celebrate the victories of my Caesar?

Here, Mark Antony, let me escape, let me postpone the arrival of your body and journey back to Rome. Let me share in the memory of the five triumphs my Caesar celebrated. Let me step up into the chariot, exulting over my rival Arsinoe, and there let me join the celebratory retinue.

Foreigners had been accommodated in tents in the middle of the roads. All Rome lived the excitement of the triumphs both day and night. There was a gladiatorial combat, and plays were staged in many districts, with actors performing in numerous languages. There were games at the Circus. On chariots drawn by teams of horses, youngsters from noble families performed feats of acrobatics and the so-called Trojan game. There the finest of Rome's youth, wreaths crowning their hair, some carrying two javelins and others with a quiver on their shoulders, galloped in two even files, split up into two teams, and acted out a chase, lances at the ready. They then performed a second charge before dividing up again into two fighting teams and finally setting up the formation known as the Trojan squadron.

For the sea-battle they had excavated a lake in the lesser Codeta, part of the Campus Martius, and there biremes and quadriremes of the Tyrian and Egyptian fleets confronted each other with vast numbers of combatants. The crowd was so enormous that some people were asphyxiated, while others were crushed to death, two senators among them.

The procession crossed the Campus Martius, passed by the Circus Dominius, attended by massive throngs. It went along the Sacred Way to the Forum and ended up at the Capitol, by the light of torches carried in candelabras attached to the flanks of forty elephants.

As Arsinoe walked along the Sacred Way, secured by chains of gold, the crowds watched in silence, out of respect for Egypt. I made sure they saw that my own gaze, as well as that of my attendants, was turned away from the wretched sight. I had ordered my followers to bribe as many as they could to do likewise, as Arsinoe passed. With so many gazes averted, my Caesar had to free her from her chains, to maintain the tone of celebration, and he withdrew her from the procession. He saved her from the death she had every reason to expect and sent her to live in isolation in the Temple of Diana of the Ephesians. There she stayed till once again she conspired against me and I had no choice but to deal with her as a dangerous enemy.

Although she was hardly a person to reckon with, I arranged the silence that surrounded her as she walked in chains through Rome, to maintain the prestige of the Ptolemies. Her ally was the eunuch named Ganymede; he sported that name as a joke, for he was an ugly brute, never suited to be a prince of Troy or a cupbearer of the gods, and no eagle on the face of this earth could have wanted to snatch him away. Arsinoe died a virgin, never knowing the pleasures of sexuality. She was never a true member of the House of the Lagids. She was a short, skinny thing. Her body was fragile; she had an unprepossessing complexion, like skin stretched tight over a drum. It emphasized her staring, colorless eyes, the only real feature in her nondescript face. Her hair, dark and brittle, seemed to grow out of the skin of a long-buried corpse. In the corridors of my father's palace, I heard tell that she was not his daughter, that her mother had had a fling, and that the ugly creature was the fruit of this frivolous, lukewarm pastime. A child conceived in passion is born with fire in it, born with color, born full of life, but Arsinoe was like one delivered in the Underworld. I mentioned your eyes, Arsinoe, as your distinctive feature, but your father, whoever he was, must have been half-blind, for he bequeathed you no light, bestowed on you no radiance. You were born gray and hostile. It was as a gray thing they paraded you in chains along the roads of Rome. Like a graceless animal, bred on dusty soils. So what if it did not grieve me to see one who claimed to be my sister walk in chains? It grieved me more when the axle of my Caesar's chariot snapped, while the procession entered the district of Velabrius, just as he was about to receive their acclamation. I protected you once, Arsinoe, with bribes meant to guarantee you a measure of respect, simply because you bore my father's name. Yet they had every right to exhibit you, for my Caesar vanquished you and with justice displayed you as a trophy of his wars. Whoever may boast of defeating me will have no chance to exhibit me, for he is not the real conqueror here. My defeat came long before, and it is I who will deliver myself to it. They will not parade me in chains of gold. Our conqueror will get no parade in Rome, no mob to celebrate his multiple triumphs.

The door of Isis' temple has been sealed tight, so I am out of the reach of Octavius's vile minions and others that have believed the stupid chatter he attributes to a Cleopatra who is neither I nor anything like me. This fellow with water in his veins set the gossip going to justify his destroying people he had envied for years. For Octavius, with his squeezed and plunging voice, bony, bleak, and abrupt, knows well he is my inferior, that neither his mind nor his body nor his glance nor his understanding of the world could ever outdo the qualities of a certain foreign woman, a Greek from Egypt, forbidden by Roman law to wed a Roman citizen, but the greatest of the Lagids, the last Pharoah of glorious Egypt. And it goes without saying that he is inferior to my Antony. His own poetasters have confessed it:

> *No noble deed Octavius did*
> *'gainst Macedonia's throne.*
> *The spoils of victory belonged*
> *to Antony alone.*

Envy lent its energies to this spindly nephew of my Caesar, to the usurper who challenged the clause in Caesar's will that required his son be taught by the best tutors Rome could supply. Octavius is a small man; he wears elevated shoes to add height to his appearance. He is stingy. When gifts are exchanged at the festival of Saturn, others give presents of silver and gold, but he offers sponges, pokers, pincers, and other knicknacks. He is graceless; his puny presents are accompanied by curt notes that say one thing and mean another.

Once again I have postponed your arrival, Antony, by all this talk of the loathsome Octavius. But time is racing by, and with it the last hours of my life. Once more, to the point.

Here in this Temple of Isis I am secure. I designed it to keep intact and undiminished the dignity of my person. But there has entered the one thing that could harm Cleopatra—my Mark Antony on his way to death. There, in front of the doors you presented yourself, my emperor, my husband, my accomplice, my happiness. We had barred the doors to protect ourselves, so we had to lug you up by the ropes with which they had tied you, Charmian and Eira, my faithful maidens, and I. Six arms could barely raise you. You were heavy, rapt in yourself. Your eyes tried to find me but they were more occupied with the vision of the Underworld. They were saying:

> *Step back, you servant of the timeless gods.*
> *You come in search of this, my living heart.*
> *'Tis not for you to take. Here I advance*
> *And lo, the gods accept my offerings,*
> *Prostrate themselves to honor me and mine.*

These words lent a superhuman weight to your body, as they marked your entry into death. We pulled harder still on the ropes, for I had to be beside you in your last snatches of life. The closeness of your body stole the breath out of my lungs. You stank of blood, you the most manly of men. You smelled like a cloth soaked with the menstrual blood of women for month after month. I had to let go the rope, and Charmian and Eira were left to drag you through the window.

"What did you do?" I asked you. "You fool, so imprudent, so ignorant and hasty!" while pale and disfigured, like a bad portrait of yourself, you babbled I don't know what nonsense. You were weeping, Mark Antony, you had renewed your laments over my death. Not even the sight of me could convince you that I was alive. Diomedes had scaled the wall after you, wanting to help where no help was possible. The remedies he had provided proved of little use. You were soaked in your blood. Olympus, the doctor, came in on the heels of Diomedes, but we all recognized that his visit was futile. We removed you from the stretcher and made you comfortable in my bed. I took off my robes to cover you. You asked for wine and I gave you some. You drank it at a gulp. Lying beside you, I embraced you. Glueing myself to your body, I kissed you. Your mouth was cold and dry. I made you promises. I spoke rebukes. I called you my emperor, ally, enemy, slave, guiding light, taskmaster. I told you how deeply I loved you, and I called you a noose around my neck, a suffocating force, my madness and my ruin. I called you my grape and fig, serpent and lion. I recalled our last, magnificent journey to Athens, then the decorations, lights, and celebrations of our first meal together, the joke we played at a party on the King of Armenia. Once again I criticized your wrongheadedness in leaving Herod in power in Judaea, and your idiotic debauchery in Leucocome, where you had scurried after being thrashed by the Parthians. I made a point of describing the sleepless night we passed together in Antioch, after you were widowed and had remarried, a night that centuries will never forget. We made love that night, till daybreak, without feeling one moment of weariness or satiety.

> *Vesper got drunk tonight and now he dreams,*
> *The Great Bear's stars have not traversed the night.*
> *The moon still stands where first she showed her beams,*
> *The Pleiades and Venus keep in sight.*

> *Hold fast, brave Night; serve Love, the best of gods . . .*

Plunged in that recollection, I abstained from life in the present and lived in memory, for no other source of happiness lay open to us. We were stretched out, the two of us, on the bed I had them bring to the Temple of Isis. Here, speaking to you, clasped to you, I spent the night, suffocating, like you, in blood. Some dream-vision came to taunt you, and to restore your serenity, I sang to you. Even when I knew that no breath of life remained in you, I still clung to you. Then I fell asleep, cradled in your rigid arms, pressed against your stone-cold breast, abandoned by the tide of your being. We were three on that sodden bed: your sword, the triumvir, and Egypt's queen. We were three: my death, my life, and your corpse. We were three: my memories, my desire for you, and my rage. We were three: Mark Antony's Rome, the Egypt of the Nile, whose pharoah I am, and the Greece of my ancestors of which you are a citizen, an Athenian. We were three: the mother of Caesar's only son Caesarion, the daughter of Auletes, and your parents' son. We were three: the war that Rome declared on us in the voice of that beardless youth, the war that blazed between us two, and the peace of our embracing bodies.

"Do not leave!" I wanted to shout at you. "Do not leave. Let me find you one last time, let me embrace you, let me fasten my lips on yours. Raise yourself a little. Kiss me while your kiss is still alive. Let the breath of your soul race to meet my mouth and heart. Let me drink of your love and I will preserve that kiss as if it were you! You go in search of the king of inhuman gloom, but I am alive and follow you I cannot!"

> *Blood gives birth to roses,*
> *Tears to anemones.*
> *I weep for my Mark Antony*
> *And my golden memories.*

I dreamed with my head propped on your chest. And once again the two of us were living out our timeless intoxication with life. It was night and, disguised as beggars, we were dancing in the streets of beautiful Alexandria. We went from house to house, pleading for wine and music. Exactly the way we did when we were making every effort to produce our first child. You were kissing me, and it was your kiss that awoke me, a kiss that left your true taste in my mouth, a kiss from your still-warm mouth, your true mouth, your living mouth, a kiss that invited me to lose myself in you, to follow you, drawing me toward the irresistible joy of your body, to final oblivion and to the fullness of our divine condition.

Now I must speak to you again. Listen, Mark Antony, to what I have always wanted to tell you. No, my maidens, do not wash from my naked chest the blood in which I am dressed. Do not comb my hair or try to perfume me. There is no costume more fitting to my words than Antony's blood. These words will sit well with my disheveled hair, with my blood-stained skin, hands clad in dry, crackling blood. Diomedes, turn your face away if I disgust you; but do not move far from Egypt's pharoah, for you must hear the words she speaks. You must note down everything I now say. Our time is short. Let them bring you water. If you need to eat, make sure your assistants write down everything, without omitting a single word. These are the last words that your queen, Isis Cleopatra, will speak. Write! Time is flying. No, do not touch me! Do not put fresh clothes on me. So what, if my face is stained, my tangled locks matted with dried blood? I realize it is improper to let myself be seen in this state. There is no need to repeat it. I am dyed with the wine of the great Mark Antony. Let no one say again I am defeated. The truth is, I am not! Let me be just as I am, drenched in him, in what he kept deep within himself, unseen by the world, in what forced him to return to me. You must understand that I am dressed in what once gave him life, draped with the hidden currents of his flesh, his secret knowledge, the source of his desire for me, the spell that made me beautiful for him, the thing that made him mine. Out of it we two formed our invincible unity as well as our mutual betrayal.

Let's begin, Diomedes. Otherwise my history will serve as material for Roman lies. All of you, who met me, who knew who I was and what my deeds were, the glory that I added to my ancestors and to Egypt, you will either die with me or keep silence about me. If anyone lives and dares to speak for me, may his tongue wither! But nothing will remain of my true story unless we make haste. My treasures will be reduced to crude ingots to be sent to Rome. Likewise they will treat my work, my achievements, and my family. They will mint coins with the legend "Egypt in captivity." They will consign to oblivion the woman I once was. Ready, Diomedes? Let your ink be of a quality that defies the centuries. Only a few hours remain. Begin!

I, Cleopatra, the last of the Lagids, Pharoah of Egypt, descendant of Alexander the Great, of the goddesses Philadelphia, Arsinoe, and Berenice, of the gods Soters, Adelphos, and Euergetos, preserve here my authentic history. The Romans will shatter to fragments all my achievements and my virtues. They will disfigure me and no one will remain to contradict them. With me, my world collapses. Everyone who knew who I truly was will depart. With me, the Egypt of a thousand years crumbles to dust. Alexandria will cease to be a city of land and sea. My children, my counselors, ministers, administrators, the priests of Egypt and of the Greek pantheon—all will be converted at one stroke into foreigners, refugees, pariahs. We have been outmaneuvered by a lesser rival. Rome cannot bear comparison with Alexandria. The usurper who commands Rome's army is a ridiculous child whose veins run with the sticky liquid of his envy.

> *Foul Envy touched his bosom with a hand*
> *Besmirched with urine, stuffed his heart*
> *With crooked thorns, breathed in it gall*
> *And through his bones and round his sour lungs*
> *Dispersed a venom dark as any pitch.*

It was not, I repeat, the Romans who defeated me. We, the Egypt of Cleopatra, the triumvir Mark Antony, we were their superior by far. Our defeat came not from Rome. They will boast that they conquered the Nile. They will write that they triumphed in battles. It is not true! No! A nightmare has been the real source of our defeat. Merely saying that for five years I have been a corpse, does not do it justice. No phrase can precisely define the meaning of our warring and our decline, for never was I so alive as then, never so possessed of fire and light. Mark Antony, you dragged me along the channels of a delta where Destiny never intended me to go. You quenched more than one of the goddesses' stars in the uncontrollable torrents of your whims. And I? I wove myself into you in a web both rare and bizarre, on which there came to be traced what I will now attempt to decipher. I pluck at that web's corners, the one nearest, facing the sun. On it appears a saying of Io:

> *O youth, you found a cruel suitor there.*
> *What you have heard is scarcely a beginning.*

I do not wish to drown myself in tears or reach my end without first telling of our hours of greatness, of our triumphs and glories. I will begin at the beginning, before we became those tireless lovers of life, before the world lay at our feet, before I restored Egypt's glory and ruled it as the greatest of the Lagids, before my dream of seeing East and West united under one crown twice became a possibility. I will not mention the chariot drawn by lions that you drove in Rome, while Caesar was visiting me in Egypt, though I am sorely tempted to linger on its description, and along with it, your character and the road we trod together. I will begin, as I said, at the beginning.

With my children, I am the last of my line. They will be dragged to Rome and married to freedmen or treated as slaves. I wish them an early death. But I myself must escape oblivion. The Cleopatra that Roman propaganda changed me into is a vacillating substitute for the real, decisive Cleopatra; the false image that Octavius constantly fashions of me, he makes in order to give himself the courage to war on me. I must elude the death brought on by history's forgetfulness. No fate is worse than oblivion; it is the completest form of death that can befall a queen.

I never kept a record of public events, the way my Caesar did. I did not jot down phrases to jog the memories of others. I let the poets and historians be responsible for that, without an Aulus Hirtius at my elbow, to eavesdrop on my words and deeds. But I now know that when Egypt falls and the Ptolemies are no more, all those rolls of papyrus will end up under water or in the fire. The papers of Mark Antony, including those that Caesar left in his keeping, will be burned. My own story, told by its protagonist, artlessly, without the skill I have admired in those touched by the Muses—may some god deign to protect it. Then one day, when the hatred of the man who wants to represent himself as my conqueror—though he never has been or will be—when his hatred has passed away, then others in a far-off time will testify to my glory and my fall. My account will be faithful to the facts.

Urgent need will help me where literary skill may fail. On stone, hard stone, I should carve what I want to say, but time forbids. Ink will record what I tell to you, Antony, you who touched me and tasted the saliva of my mouth, and to those yet unborn. Your ears still hear me, Antony, still are nearby, and cannot leave till I accompany them. I am their missing part, their key component. Without me, they will never rest, will remain a mere shadow of themselves, cannot depart. Here they stay. I should not speak in a loud voice as if declaiming to you, like that other queen who in defeat wailed her woes to Darius: "Can he listen to my voice from the underworld?" A murmur will suffice for your understanding, for Cleopatra is flesh fitted to the labyrinth of your two ears, the one thing your body lacked since birth. Without me, you cannot leave, for your condition is defective. When my story ends, we two shall go together.

It's you to whom I speak: you who shared my linen bed, and those who may not dwell in Africa or Asia or Rome, who may listen to me beyond the regions of Gaul and the wild, turbulent Atlantic. Listen! This is what I was. These were my deeds. The last hours of my life I will spend in relating my history. Can a better death be imagined?

> To weep, to moan our lot, when needs require
> We stir the hearts of friends, is time well spent.

Even more so in my case, for my time cannot be weighed in the common balance, for in itself it forms part of the booty that belongs to him who, in his arrogance, stupidity, and error, believes he is my master. My time is more precious now than ever, it gives me joy to start upon these memories. Something akin to life itself gathers to my heart and touches me and warms this chilly flesh. Suddenly I am alive, and I recall . . .

Diomedes the Informer

"When they collected excrement from the sacred crocodile to annul the generative power of semen, they
offended our guardian and brought death to Egypt.
When the Queen cuckolded her brother and frolicked
with a string of Roman generals, she offended Eros and
brought death to Egypt. When she made a present of
Alexandria's youth for the Romans to use as shields in
their military campaigns, she offended Osiris and brought
death to Egypt. When, instead of governing, she braided
her hair in unnatural styles, fixing it in place with fruit
juices, she offended Isis with her vanity and brought
death to Egypt."

The obscene prophet who spouted this endless succession
of nonsense had been rushed to Alexandria by Romans intent
on lowering respect for the Queen. His outlandish cries halted
the Queen's dictation. She had described herself as dead but had
been firing out words like arrows. She had just described herself
as alive, but her description coincided with the prophet's outcry.

Now she fell silent. Her tense, arrowlike words dropped
to earth and she burst into tears. Without tension to support

her, her body changed from a flourishing tree to a flower ripped up by the roots, from the stone in a sling to a pebble lying on the road, from the hurtling wheel of a chariot to the tile shaken from the rooftop by its passing.

Reversing the direction of her words, her declaration of life, and bursting energy, she turned listless and tearful. Why? What could it matter to her what a longhaired prophet was bellowing, a man who misread the past and was blind to the present and future? Like the boastful son of Lacares, he had come to plunder the fallen, like a vulture, a foul hyena.

Cleopatra leaned back on the soft cushions and the mattress of her gilded bed and there she stifled her sobs. Charmian and Eira were sobbing and howling. Down below, at the foot of the mausoleum dedicated to Isis, the official mourners, dressed in black, their hair down, had been waiting for the queen to stop dictating. They had not dared to open their mouths but now they, too, joined in the chorus of grief. They wept for Mark Antony, for Dionysus, for Osiris, the father of the gods. They wept for the pain of the queen. I myself went over to the window and saw among the women the figure of the lean prophet, his shouts drowned out by the lamentations. In a trance, he did not hear them. He believed his lies from beginning to end. He had forgotten he was proclaiming falsehoods.

Right at the foot of the tower, a dense ring of Roman soldiers used their sharp lances to hold at bay the crowd of Alexandrians. The soldiers were unsettled by the behavior of the mourners, who were swaying back and forth, tearing their hair in the extremes of grief. The points of the lances almost touched their chests. Between the backs of the soldiers and our own white walls was only a narrow passage cluttered with their weapons and baggage.

"If only we had with us a platoon of brave men," I thought. "Right now they could slip silently down ropes and plant in the backs of the Romans their own daggers, lying there idly on the ground."

Surrounding the tower and the ring of legionnaires, the people thronged in their grief, echoing the cries of the mourners at a lesser volume. There were children, women, elderly men, and the usually restless youngsters—all now stunned to inactivity by the appalling turn of events. Sellers were carrying empty baskets. Dogs snuffled around. It was as busy as market day, but without any of the customary piles of merchandise. Alexandria was starting to feel hunger pangs. Carts, loaded with grain, vegetables, and animals, were being waylaid on lawless roads, most frequently by Roman garrisons, who seized them violently, eager to add to their stores of war booty.

From the window I managed to see on the central balcony of the royal palace the commanding officers of the Roman army, as they surveyed the scene. They were staring at me with curiosity. I half-turned away to look at Cleopatra. I don't know if it was my gesture that woke her, or what else it was, because her tears lasted no longer than the time it took me to see what I have described. She got up, almost leaping off the bed, and resumed speaking in a voice now hoarsened by rage. She forgot Mark Antony was dead. She forgot that Octavius, today known as Augustus Caesar, was in Alexandria. She forgot her time was running out implacably and she returned to the topic of what, in her opinion, had caused her downfall. She began on a furious note, spitting out incoherent phrases that I will not bother you with. Then she sat back and lowered her voice to a murmur broken by sobs. The tears that flooded her cheeks could have been from pleasure, because her words carried us away to her happiest days in Alexandria, as she sank her arm into the plump cushions and put the full weight of her upper body against it.

Cleopatra

"O Antony!" she cried, it wasn't you who brought us, you and me, to this grievous end. One kiss from you, the mere taste of your lips, was enough to intoxicate me. When you put your mouth on mine, delirium seized me before I could close my eyes. From you, I drank an unknown substance that made me stumble. But instead of falling, I turned my face to the sky. My chin jarred against the sharp edges of well-rounded spheres, my forehead banged against them, and then my chest. Every kiss brought to my skin a need for more kisses. At every kiss, Antony, I opened up to you, my shoulder, my hand, my thigh. My skin was cut to ribbons, my veins chopped small, simply because I was returning your kiss. I was kissing you, Antony, and unfolding. The stars transformed me into part of the racing air through which they fly. Antony, Mark Antony, just to kiss you! In your kiss, I flew, I opened out, I came apart, ignorant of pain. I wanted more kissing, more flying, more ranks of stars to beat against. Free from earth, weightless, indifferent to every form of grief and all the humiliations flesh is heir to. The things that each of us, when separated, would describe as obligations, needs or acts of drudgery, became, when we two shared the work, a joyous celebration.

We never, never lost the thing that bound us two together—that sense of power! If you, Antony, and I had been destined to die at the same moment, then death would have lost its sting. Together, you and I could overcome any obstacle. You were my life and death.

Life itself was a smiling game of delirious excitement. We played games because happiness overflowed in us; we laughed because life after life was there for us to live! How many ways we found to be happy! So happy that at times we became children again. Nothing in my whole life gave me the glory you gave—if the meaning of glory is to be elevated above the ranks of ordinary humanity. Antony, I loved you because you created me, because in you I was born a second time, and because whatever you drew from me was sublime and ripe with laughter.

Because I loved you, I had to return to the world, infused with the power you bestowed on me. Out of the two of us, I decided to produce a sun that would radiate well-being on our peoples, even as it expanded our glory. My strength increased with my love, my ambitions fed full on their own appetites, the perfection of our loving bodies had both the power and the duty to touch our peoples with the same perfection.

But you shared neither my needs nor the will to satisfy them. The effect of our soaring flight—the word "flight" contains all my meaning, even my skin opening like a flower—it had different results for you. I was so happy. Joy let me play like a child. As I burst open and tore apart and soared high, I was growing; my will was gathering strength. One aspect of my being was brought low by your love, but the other, the one visible to worldly eyes, grew ever more perfect, more complete, more lived-in, solider. It shone, like a blue-green moon over trees and rivers. I was growing; my will was gathering strength. My happiness was like the tiny fibers of those eager roots that drink with zest all the forces of the earth. My stem, leaves, flowers, fruit responded to that zest, as if it were their source of life.

Because I was so happy, I grew more sensible, apt, swift to act, and imaginative in dealing with the issues of my kingdom. Merriment made me more accomplished, firmer. Who could defeat me now?

Antony, however, simply grew more himself with the sheer happiness of love. His inclination to be a child in all things strengthened. Gone was the grimly powerful face, replaced by a full moon shining down on all. He was totally a child, all games and whims and drunkenness. The unrestrained laughter of a child, caprice without peevishness, the endless intoxication of the night.

But the child was also the offspring of an idiot, suffering uncontainable puerile rages, the freakishness of a boy general, the infatuation of juvenile poetry.

You had already been inclined to playfulness; your devotion to pleasure was notorious. When Caesar left you in charge in Rome, you toured the streets in your chariot drawn by lions. But now, under the influence of our happiness, you turned yourself into the young lion that true love tames. Learning docility, you were transformed into the innocent who knows neither how to attack nor how to defend himself. Lost were your warring instincts. But like a domesticated lion, you could still inflict wounds at the times when you forgot your own strength and failed to remember your situation.

With so much happiness always on hand, Antony turned himself into a toy. In his walk, in the face he showed to the world, he incarnated an obvious joy that defied all limits. Where the delicate fibers of my being drank in the earth's strength, his merely fingered the water. Hence the mouth of those tiny roots stiffened with cold in the very presence of the fertile earth. They reached the water but they did not drink; they danced there but absorbed nothing. Our happiness did not help Antony to increase his strength. It did not make him grow or even maintain his power. Merely crazed with love, he turned toward the darker side of himself. There everything shattered to pieces. And as things flew apart, he lost his vigor. His caprices mounted in both number and size. Our love goaded them on. The love potion we both drank produced different types of intoxication in each of us. Mine fed my sanity. His made him twitch and tremble; it kept him day and night in a state of nervous excitement. It ruined him.

Here I refer to the first time we lived together. This was the way our story started. These were the characteristics of Antony's first visit to Alexandria. We had met in Tarsus, where he had asked the Queen of Egypt to meet him, in hopes of renewing the alliance. How many weeks did we spend making love? How many months? The chronicles of Egypt state 120 days and some hours. Each one of those hours—said the private chronicle of my heart—was 120 times more ample than what we normally call an hour. Antony, for me you were the very definition of happiness at its maximum.

One morning, one of those first happy mornings, when we had gone fishing on Lake Mareotis, you exploded with rage because the fish refused to bite. Again and again, you insisted on changing rods. You were wasting time, instead of attending to the urgent business that the needs of your soldiers and the nonstop mail from Rome required. Your repeated efforts proved useless. You were shifting about more than the fish were, bellowing stupid, pointless curses in your rage. It was not a sight worthy of a triumvir. I ordered my servants to attach a magnificent salted herring to your hook. You felt the bait taken, pulled on the rod, and shouted with infantile glee. When you saw the joke, you laughed till you cried. Between the tears, I said to you, "Leave the fishing to fishermen and return to the proper business of a triumvir." You kissed me, laughed again, but did not heed my advice. My calling you back to the realities of the world had no effect. From me you wanted a bridge to convey you out of this world. For you, loving me meant turning your back on everything that befitted the mouth of a governor, the eyes of a king, the mind of a triumvir. You used my love to turn your back on everything that required life, nourishment, commitment, tact, astuteness, moderation, and dash. That was why you loved me.

I was different. Love's intoxication developed in me an appetite for governing and for life. My love for you, Antony, meant having your children, ruling my subjects, increasing my wealth, and adding to the size of my kingdom. My love for you kindled my intelligence; my power of decision learned shortcuts; my ambition caught fire. I wanted to live more, have more, do more. Handsome Mark Antony, Dionysus, your beauty was my delight and my strength. And it became my sanity. Joy brought me well-being.

To kiss you dressed me as a queen and grounded me as a woman. For you, our happiness was a cup to be drained at one gulp. Ruinous forces were let loose. To kiss me was the undoing, the complete destruction of the triumvir. What I call good did you harm, Antony. I did not cloy you, just as fine wine does not cloy the palate. But I could not inspire in you an appetite for greater things. When you saw me, you became blind to yourself. Your joy in me meant turning your back on what was alive, on everything the good earth produces. Intoxicated with loving happiness, you let your eyes stray from yourself; they stared in ecstasy, frozen motionless, indifferent to the world. Oblivious of your own body, you spun about. You were spurning the world; when you looked at yourself, you did so out of blind sockets, empty rims.

If anything disturbed your trance and you were forced to recognize what you had become, you exploded with rage. Fortunately, I was spared the sight of your conduct at Brundisium, for I had left Rome and, more concerned with my future than my past, boarded my ship for Cilicia. Your love brought me the highest imaginable glory but it also inflicted on me the thickest darkness of sorrows. Your madness and your limitless caprices— ever more insistent, frequent, irascible, and unreasonable—did to me what nothing else could—they destroyed my inner strength. Thanks to you, Mark Antony, I learned to dread each dawn, to see day break without glimpsing the very thing that first made me what I was. I mean, a certain coloring, which left me quick to find ingenious solutions, take nonstop pleasures in excess, and voice memorable words. That lively coloring of my mornings and evenings, the unquenched flame that had lit up my life—you left it dimmed where you did not extinguish it. I became vulnerable and open to harm. You turned me into a corpse prematurely, destitute of vital breath. All thanks to your insanity and idleness. Our love gave you no hunger for life, for building, improving, growing. The best moments of our lives were merely your chance to escape reality. You did not use them to make yourself master of Rome, lord of the world, a second Caesar. Your wallowing in our love served only to feed your appetite for self-destruction, for flight, for indulging your caprices to excess; and it was all because you were rotten inside before I ever met you.

Hear, O Selene, from where my love was born!

Antony, you were riddled with rottenness. As rotten as a woman who was once a queen but today is forced to share a bed with the friends of her master. Rotten with the rottenness of a man who fails his city in time of war and who knows that, though he still lives, he has forfeited his last chance to defend his mother, his wife, and his daughters from the assaults of his victorious foes. Rotten as the ignorant fool who cannot see that we nourish our lives on something other than grains, fruits, wines, and spices. Rotten as a king who drinks himself into a stupor, day and night, without attending to the duties of his throne, sowing hunger and hatred throughout his kingdom. Rotten as a leper. Rotten as a prophet who speaks his prophecies in words no one understands. Rotten as a poetaster or a second-rate musician reduced to beggary. Rotten as the man who sleeps with his own mother, forgetful of his condition as a mortal and blind to the anger of the gods. Rotten as a child who, born in the desert, is abandoned to live with beasts, forever ignorant of language, of the names of the gods or the story of Helios, a creature who sheds his human dignity as he dines on thistles and tries to shed his skin like a snake, when the sun beats down with scalding heat. Rotten as the ignoramus who does not realize that in every tree there is life and that within all things, all living beings, the words of the gods lie hidden, awaiting revelation. Rotten as the rebel who defies his own innate wisdom and insists on living his life as a blasphemer, trusting only in the power of his own brain, hoping to crush the helmets of his foes with a blow from a stone and a kick from a horse's hoof, even as the enemy armies sweep forward in waves of terror. Rotten as the man is rotten who in a fit of fury beats his own mother after he has grown up in the darkest corners of the house, where like a dog he was thrashed with a stick. Rotten as the sluggard who does not know how to work, how to desire and act, even how to dream a reasonable dream.

Why was it you, why did it have to be you I tied myself to? Why you? You had corruption sown in the depths of your being. The roots of your life were dead to nourishment. But it was you whom I joined in a single life. Is love more fully itself only when it finds rottenness, impossibility, death, and violence? If so, then I too have been eaten away by rottenness. Since first I became a woman and desired a man, I, too, must have been rotten, since only in love did I find the means to burst with happiness, and only with this happiness could my intelligence and other powers attain their fullness. Only when love was satisfied, reciprocated, and rendered happy, could I feel complete. So, if it was only through love that I knew how to be myself and if love is born only from rottennness, it must be that I was a decomposing corpse from the first moment I kissed a man with desire. For it was from that moment that I knew how to gather my strength—with a man standing beside me as my accomplice and my beloved. Only then did I feel whole.

Rotten are they who feed only on love and wish to satiate themselves on one single person, rotten to the heart of them, whether king or triumvir or Caesar, woman or man. And Mark Antony was rotten from birth so it served me nothing to be a scion of the House of the Lagids, to reign in Egypt and set my mark on Rome.

The idea of rottenness both appalls and obsesses me. Who will mummify our bodies, Antony? I am going to speak my innermost thoughts aloud. They have left us alone with your corpse, denying entrance to anyone with the skill to mummify us. I am alone and there is no one nearby who can care for your loving body as it deserves. No one will care for mine, either. They have left us alone, you and me here, to die in a manner unworthy of a human being, to die like kaffirs, without form or ceremony. Is there a sharper sorrow, a bitterer disgrace, a crueler punishment? Does one need to be Antigone to know it? We deserve it, you and I. Did we merit this isolation, for being the lovers that we were in our first days here in Alexandria? Tell me, Mark Antony, could I have loved another who was not you? Could he have been totally different from you? Did Destiny trap me? Did it place beside me, here in this cage called Egypt, only a man doomed to failure? For there was no one else beside me. No one else forced the bars of the gilded prison where the Lagid Queen lay confined.

Was there no second Caesar for me? A complete man with whom I could have been reborn? Did the only true man die assassinated by his own followers? Were you my better-than-nothing? Certainly in Egypt there was no man with the power to seduce me. The kings of Nabatea and Judaea had no Rome with which to woo me. Was it this lack of choice that destroyed me as a queen and as a woman? Was it this that cast a stormcloud over me and made me grasp at the ungraspable?

Could I perhaps have learned to feel complete beside a man of lesser strength than I? One with less authority, fewer riches? No. My self-respect as a woman made that impossible. Men know how to love a female slave. But we women who have nothing slavish in our natures, who are owners of ourselves, who have enlarged and cultivated our personalities, who have achieved an understanding of ourselves, who live our lives to the limits permitted by the gods—we do not know how to love a man who does not merit it in the eyes of the world, a man who lacks power or intelligence or that jewel of jewels, genius. The rich, old women of whom the poets sing, they who can be seduced into loving a man who covets their possessions or, worse still, who would see them dead so that he can inherit their wealth, what of them? I do not belong to their world. They need to placate their vulvas. To satisfy their carnal appetites, they stoop to buying love, like the graceless men who must pay cold cash for what is freely granted only by looking a woman in her eyes and desiring her. Such men seek a commercial transaction and nothing else; they use their coins to protect themselves from the women they abuse in the pursuit of pleasure. What does any of that matter to me? Nothing is further distant from Cleopatra. And yet they tell me that in the streets of Rome the people sing that Cleopatra is a prostitute Antony fattens with pieces of the Empire. They chant:

> *Cleo is a dusky whore.*
> *She costs a pretty penny.*
> *Mark Antony must pay and pay.*
> *If not, he don't get any!*

I had my servant sing me the latest chant. Ugly words, ugly tune, typical of Rome and its musicians. The only part worth hearing was the voice of the Egyptian who sang it. He was trembling like a leaf in an angry wind, but he sang with a voice that the Nile, the sun, the Mediterranean, the proximity of the desert, the papyrus, and the lotus flower produce in the people of Alexandria, the heart of rich Egypt—all the while knowing the penalty for being the bearer of bad news.

Mark Antony, I say it again: you were my destruction. You were the only one with whom I was made a complete being, entire. Caesar, I tell you, was different, altogether different. Neither he nor I ever had the illusion of forming a whole, for we never succumbed to the arrogance of locking ourselves into a closed circle, never tried to make two into one. Antony, you were my glory. Out of you was born the best of me. Out of you and only you was I born complete, you my father, Antony, and my mother!

We were our own worst torments, Antony. We let ourselves be swept away by the foolish fantasy of creating the perfect unity.

In my grief, I have lost the thread of what I was saying. I wanted to describe what you and I were like and how we drove ourselves to our defeat. It was never within Octavius's power to destroy us. He had no part in our story. You and I hurled ourselves to this terrible conclusion. He merely took advantage of our collapse, like the son of Lacares and the others, who squalidly grabbed at the possessions of the vanquished, snatching their booty from the leftovers and boastfully representing it as a triumph.

After that incident, the joke of the salted herring, Antony still did not pay serious attention to the matters of state. Thanks to this neglect, his wife and his brother were able to involve themselves in a war against Octavius. That would never have happened, if he had listened to me. When I drew it to his notice, he cut short my lecture. But he never left off loving me, in his way. My insistence that he return to face reality and use our love as a citadel to make more of himself merely drove him to look for easier and more comfortable ways to turn his back on everything. He was determined to use our love as a means of escape. He loved life so much; yet he was set on eluding it. Can someone explain to me what motivated such behavior?

What wonderful days, our first days together, in my city! Antony was there because he wanted to experience the giddiness of being with me. With me he escaped from the eyes of his own conscience, but the minute I begged him to face himself and see what he was doing, when I implored him to turn his mind to the business of government, to attend to his work as triumvir, his only answer was to take another woman into his bed. A woman who was neither especially beautiful nor rich nor powerful, with no reputation of being able to give pleasure to men. In short, a pretty slave, who smelled of the foul water from cleaning buckets, a mere washerwoman. But he had not ceased to love me. He had lost all for love and now the fool wanted to make me a loser, too. He wanted to ruin me as he had ruined his own power and position . . . Our love sent him searching through a labyrinth without the thread of Ariadne. He was trying to finish himself off and to finish me off as well. He was set on blinding us both, blocking every access to the outer world, and separating us irrevocably from it. He was trying to make us into something else, take us somewhere else, to damage us one more time, so that we might finally destroy ourselves forever.

I burned with love for him, but I did not neglect Egypt. During the hours I dedicated to my duties as a monarch, he took up with the slavegirl. And not only once. He let me know it, pushed it in my face. He wanted to batter and bruise my loving pride. Not content with that, he stirred up an endless number of complaints against me. His theatrical displays of jealousy assumed an almost grotesque tone. He started by alleging that the reason I left him alone for hours at a time was to caress the dusky skins of princes and servants, men who, it goes without saying, existed only in his sick imagination. One scene of jealousy followed another, every time more violent. He mocked our love incessantly by using the slavegirl whom he had taken without desiring her. Then, in return, absurdly, he made me pay for it, torturing me with his rages. He parodied our love with her. But with her, he could not match our joy, for he had fallen prey to a frightful melancholy. Nothing made him smile. Certainly, the wine he was drinking in ever greater quantities brought him no smiles; it only left him more irritable and consigned him to yet deeper depressions. More for his depressions, I think, than for his attentions to the slavegirl, I, too, began to neglect my duties. He continued to ignore his work, but at least he put aside the slavegirl and, for the moment, his outbursts ceased. The slavegirl disappeared. Somebody did me the favor of making her disappear, and I lend no credence to the rumor that she was carrying Antony's child at the time. He and I returned to our old happiness, to parties, to laughter, as if nothing had happened—and not because we were pretending. Our mutual attraction far surpassed our squabbles.

We were back in our bed. We rarely left it. Antony was making love to me with an exasperated insistence that gained energy from its very repetition. We left our bed only when we received news that his idiotic relatives had provoked a war in Italy. It could bring them nothing but headaches and losses. Yes, his wife Fulvia and that imbecile of a brother had declared war on Octavius.

Mark Antony embarked because I practically threw him into the sea. The tame lion, like every cat, seemed scared of water. He did not want to go. But as soon as he landed on the Italian coast, he forgot his fears. He extended his claws and defended himself with his old wilderness strength, fighting with both fury and cleverness.

His indifference to his private life even included me. He stopped writing to me. I never for a second considered forgetting him. For many reasons. One was that just before leaving, he had resumed his role as a governor. Once more, I felt he was back at my side, as in the best days of the past. Another was that, a little before he sailed, I had become pregnant with his Egyptian heir. Our son, I thought—our children, as it turned out, because they were twins—would incarnate our love. Rome and Egypt would be blended into one. Now Caesarion would not be alone; he would have siblings, and their father would take pains to legitimize his inheritance. The children of Cleopatra would be masters of the greatest empire the world had ever seen.

A third reason for not relinquishing him was that the slow-witted but aggressive Fulvia soon died. He was a widower, and, in my stupidity, it never crossed my mind to doubt that he would return to share my reign, that I would be recognized as his wife in all four corners of the world.

I nourished the fond hope that he needed me as much as I needed him. How could I have been so bereft of common sense? Even when he was in Alexandria, hadn't he ceased to need me? Hadn't he warmed his bed with another woman? My situation was desperate. Cleopatra could not feign love with another, but neither could she cease to feel desire. Desire, Mark Antony, desire for love, desire of the flesh, desire for conversation with an equal, desire for the company of a peer! They all amount to the same thing, to one appetite, a single need to satisfy different cravings. Affection, the pleasures of the flesh, company, a man who watches over us and guards us against the world, a judge, and an accomplice. Even in the worst moments, Mark Antony, you talked to me; with the sweet light of your conversation you illuminated for me the last and least of your thoughts. Even at those moments, you caressed me with affection, you gave me pleasure. Even then, you talked to me endlessly. With nobody else did I speak with the intimacy you and I shared. With absolute certainty I believed you were my other half. From the very first day I idolized you. You calmed me, fulfilled me, and satisfied my need for companionship as no one else did. Only you, my divine Antony, Osiris himself.

When he returned to Rome, I was still close to him. We were not separated, no matter that he had crossed the Mediterranean and had stopped writing to me. He was my other half, my partner. His journey was a mere detail, a highlight that set off the general picture of our love. Neither his tantrums nor his slavegirl nor his jealous accusations nor his depressions nor his foolish drinking bouts nor his mind distracted by each and every fanciful gust of wind—none of this mattered. Only his company. Perfect, I would say, if it had not been that desire unsettled him at times and left me unsettled for him. But I would soothe him and myself with the silky certainty of our love. Then I received the news: he had married Octavia, the sister of Octavius, as a "token of reconciliation," as the courier babbled it in his report. He paid with his life for such ominous news. And my hopes died with him. I was still not ready to deliver my twins, but I gave birth to a grief like no other. It did not resemble Antony's depressions, griefs that were dark enough but lacked depth, coming and going without rhyme or reason.

His marriage restored my sanity. It was impossible for a triumvir to marry a woman whom his people had never regarded as a citizen. I could be the queen of Egypt, I could have a statue of gold dedicated to me in the temple of Venus Generatrix, Caesar could have Rome worship me. But for all that, and for all my being the wealthy heir of Alexander the Great, never could I be anything but a foreigner, an Egyptian. So my despair had neither name nor direction. Since the moment he had left, I had not ceased to be by his side for even an instant. Recalling our moments of greatest sweetness, I mean our rapture in Tarsus, forgetting his craziness with the slavegirl, I held him to be my ideal, the perfect companion, the incomparable one. And he truly was incomparable! For, who could match him? The Queen of Egypt, Isis, could have no lesser lover, no one inferior to herself in power and beauty, in energy and intelligence. There was no man to equal him. What of Octavius? Someone fooled by the glories that he claimed for himself on our defeat might be tempted to ask that. Octavius does not have a shred of real flesh in his whole body. Octavius will preen himself over our ruin and this will give him the look of the Caesar he longs to be. But he will be a mere fraud. The man is a nonentity. Cleopatra could never have bothered with him. I said I needed to have a man the equal of Antony, not cheap glass masquerading as a diamond, not cheap iron dressed up in gold leaf, pretending to be the genuine thing. For that is what Octavius is, despite being the nephew of the great hero I loved and whose assassination robbed Cleopatra of her man.

I did not drown my sorrows in drink. I could not comfort myself in Antony's way, telling myself I'd no reason to be sad or taking another warm body into my bed. Antony had married somebody other than me, he had married a Roman, therefore (I don't know where I get the "therefore") he had made his fortune. Octavia was good-looking (I had no doubts on that score). She was much younger than I. She was accommodating. The triumvir had clearly had excellent luck.

My Roman had forgotten me. He was not preparing the immense gifts I deserved to receive on behalf of his twin children. He had betrayed our alliance. But enough of that! I was not going to toss stones in the air for the pleasure of having them fall on me a second time. Nothing of the sort! We would continue to be allies. He had no reason to go back on our alliance. He would continue to be my patron in Rome, as I would continue to be his Egyptian friend. It would not become a personal matter.

Nevertheless, my grief brought down on me a sense of total death, the way the footprint attracts the hunter's dog. I lost all hope of ever seeing him again. I had lost the Roman Empire both for myself and for my children. If it had not been for my wise attendants who managed to cope with the affairs of state, I might have lost Egypt itself. I do not know how I did not lose the twins I carried in my womb, hidden deep inside me, invisible to the world.

One detail made things even worse; the other triumvir, whom I had long considered my enemy, bore the same name as the new wife. I gave this an exaggerated importance. Octavia was the sister of Octavius, but what I could not bear was the similarity of their names. Now that I was no longer Antony's partner, it was she who had supplanted me, a woman from the opposing side, Octavia. Of course, she had to be his perfect counterpart, his complement. With her beside him, he was sure to be serenely happy, he had to be—or so I imagined—at peace with himself and others. Now he must surely have what I had been incapable of giving him, a harmonious pact with the world at large. The torments that had persecuted him when I was at his side, could not be harassing him now in Rome, of that I was sure. He would not be replacing Octavia with a slavegirl. With her as his wife, life would run smoothly. With her, the ugly side of his disposition would be erased, beaten down, exorcized. Antony and Octavia had to be mirrors of each other, complete partners, beings finally brought to fulfilment.

I felt not only abandoned but defeated, even destroyed. I had loved nobody more than him, never. With no other was I so wildly, so wholly in love. With nobody else had I felt so solid, so strong and secure. But now my love meant nothing to him. His Octavia, the perfect partner, bore the name of the second triumvir, the usurper who had snatched from my son the inheritance his father had freely left him; with him for a brother-in-law Antony would live a life smooth to the touch, like the finest sand. Time would do no damage to him and his wife. They were two perfectly happy creatures. And I was the displaced one, a woman without use, a victim of robbery. A nothing. And the nothing did nothing but lament her situation. I had handed myself over to my grief.

One morning a shaft of sunlight fell on my bed and awoke me. A draft of cool air accompanied it. My faithful Charmian had raised the canopy of my bed and set beside me a basket of rose petals, and so that I could enjoy their aroma more, had half-opened the balcony door. Every day she tried to delight me with this or that little surprise. The sudden ray of sunlight, the cool breeze, and the smell of rose petals transported me aloft to a time when Mark Antony did not exist for me, when Cleopatra was therefore fully alive and in her heart there glistened a pearl of happiness.

But they did not bring to mind a particularly tranquil and joyous moment. My mind went back to the time when I had been deposed from the throne of Egypt by the clique around Ptolemy, my brother and husband. General Achilles was in pursuit of me. Along with my personal bodyguard, I took flight in the hope of mustering reinforcements. The troops in Pelusium had sided with us and agreed to admit us into their city. The petals and the breeze had wafted my thoughts to the light, four-horsed chariot in which General Aristarchus and I were riding. Roses and wind carried me back to that journey across the desert. After several days of headlong flight, we were in the final stretch, heading toward the walled city. The sunset and a low breeze had distracted me from my sorrows, for the general had a sweet-smelling mouth, scented with roses, and neither the sand nor the speed of the light chariot could dissipate the smell. It filled me with desire for the man who would lead the army with which we planned to recover Egypt. The smell of his mouth transformed the warrior-in-arms into a handsome hero who delighted my heart. It drove away all thoughts of my predicament. There in the twilight, before we reached Pelusium, I recovered my strength, I felt confident of my power, for my heart leapt with joy at the breath of Aristarchus. If life had rushed into me then on the road to Pelusium, a queen without a throne; if the caressing scent from a mouth that smelled of roses had been enough to recover my composure when I was cornered and lost; if that alone could set the heart within me leaping with joy, what then of now? Here on my bed of sorrow, had it not happened again? The combination of the scent of roses, the cooling wind, and the light shimmering through the canopy of my bed had restored me. For a second time, thanks to the petals, the breeze, and the light, my heart raced with Aristarchus toward Pelusium and returned to life in the instant. Thanks to them, I regained my sense of my own identity. I knew who I was, what the wind was, what the petals were, what the sun was. My life was there to be lived; with the stroke of a feather I could brush away Mark Antony, his betrayal and his caprices.

I got up from my bed, almost dancing. I called my ministers together and spent the morning bringing myself up-to-date on the affairs of state. Nobody referred to my depression or to the Roman. He was now dead to me, a stranger I had no cause to mourn, for he was long gone from us. While they combed my hair, I heard a maid whispering that the acrobats and comedians from Thebes were putting on a show that night in Alexandria. That night, Apollodorus and I exchanged our fine robes for the simple, white, woven garments of shepherds, and without advising the palace, we slipped out. In our disguises we watched the show. The witty comedians left us chortling, while the acrobats kept our nerves in suspense. Indistinguishable from the common people, we made our exit, doing what everyone else was doing. Here and there we halted to listen to the street musicians. We applauded them, and then we danced, hugging each other like youngsters, mixing with the simple, happy crowds. Apollodorus and I—as well as the children developing inside my happy flesh—got drunk on cheap wine. My faithful servant bought a pint of it for a few pennies from a woman who made us drink it out of grotesque cups. Mine was in the shape of an elderly man, with long, floppy legs that wrapped around his neck. Apollodorus got one like the torso of a woman with three breasts. Both were painted in startling colors.

I make mention of my unborn children here, for while I was taking large swigs, I felt sure, for the first time in weeks, that my children were indeed going to be born. I had been living in a dream, a dream deeper than life itself, but the wine, instead of merely sating, had awakened me.

In that dream, what had happened to me had been happening to somebody other than me, to a different person, one had no connection to the real me.

My final month with my twins passed unnoticed for me. My pregnancy with Caesarion had been very different. If I forgot him for a moment, Caesar was there to remind me. According to the gossips, he had played husband to all the wives of Rome and wife to all the husbands. Now for the first time ever, he was going to have a child. He believed, furthermore, that the gods had decided his only son would be born to him from the throne of Egypt; the reason was that a grander destiny awaited him. Grander even than that which history had already conceded to him, the greatest general after Alexander the Great. My life with Caesar was totally unlike life with Mark Antony.

That night, on my return to the palace, after Apollodorus had left me alone, I slept with no more dreams of decapitated bodies whose heads had been hidden for me to find in one or another corner of the palace. I slept without dreaming in the unnerving colors that brought panic to my nights. I slept without hearing uncanny music in my dreams.

The next morning I told my trusted advisors to start think about which king they were going to look for as a husband for Cleopatra. I had no intention of spending my life among eunuchs. That was not a suitable fate for me. But I did not want some boy-man in my bed. I refused to favor anyone with my desire unless he could prove a boon companion. The queen had a weakness: she needed a man she could count on for company.

The second day of my recovery, I dispatched from Alexandria a splendid wedding present to Antony and Octavia, along with another gift for Octavius, to congratulate him on the healthy direction his government was taking and on the recent renewal of his friendship with Antony, whom, I wrote, I still considered, like Octavius himself, a close ally of Egypt.

The third day of my recovery, I spent without any taint of displeasure. I was fully mistress of my throne and of myself again. I told myself that the storm had passed, and for good. I forgot that I had said I needed a man at my side. I looked at myself and saw nothing that resembled a weakness.

By the time the fourth day had arrived, I felt completely and permanently cured of the pain of Antony's desertion. As soon as I got into bed, I started to enjoy the stillness of the night. Sleep slowly possessed my eyelids, more delightfully than usual, thanks to my fatigue. But then

Savage Love seized me by the hair
And would not let me sleep the whole night long.

It said to me: "Cleopatra, queen of Egypt you may be, / But my slave you remain, ten thousand times the lover of Mark Antony. / Do you think you have grown so robust that you can sleep here all alone?" I leapt barefoot from my bed, half-naked. Not waiting to rouse my maids, I hurried out of the sleeping quarters and, untrammeled by sandals, my feet felt an urge to walk and walk, to escape my dread desire. Without a second thought, I left the palace and began to run, as if running would let me escape the memory of my nighttime strolls with Antony.

The streets of Alexandria were empty. Men's voices, the creaking of wheels, the bumping of boxes on carts, the grunting

of beasts of burden, the songs of birds, even the barking of dogs—
all quite absent.

Trembling from my bed and its dream, driven by insatiable
desire, I dashed all alone both hither and thither, for it was impossible to find the only man I wanted to kiss. I did not walk,
really I ran, fleeing all the places where tyrant Love knows how
to ensnare his victims.

My despair got wilder and wilder. If I had leapt terrified
from my bed, I was now terrified of every single thing. My eyes
saw all objects in a bright light that glowed with a painful intensity and almost burned me. Everything lay in semi-darkness—
for it was the middle of the night and the street lamps had been
extinguished by the watchman—but a light shone with a dangerous insistence from every object.

It was a moment of dreadful darkness, though darkness is
hardly the right word when everything glowed bright enough
to hurt me. My grief was literally splitting my heart in two and
mockingly rubbing one half against the other. In the recent past,
I had not been strong enough to bear the sight of the sun. I had
stayed in my bedroom, wanting to know nothing of Egypt. I had
suffered, drowned in my miserable tears. But all this was nothing compared to the grief that possessed me now; and it had come
without warning, because I believed myself free of him, free of
my sickly attachment to Mark Antony, the man who did not love
me. Now the very objects of my world were hostile to me. The
universe had sided with him: it had joined him in his rejection
of me. I was a mere nuisance, a superfluity in the world. I needed
to be cast out violently from land and sky and the winds the gods
unleash. Objects touched me and called out, "Enemy, enemy,
enemy!" It was a fearful moment, but when I compare it to the
moment in which I now speak, I envy myself that experience. I
would choose to be back there, to be that woman again, once
more to be Cleopatra.

Then at some point, my eyes glimpsed a sharp piece of metal on the ground. I picked it up, grasping it firmly. A little farther along, some fist had used the metal to scratch a message on the wall and then tossed it away to avoid suspicion. The message read:

My name is not Cleopatra.
I wasn't born a woman or the child of a drunken king.
My father drank water and kept bees.
I am a slave.
I wasn't, I won't be, I don't want to be a Lagid,
But the mystery of my soul is as deep as that of the wretched queen!

Beside the words, he had started to daub a face with a huge nose and pronounced wrinkles on the neck, as if in mockery of me. The sketch got my nose right but those wrinkles belonged more to Arsinoe than to me.

"Wretched queen!" What a slap in the face! Seeing my name written with such contempt, I saw with total clarity how the rejection of Mark Antony had torn me to pieces, that my face had become a shapeless lump. I thought I saw that when morning came to this same street, two or three dozen women with faces exactly like mine would be walking here. My hair was disheveled, and the same lack of care was apparent in my face. These women, my counterparts, each one of them would be exactly like Cleopatra, though none with hair as disordered as mine. So there was nothing unique about me anymore! I was a mere nobody, Antony, because you had erased me. I saw your hands, your fat fingers with the palms too big for them, I saw them molding one of those shapeless faces out of clay. I saw your hands holding the sharp metal I had just picked up from the ground, and with it you scratched features into my face, without any bleeding, as if I were clay also, but for all that, I suffered excruciating pain.

This horror at seeing myself erased by you and then repeated in so many other women had a red-stained edge to it, the color of blood, and it came with a pain beyond bearing. Then it took pity on me and withdrew its fangs and was replaced by a chill breath of wind. The breeze on my face spurred me to tears and I felt a sense of relief. I remained motionless, while my grief disfigured not just my face but the whole city. I wanted to die. I thought I was dying. The wet tears on my face turned to fire, became rivers of lava, and, the worst of all torments, the sand frozen by night. And I, the queen, was the victim.

At first I had not heard two men approaching. They were chatting and, after they saw me, they used their lamps to read the inscription on the wall. Then they started to shout. By now I've heard the story of that meeting told a thousand times. I can imagine clearly, I can see and hear that before they saw me, the two friends were exchanging laughs and teasing phrases about the endless party they were returning from so late at night. They were Philostratus and Crinagoras of Rhodes. But they had not a drop of wine in their veins, for they had been dining at the austere table of Olympus, the sage who has since become my doctor, and who now, in this final hour, remains faithful to me. They had sat in the open air, their only light the pale starshine, but they had spoken and listened their fill. Around this table pranced neither musicians nor dancers, neither comedians nor poets. They wore no garlands and reclined on no cloth of gold. They had only the herb garden of Olympus and his secretaries and students, men who clad themselves in coarse white wool, the plain dress of shepherds. In all this, there had been a gentle, moving simplicity, even though a student, who was not of their number but was studying mathematics, an arrogant youth with the long curly hair of a child—years later he would give himself out to be a prophet—had irritated them with his impertinent questions and his drinking of wine. They were making fun of his drunkenness and his questions at the time they bumped into me. On seeing me, Philostratus exclaimed, "There's another drunk, and this one's female! What kind of milk are mothers giving their children nowadays that they grow up with such feeble bones? One cup of wine and they fall over and talk drivel!"

But in spite of chiding me with his first glance, he spoke to me in a softer tone, perhaps because he felt compassion for my near-nakedness and my pregnant condition. "Little girl! Where are you going? May we accompany you?"

"Don't talk to her! Let's get out of here," Crinagoras said to him. "Can't you see what's she's written here and how provocatively she's showing off her . . . Let's beat it. Look what she's written. Find out who she is."

"She didn't write that!"

"She's got a sharp piece of metal in her hand."

"But she isn't the one. Don't you remember the poem?

The man whose dust lies in this deep-dug hole
Toiled as a slave while he was here on earth,
Yet earned he merit of an equal worth
To royal Darius, by his honest soul.

It's by Anyte. From 'The Tomb of the Slave.' Anyte, the one Meleager called 'the Homer among women.' It was going a bit far to say that, don't you think?"

Crinagoras hastened to reply, "Love for poets always does go too far, oversteps the limits, and with Anyte being a woman—well, she had twice the reason to overdo it."

Quoting Anyte, they had forgotten me. I too had forgotten myself, sinking deeper and deeper into that cauldron of grief where everything rang loudly and glittered sharply. I hadn't seen or heard them until Philostratus, remembering me, dried my tears with the edge of his rough, woolen cloak. Only then did I become aware of them there in front of me.

"Why did you scratch that up there?" he snarled. "You're asking for trouble, you know. You're endangering your child and everything. And for what? To travesty a poet who's been dead for hundreds of years."

"I didn't scratch anything on the wall," I said, without checking my tears.

"Why are you crying, pretty girl? You're about to have a child. You have life and happiness ahead of you. Have you quarreled with your husband?" Raising my face, he said to Crinagoras, "This woman's no beggar. Just look at her face. Where do you live? Calm yourself."

I could not calm myself. My face, beneath the edge of his cloak, felt that it was breaking asunder in every slightest part of itself, that Antony had obliterated it, exhausted it, robbed all its features of definition. How could he have done that to me? Had I imagined it all, that we had loved the way we had loved? Had I meant nothing to him? Had it happened only inside my head, in my imagination, for me alone? Did his Octavia have what Antony needed? Why didn't I have it? I wanted to die.

"What's the matter, little girl? Love troubles, eh? You're lovesick. Is that it?"

What made him think that? Was it so obvious?

"What else could hurt a woman like you, with such strong features? Look at her. She has a really striking face, with so much character. Any painter would want to paint her portrait."

A voice from behind then spoke up. "They've already painted her, man."

Did I know him? Had I met him before?

"She's still crying."

"You two, you better not touch her. Get out of here. Everybody knows that's Cleopatra."

Philostratus and Crinagoras swung round to the man who addressed them.

"It's you!"

"Yes. Have you sobered up yet? We were just talking about you before we found her," Philostratus said to him.

"Sure you were. I was right behind you. What you were saying sobered me up. You made me feel ashamed of myself. You're right. I was impertinent."

"How do you know it's Cleopatra?"

"For God's sake. Everybody in Alexandria knows it. Crinagoras, Philostratus, you only need to live near the Nile to know it."

"Let's take her to Olympus's house. He'll look after her. We're not going to leave her here."

"What makes you think it could be Cleopatra?" Crinagoras asked nervously. "All by herself? Half-naked?"

"Are you our wise queen?" Philostratus asked me, without ceasing to wipe away the endless flow of tears that poured from my eyes, now loaded with even more feelings, shame, humiliation, anger, rage, gratitude, surprise . . .

I admitted I was. How could I deny it?

I don't know what the old man said to me but it had an extraordinary effect and calmed me down. If I could recall his words, he would be saying, "And do you weep over Antony? I have to tell you: forget him. You are the most desirable woman in the kingdom. You were Caesar's woman. You are not a Roman. Your customs are beyond their understanding. The legend of Egypt is yours. If he is not here with you, if he happens to be with another, it is because he is inferior to you. Let him go. I do not know if there is another Caesar for you, but if there is, it is not Antony. Stop worrying about being left alone. Surely some god will come down from the heavens to spend his nights with you."

I know Philostratus did not actually say that to me, but it was what I was hoping to hear. But he did tell me what I needed to calm me down, and he took me to spend the night in the house of Olympus.

Prudent and serene, they sent a servant to station himself at the palace gate, to advise the guards of the whereabouts of Cleopatra as soon as day dawned, or before, if he heard any sign of alarm. They sat down at my side, prepared to stay awake with me if I did not fall asleep. But I stayed awake and spent the night in what proved to be a refreshing cure for me, owing to their conversation and a long skein of anecdotes.

By my side, without a pause, Olympus, Philostratus, and Crinagoras spoke on and on, tackling one subject after another, seamlessly. I imagine that over the table they had so lately left, they must have discussed other subjects, the abstruse topics over which wise men bother their heads. With me, however, they shared stories and fables, a lifetime's collection of incidents, like three nurses intent on soothing their child to sleep with a lullaby of words.

The nightlong talk those three sages bestowed on me finally cured me of the pain of Antony's desertion.

As a consequence, I included them in my court. When Antony returned, they learned how to appreciate his mind and gave him their genuine loyalty. Olympus is still my doctor and is the one living soul who now visits me. Where Crinagoras of Rhodes has ended up, I don't know. In my isolation here, shortly before the dying Antony arrived, I was told of the fate of Philostratus, my poet. The Romans cruelly humiliated him in the streets. They stripped him of his clothes and forced him to walk down the street on all fours, like a dog. They made him eat, like a dog, the manuscripts of poems dedicated to me that he kept in his house. "Gobble down your Cleopatra," the centurions bellowed. "All she's good for is to be food for dogs like you." Then they made him swallow cattle dung till he could swallow no more. "Gobble down your Cleopatra, dog," they kept chanting, chanting, chanting. "Gobble her down, gobble her down, gobble her down."

These soldiers of Octavius kept up their torture till they suffocated him. Like Antigone, I wonder, "Will they torture me?" And I answer with the reply that Creon gave her: "No, your death will suffice." What this tyrant does not know is that my death has long been a gift from Antony, who also tortured me. What does it matter what Octavius can do to me?

As I said, Mark Antony, you came back. Two years after you had left me in Alexandria, you returned.

You sent me a long, persuasive letter. I feel a desire to repeat it here, so sweet a letter! You did not know I had learned it by heart. From time to time I repeat it, to bathe my tongue in honey. If I still had a tongue, I would want to drink its words now, but I am totally lost to everything.

In that letter you begged the queen of Egypt to take her twins and herself to Antioch, so that you could know "the twin fruits of the best days of your life." Inside the five sheltering walls of that city, our glances met again. At once the bond that united us, the knot of mutual pleasure, tied our bodies together, binding us with its protective force.

The two years that had divided us were transformed into the four steps that our bodies took to form an embrace, fusing us together, one into the other.

Had you really been widowed and then married Octavius's sister? Had I really forsaken my better self till I was restored to health by the city's sages? All that disappeared the second we saw each other. You had never gone away; you had only drawn closer.

You and I had found a route that bypassed every wall, every rampart, every form of separation.

A few days later, we celebrated our marriage Egyptian-style, convinced that nothing could separate us ever again. We forgot that

> *Nothing lasts for those who are born to die,*
> *Both fortune and misfortune hurry by.*

We were drunkenly happy, with a happiness that made us unique, vigorous, indefatigable enjoyers of life.

We minted coins with both our images on them. Wishing to fix forever the two aspects of our love, I stamped on my seal the word: *methe,* intoxication, for the gold of our laughter, our joy, our being together, and for the desperation with which we possessed each other, the madness of losing ourselves irretrievably, the torment in which our woven sheets wrapped our bodies. It was a torment that we in our drunkenness would not forgo. I wanted to see you every day, Antony, never to let you out of my sight for fear my exasperated need for you would tear at my flesh. You brought me no peace, no serenity. You brought me intoxication and fever. The wealthy queen of Egypt lived on the verge of starvation. Not that the delights of your love did not satisfy me to the full. Not that you did not come to me with laden hands, giving me more than any man had ever before given a woman. But you, too, were scourged by our hunger for each other. Love obliged us to live on our nerves. Nothing induced calm or repose. Nothing reduced the anguish of love's arrows.

Temperance, that good without equal, had no place in our style of life. Like a tongue of flame, we set ourselves under each other's heels. But we did not want to remove that burning pain, for the mere notion of losing each other again was worse than seeing ourselves devoured by a thousand tongues of fire.

We both donned the same garment of Deianeira, the one she wove with her own hands for her beloved Hercules to wear. Out of jealousy she dipped it in the blood of the centaur Nessus in the hope of recovering her hero's love. Do you recall the story? Hercules was returning with her to the walls of his city, when he encountered the turbulent waters of Evenus, swollen by winter rains, more turbulent than ever before. The river was full of treacherous whirlpools, and Hercules, instead of reminding him that he had recently defeated a river in order to gain his bride, thought only of the rapids and feared for his wife, who was not familiar with the fording places. Hercules! All you had to do was grasp her by the waist and carry her across like a child. You had just come from a victory over the tumultuous rivergod Achelous, but fear for your Deianeira stole away your confidence in your own powers. You thought fainthearted thoughts about how to get your beloved to the opposite bank without any risk.

And what did you do? Trusting the words of the fierce Nessus, you let her cross the river on his back. When the centaur, emboldened by the current, caressed her flesh, she cried out and you wounded him with a poisoned arrow. Treacherous to the end, he said to Deianeira, "Your beauty had destroyed fierce Nessus. I leave you, my beautiful one, this present. Keep my blood where daylight cannot reach it. If one day Hercules, in his blindness, fails to recognize your charms, soak a robe in my blood. Make him wear it and he will adore you once again." And other things, too, he said that I will not repeat here.

When Hercules returned victorious from his labors, his eyes were glutted with the beauty of a young captive. It was then that Deianeira bathed the tunic in the centaur's blood. It consumed him in agony.

We both put on the tunic of Deianeira. With us, the centaur got his revenge without needing to lie to its weaver. We were both like the fleece of the white sheep she used to daub the tunic. We devoured ourselves, we turned ourselves into fugitive smoke there on the bed we made for ourselves.

We set about destroying each other; there hardly remained a visible trace of us, only a mere scattering of ashes where the tree once grew. We continued bubbling away, as if on the boil, and nobody could see the damage the fire was causing.

It was the arrow that kills the one it does not strike.

Clad in the precious garments that Love prescribed, our limbs contracted little by little; they narrowed, became enchained. On the one hand, our presence drew the eyes of the world, the presence of you and me side by side, as if the cleverest artisan in the world had fashioned us, creating the visible statue of Love itself. Who, when he saw us, would not exclaim: "They love each other!" We were fairer than the fairest, because you and I together composed one figure, entire in itself, the purest of forms. The gift of the ancient centaur had been put on. "From hereon he will see women but none will please him like you do. None will please you except him. Thanks to that garment, the two of you will feel your very entrails shiver with delight!"

From that time on, after our return from Antioch, we were possessed by convulsive cramps. Under the sway of the jealous Deianeira, the double Hercules, the queen of Egypt and the triumvir Mark Antony, were like two children out of control.

The arrow infected with the poison of the hydra of Lerna envenomed two lives more. The dusky hydra imprisons us now; its venom circulates through our veins; its stabbing pains burn our flesh and transform it into hot coals. We bubbled, as if boiling, and nobody warned against the fire, though it blazed unremittingly around Mark Antony and Cleopatra, obscuring them from the world. The bonds of love converted into the shirt of Deianeira defeated us. Now your blood, which a dagger let loose from your body, bathes me, Mark Antony. Look, I am relieved because it has set you free of me.

Let Octavius hear this: It was not you, you vile, bloodthirsty, merciless, wretched Ocatavius, who defeated me. Once more I say it. What were you? You had no part in our story. Confess it! Whom can I blame for my condition? Whom would I like to tear to pieces?

Sixty thousand infantry, twelve thousand cavalry, the four hundred ships of Rome, the problems of supplying our troops when Agrippa had seized control of the neighboring islands, the desertion of the kings of Thrace and Paphlygonia, Delius's going over to the enemy and taking our battle-plan with him, the surrender of our land forces, the defection of the legions stationed in Cyrenaica, the ships I sent overland that were captured and burned by the Arabs of Patras—none of that had power over us, because Love held us in its sway. And now here I am, undone, in shreds, my powers of no avail, but even as I see you dead, Mark Antony, I fall in love with you again. Once again I put on the tunic of Deianeira, though I know of its burning intensity, but I am determined to see you and me become One.

I should have listened to the gods. My mistake was committed before I met you, Mark Antony, before I met Caesar, before I knew the hope of being the love of another, the dream of achieving completeness in the arrogance of a fulfilled couple.

Antony, neither you nor Caesar, nor anybody could have given me that One, for a mortal is nothing without the gods and the earth. The river loses its gleam, its generative powers, if the gods do not infuse it with life. The Nile is the gods because it contains them. Let us imagine the unimaginable: that the Nile became merely running water, that it lost its divine identity. Well, so what? It is impossible to imagine it but let us suppose that the giver of life losts its godly powers. Its dark waters would not even wet us. Its silt would be sterile sand. But the river knows nothing of such foolish arrogance. The river is the breath of the gods and does nothing to hide it. It runs full of life and it bestows it on us, because it is life itself. Hear this, Antony, though you hate me to speak of Caesar: His attachment to me made me haughty after I thought that, with him as my ally, I would receive obeisance from all the kingdoms of the world. Listen now to what I say of you: So great was my joy, so profound the intoxication you filled me with, that I loved you in the firm belief that we would one day encompass everything, that our love would contain the Nile, the air, the sea, the sun. Nothing, nobody, would be lacking. We were to be complete. We needed no tunic of Deianeira to ruin us! The bonds of love could have remained untangled and we would still have known defeat, for we were convinced that you and I together were One in the world's despite, the One that outrivaled all beings mortal and divine!

So our ship sank all the deeper in the deepest of waters. Because we were happy, because we thought we were complete in the possession of our happiness, because you came back to me and abandoned me yet again! It meant nothing to us that the scant breath of Octavius blew on our sails and snapped the yardarm, and the sky darkened with rage, and the whole universe, including the Elysian Fields and the world of the dead, turned against us. The great battle between East and West, between the Tiber and the Nile, between Octavius and Antony and his Cleopatra—the conflict that poets will sing for centuries to come—none of that ever happened. We fled from Actium before Octavius could smash us down and postponed the final encounter. When he did come to face us, the issue was not fought over you or me, or over the oneness that we thought we were building piece by piece. Antony, neither of us listened to the truths of the gods. Because we were the river that thinks it owes nothing of its power to the divine, because we were a rootless tree, a sky overcast, the couple who believed they were self-sufficient—that was why!

It did not matter, Antony, that you were a successful general but an ineffectual king, that you were not adept in satisfying the wishes of others and were even incapable of perceiving your own, that you never knew what you wanted, that you were often a sundial buried in shadow. You were great when you had my Caesar to advise you, but you were not vanquished because you lost him. You were vanquished because of what I have been telling you, for loving me to excess, because I returned your love, convinced that we two made one, that we formed a perfect unity. We lost. We were our own defeat!

Betrayal

Everything, everything is the handiwork of Death.
—Virgil

Diomedes the Informer

Cleopatra was short in stature but possessed an extraordinary physical beauty and grace in her movements, as agile and elegant as an animal or a nymph. Her manner of speech was quick and confident, and in order to fulfil my obligations as her scribe, I was forced to devise a form of shorthand that my assistants would know how to decipher. She had personally approved of my entering into her service when I was a mere youngster, but would not have done so had she had the foresight to see how much I would end up weighing. I tend toward obesity, the sole trait I share with the Ptolemies, and my body, though formerly obedient to my will, has never enjoyed either speed or agility or grace. Now, thanks to my weight and my advancing years, I am the prisoner of my own legs. I was not so at the time when the events of the story I plan to narrate took place. The hand with which I write now is appropriate to my weight. I am slow. I weigh every word as I go. Between one line and the next, I stumble over my own thoughts. It is incumbent upon me to confess to this characteristic, though it is nothing in my favor, but I will not trouble you with it again.

Cleopatra had this rapid way of speaking and told her stories with a liveliness that I, old and fat, cannot presume to imitate with either my hand or my head that now requires an effort to raise when I wish to see the stars twinkling far above. My weight stoops me the way Nature bends an animal, obliging it to peer down at the surface of the Earth. Only mankind has a face wholly to the front, but some of us, despite our humanity, have become animals in this respect.

The passing years have effaced much of what I remember of Cleopatra, but some things I can still recall without the least distortion, right down to the most trivial details. The one advantage of being torpid and heavy is that one proceeds more slowly; and at that pace, memory holds fast to certain things as if nothing could budge it, as if it were fixed, firmly rooted. But the words of Cleopatra were beaten down every time I tried to recount them. It happened so often that now they hide themselves from me, together with certain incidents to which I had been eyewitness, flying from me like birds that flee before the drums of rowdy men. My interrogators wore themselves out trying to convince me that I had not seen what I really saw. That what I knew to be the truth was actually falsehood. How many times did they come and ask me about her, only immediately to contest every statement I made, every phrase, every account of every act that I tried to affirm. For long years I had submitted myself to the authority of the truth with a dedication I now repeat here, but I started to weaken and make concessions, first with my words, then with my point of view, and finally even in my memory. But I will tell no more lies. I will fill in the gaps where terror caused me to forget. From my stylus will come nothing imagined.

Since I know I am soon to die, I cannot cling to the argument that Theodotus employed to advocate the treacherous beheading of Pompey: "The dead don't bite." Maybe they do not bite the living but I'm not certain they do not bite the other dead. I write now because I wish to repair my errors, but already I realize I have failed! The words I have attributed to Cleopatra do not convey the lively way she spoke. I falsify them by calling them hers. That alone should be enough to disqualify them, but there is a defect even more serious: they have been deliberately altered by the powers of Rome.

They pretend to describe the real Cleopatra; they even believe their own pretence, but they end up reinforcing the version created by Caesar Augustus. (Cleopatra always called him "Octavius.") They focus on one aspect of her, representing her as a creature who saw life through eyes blurred by her feelings. An insulting straitjacket for a woman of her energy, complexity, and violence. Could the great Cleopatra have been merely a tear-stained creature, weeping for her sentimental misfortunes? She had been educated by sages, constantly surrounded by refined and worldly eunuchs, by prudent and intelligent maidens. From childhood onward, she had witnessed palace intrigues. She had shone as a governor, excelled as a cunning strategist, and managed her affairs with consummate skill. Could she be this weepy weakling? Not anywhere on this planet called Earth. Nowhere where a man is called a man, a woman, a woman; courtiers, courtiers; youths, youths; slaves, slaves; soldiers, soldiers. Nowhere in the world of Cleopatra. She was of another order entirely. And I intend to portray her as such—even as I flee for my life, on horseback for my legs no longer support me—as a woman born to command, with the glance of a queen; a woman of method, order, skilled in languages and in seeing through pretences. Get away from me, all Romanness, Rome and its Romans. Away, I say! Far from where my hand is writing. Away, I tell you.

With this abjuration I need to begin before inscribing the words of Cleopatra, taking care not to alter them, in order to preserve the one thing she asked of me, her memory.

I wish to repeat what she began to dictate to me before the corpse of Mark Antony, covered in his fresh blood. She wore hardly a shred of clothing on her body. She had pulled off her clothes the night before, to cover him. Almost naked, she had spent the night in his arms, murmuring to him. We did not attempt to separate her from him, not even when his corpulent body stiffened and ceased to show signs of life.

Before day broke, before we shrugged off the sullen heaviness that had befallen us in place of the comforting sleep that carries whole and entire to realms where neither sadness nor joy can touch us, before we were fully awake and alert, Cleopatra sprang up, slipping out of the corpse's embrace, where she had seemed part of its death, painted with blood and frozen into immobility.

She spoke to me, with her hair disheveled and matted. But she addressed me with an intelligent glance in her distraught face. She had abandoned all her attempts to chafe life back into Mark Antony and stood frozen. Her scanty garments had the look of sculpture, heavy, dense, and thick. They still retained a stiff charm in their folds but they no longer seemed to be woven of threads. The bloody fabric possessed an unearthly weight and volume.

Standing there, heavy as lead, with the proud carriage that always obliged us to adore her, as if she had dressed with an eye to elegance, adorned, as it were, for a ceremony of some importance, but with the blood always threatening to stream off her, she looked at me and began to speak, gesturing that she required my full attention. She ordered me to take her dictation and to take it accurately. I began to do so the

second she opened her mouth, calmly and coolly jotting down
her words, striving to preserve the precision and clarity of her
thoughts. As is obvious, I have skipped some truths. My false
memory, my slave's memory, my Roman memory, wanted to
imply that a certain madness raged in her words, out of
control, as if she were beside herself with the grief induced by
her farewell to her husband, to her sons, to Egypt itself, and
along with Egypt, her farewell to autocracy, to power and
riches, to beauty and all its charms, to life itself as it surrendered to the blind, insensate greed of Rome.

She wanted her story recorded. She was looking back to
a world that she alone had known, one that could survive
solely in her words. All the rest I have set down here, expressing it through her voice. The absurdities that I have attributed
to Mark Antony, the feelings that verged on extremity, the
recriminations, the tone, especially the hysterically vindictive
tone, stripped of her characteristic self-possession—all that
came from my stylus under pressure from Rome's leader,
determined as he was to destroy the memory of a great queen.

What is true is that Cleopatra's voice retained its firm
tone till the very last moment. Till then she remained in
control of herself, a peerless creature who at no point succumbed to sudden fears and fits of anger, a woman who knew
how to be beautifully persuasive. It was the voice of a queen
and the silence of a woman, both of which I disfigured by
distorting the way she spoke.

While she was attending to other business, using my
secretaries and scribes, I was carefully checking the words she
had dictated. I had noted them in own handwriting on the
scrolls—less cramped than usual—the way I had done with
her other narratives, decades before, along with her successful
negotiations with neighboring sovereigns as she maneuvered
to make stealthy additions to her realm, her plans for outright

conquest, and her sensitive dealings to preserve and strengthen
her domestic power. It fell to others to write down her
financial dealings. That was never my job. Nor to record
entitlements, the revoking of entitlements, and the other
official decrees of this queen of kings. Still, all the royal scrolls
were kept together, regardless of their content, and treasured
as the principal legacy of Cleopatra to the world. To me, she
dictated her thoughts about the art of government; her personal version, far from reliable, of the expedition against the
Parthians, and a concise history in verse of the Lagids, which
she stamped with a false signature. She had her maids compile
a volume of tips on how to look beautiful, with hints on
hairstyles, skin lotions, the starching of clothes, shaving kits
and ointments, intended to be a present for any friendly king
in whose territory the women were dismal frumps, so that
they might acquire a touch of style. The scroll was scrupulously edited, but of course, it did not give away all her
precious secrets. It was signed with Cleopatra's name to add
value to it, though it was common knowledge it had not been
actually written by her. I must point out, once and for all, and
before I forget, the total falsehood of a rumor circulating here
and there, that Cleopatra wrote kitchen recipes, with ideas
about how to decorate a room for a party, detailing the layout
of the table, the reception area, the dresses and perfumes, with
an addendum on mixing drinks and seasoning dishes and
suggestions for the best songs and dances to accompany the
occasion. That is a libel made against her out of malice, to
reinforce the image of her that the Romans want to convey,
of Cleopatra as a flirt, a mistress, a trivial housewife given to
fits of pique. She has also been credited with a "Treatise on
Weights and Measures," another on agriculture, and yet
another entitled "Secrets of Alchemy Revealed," which
contains a legend that she knew how to create gold. In one

way that legend is a complete lie, but metaphorically it contains an element of truth, since her astuteness and versatility in business matters meant she had the knack of striking highly profitable deals.

Speaking of alchemy, she increased the riches of Egypt to an immense degree, multiplying them many times over, while hanging on to what she already possessed and preventing the Roman vandals from stealing any of it. She knew where to invest gold so that it brought in a one hundred percent profit. She bought groves of Jericho balsam, paying Antony a mere trifle for them, and then rented them out at 200 talents per year. In Nabatea, she cornered the market in pitch. When she could not exploit a thing for quick and easy profit, she put her ingenuity to work and eventually brought in gold in abundance. Gold poured into Egypt from all points of the compass. She even debased the coinage, minting coins that did not contain the legal amounts of precious metals, and inscribed on them whatever value suited her. Initially this caused an uproar, but then she flooded the market by minting even more of the same, plus others worth even less but all with the same face value. Confusion confounded confusion. She left her mark on the Roman world by this debasement of the currency. And in other ways, too. On her trip to Rome with Caesar, she took with her Sosigenes, the official astronomer of Egypt and, working together, they adjusted the calendar to make it coincide with the agricultural cycle. She worked tirelessly beside Caesar, organizing the census and showing him how to operate a customs and excise service. She applied herself to improving the appearance and the comforts of Rome, giving instructions to drain the Pontine marshes and Lake Pucinus. All without neglecting the affairs of Egypt, on which she kept the closest eye, despite her distance from home.

Cleopatra did dictate to me, at one point, a funeral
eulogy over Caesar. We keep it in a separate place, apart from
the other royal documents. She did not consider it quite
proper for the monarch of Egypt to lament the death of
Caesar publicly, either as the father of her son or the ally who
consolidated her position on the throne, in case people might
read into it a submission to Rome. So she forbade copies of
"The Funeral Eulogy over Caesar" to be circulated and
stopped her signature being stamped on the sole existing copy.
We made copies of all her other works for the library of
Alexandria, for the library at Pergamum (which Antony kindly
presented to her), and for that of the Seleucids, as well as extra
copies to be given as special presents to visitors and envoys
and to be sent out via her embassies.

Recently we made an inventory of all the scrolls, as
detailed and orderly as the queen herself. Augustus made us
hunt down every single one, so determined was he to silence
her voice. He ordered that all the copies be placed at his feet
before being burned, treating them like living prey. I said
"hunt" deliberately. When he got hold of one, he had it
locked away, forbidding anyone to touch it, let alone read it.
Someone once said, "I hope there isn't a curse on it," and he
exploded with rage, swearing that he was not going to allow
legends to be created about the pamphlets of a slut. Perhaps
this is the reason he had all those who hunted down the scrolls
executed.

I was the only one left alive. It was no accident.
Augustus wanted me to corroborate, as an eyewitness, his
most fantastic misrepresentations of Cleopatra. All the others
whom he used to track down the scrolls, he had eliminated.

If I were to comment on his image of her, I'd have to
say that nobody perverted it as much as he did. His contempt
for her was rooted deep in his being, above and beyond the

natural Roman disdain for all things Egyptian, above and beyond the misogyny that resents a woman controlling a kingdom. She was also the mother of Caesar's only natural son, and at any moment he could have asserted his rights to his father's legacy. Caesarion was an obstacle to many of his ambitions, a living impediment, and an invincible one if his mother sided with him. As soon as she was overthrown, he had Caesarion decapitated by the hand of his personal tutor, his guardian. To his failure to implement the terms of his uncle's will, he added a reckless disobedience to his wishes, a mocking defiance. As Cleopatra has already stated, Caesar left explicit instructions that his son be given the best of educations. But Augustus ordered the tutor—whose salary, incidentally, was not paid out of his father's legacy but out of the pocket of his mother—to cut off his head, so that Caesarion suffered the same fate as Pompey's child, beheaded by the hand of his protector.

Thus Augustus hurled himself into the business of eliminating her, even her image. So how did some of her statues survive? It was the work of Archibius, her friend, who gave Octavius-Augustus two thousand talents to save the statues from the obliterating fate that befell those of Mark Antony. But it wasn't the money (though the miser stuffed it gladly into his pocket), nor the plea of Archibius that saved the statues from destruction, but the desire of Augustus to confine the queen to her fancy hairdo and in her woman's robes, void of ideas, plans, and strategies, for those stone effigies with their bronze and gold adornments are unthinking objects. On the other hand, he did not leave intact one tablet, one scroll, one inscription, so furious was his rage against her memory.

Now I am employed in destroying those scrolls, without still having finished saying what she was really like when she dictated the last of them to me. Before she even spoke, I knew from the way she looked at me that she was dictating. It was the voice of a queen, as I told you. More than once the Romans have written that on that fatal morning Cleopatra had scratched her whole body, pulled out chunks of her hair, and thrown herself down in grief and despair. Not so. I saw her without a single scratch. There were no bald patches in her hair, though it was matted thick with the triumvir's blood. I was an eyewitness. Her body was in no way damaged. As night drew on, she tenderly hugged the body of the man she had loved, unafraid of the presence of death. At daybreak she spoke. But she did not speak the words that the mirror of my slavish mind has reflected here.

Remember, I penned them in an enemy city. For I am now in Rome. Here old age has suddenly overtaken me. Here my legs refuse to serve me. Here I have grown elderly, and like any elderly soul, I have become a little child again. Here I once enjoyed moderate wealth, thanks to Augustus. I am as sure as I am in Rome that, on that fatal day, Cleopatra did not inflict a single scratch on herself nor tear out one strand of hair. Why did the Romans scratch her in their version of her grief? In order to add a touch of pathos? No, enraged against her, detesting her, they depicted her in this final portrait as a queen wounded by her own hands. They loathed her but at the same time recognized her power. Nobody but herself, they implied in unwitting tribute, could wound her, but their hate also portrayed her before the world as unhinged, as a woman who had lost control of everything, even of herself.

The day Mark Antony died, her voice sounded solid and firm as she began to dictate. Without any alteration in tone, she moved her feet, as if preparing to take off her shoes. Her maids darted forward to help her, but she checked them with a raised hand. Down onto her spotless white feet, the blood dripped from her robe and highlighted her sorry condition. With the sole of one foot, she rubbed the instep of the other, for the drips must have given her an itch there. The natural-ness of the gesture, the way she wiggled her toes, was deeply saddening for me. The heart in my breast, usually so carefully guarded against any emotional shock, received a heavy blow. I almost lost my composure. The manicured feet of the queen, painted with the blood of the arrogant and once-powerful triumvir, sent a shock wave through me. Her feet kept mov-ing and moving. But not from place to place. They made simple little gestures, delicate but demonstrative. In a way they were expressive of the queen's countenance. It wasn't because this was the first time I had seen them without sandals, but because Cleopatra's life normally was so attached to all the rituals proper to the dignity and elegance of her position. She surrounded herself with an unalterable aura of glory, and never lost even an iota of her autocratic majesty. If she did act drunk or confused from time to time, it was always a studied drunkenness or confusion. If she set ceremony aside, it was to burst into triumphant celebration, but even then the joy that shone out of her was glorious and covered her with a veil of awe. If she disguised herself as a slave, it was so that she could go out and dance with Antony in the streets of Alexandria. As the pair of inimitable party-goers went from house to house, begging for drinks and followed by a throng of musicians, they were acting out another scene of her glory. Only on one night did I see her fail to act majestically. That was shortly before she had them stamp *"methe"* (intoxication) as her name on her ring. One afternoon in Alexandria, on the beach near the Hippogeium of the Mercenaries, I accompanied her and Antony. She had summoned me because the two of them wanted to state in writing their purpose in the upcoming war against the Parthians. They thought Ares would favor them,

for they had Eros as an ally. As Eros is superior to Ares, Ares
would obviously bow to his force. They soon forgot my
presence, the war, and the Parthians, and spoke only of erotic
matters, if they bothered to speak at all. They were there to
amuse themselves with masses of kisses and caresses, in order
to reinforce their alliance with Eros and guarantee their
success in battle. At least that was what they told themselves.
Up to this point they were still acting out yet another scene of
their glory. Then in a burst of high spirits, Cleopatra stripped
off all her clothes and dragged Mark Antony to the sea's edge.
There she stripped off his clothes too, and the two of them,
like undisciplined children, rushed carelessly into the water.
They pressed on through the foam and hugged each other. I
had never learned to swim and from the shore I nervously
watched the two heads bobbing in the distance to the action
of the waves. I was scared of the sea, of both its currents and
its creatures. I had never seen anybody on the beach of Alexandria enter the sea out of choice, still less frisk around in it, as
those two were doing, leaping among the waves. With good
reason the people of Alexandria fear the sea. But this was
Cleopatra and her Antony, and they loved each other, and the
sea seemed to carry them on its bosom. I lowered my gaze
when they came out of the water, arm in arm. I can't say why
but at that moment I thought of Robirius. I thought about
why we, who so often fed the avarice of the North, insisted
on being ourselves. I thought that the opulence of Rome
existed at our expense, that the Romans depended on us. At
the back of my thoughts, I heard the laughter of Cleopatra
and then the voice of Mark Antony turning into moans. Out
of delicacy I turned my thoughts back to Robirius, who was
reputed to be the moneylender to King Auletes. He certainly
lent the king great sums of money at exorbitant rates of
interest, sums that were then showered on senators and

consuls and other powerful Romans to ensure they voted in
favor of furthering the aims of the throne of Egypt. And who
ended up paying for those sums and all that interest? Egypt
itself! The Egypt that had rewarded Robirius with a public
position, for Ptolemy, you see, had kept him on as his Minister of Finance till the end of his reign. The Roman had
practiced corruption, unimpeded. There was no transaction
that did not pass through his ministry, and for each one
enormous bribes had to be paid, and their only function was
to add to the wealth of the loathsome Robirius. This went on
till Cleopatra assumed the throne. She got rid of him, a good-
for-nothing whose only aim in life was to line his pockets. I
was thinking about all this, for no particular reason, while
Mark Antony and Cleopatra frolicked on the beach. Then I
half-opened my eyes and peered through the lashes. The
ladies-in-waiting had hurriedly picked up the clothes so
carelessly cast aside and had spread a blanket on the beach.
They had lit candles on three sides of it and then left, forgetting all about me.

I was sitting under a palm tree. The shade of its trunk fell
directly on my body. It was easy to miss me. Nobody had
noticed me while I was making my mental journey to
Robirius. The sun was setting on the waves. Under its thin
silvery light, from behind my lashes, I watched the pair. His
penis erect, he was stroking her thighs and passing his lips over
her breasts. They had now changed all their laughter for sighs
and moans. They stretched out on the blanket and he pene-
trated her. They continued with this game till night had fallen.
The only light was the candles, until the half-moon appeared.
I did not dare move or even think of moving. At that time of
my life I had touched neither man nor woman. Ever since my
thoughts had left Robirius and returned to the beach, my own
penis had been erect. Thankfully, my throat was accustomed

to spending its days in silence, so I had no problem in stifling my moans. I was enjoying the two of them. I did not need to touch them. I had them. I saw them. I felt them, the buttocks of Antony, the perfectly shaped breasts of Cleopatra, who was infinitely more beautiful in her body than in her face. It was not simply that I did not need to touch them; I did not want to touch them.

I had ceased to be a child. I had become a youth and then a man, writing down what others dictated, lending my body to the voice of others. As long as I was taking down dictation, my mind and my inner voice followed their own courses, as if my consciousness could split and be in two places at the same time. That was happening on this occasion. I was in two places, leaning against the hefty trunk of the palm tree, my hands stroking my penis, never so painfully erect as it was right then, but I was also lying on that soft blanket of linen that the ladies-in-waiting had staked to the sand. I was the body of Mark Antony but at other times the body of Cleopatra. Bodies of gods. He ejaculated twice. I ejaculated with him. And in her body I was shaken by orgasm. But it went beyond mere amusement. The second time, bent double with pleasure, I rolled on top of my scroll and stylus and smudged my notes.

That was the only time I damaged anything dictated by her. Before, that is, I became the betrayer of the scrolls, at the time I guided the underlings of Caesar Augustus to every one of the copies and when I, who had been the hand dedicated to perpetuating her voice, contributed to the death of the Queen's memory. But this minor error should not be added to the list of major damages, because it was only the key words that scribes would amplify on wax tablets into koine, the common tongue of the Mediterranean.

Before I became a traitor, I was the one who jotted down
her words and gave them permanence with the sharp point of
my stylus, sheltering them against the annihilating winds of
time. I was faithful to the dictated word. But later I was responsible for the fires that obliterated them. I don't have time to
explain why I did it, nor do I care to. I have not resorted to this
ink to write my apologia. I will only say that I needed to
remain alive, and that I did remain alive while so many others
perished. And there was no one who spoke to me about her
who did not reject what I told them. I am human and I need to
relate to other people. That's why I became a connoisseur in
false truths. So deep are my lies, that now that I want to put to
rights the wrongs I have done, I find I have taken the same path
as her enemies. And what started as an imposed task has become
a routine. I have filled my pockets out of a base motive. But the
money has not served to buy me a protective space. Thus I
spend the years listening to them explain one version after
another of Cleopatra's character, none of them remotely like
the truth. It's decades now since I refuted them—but, to be
plain with you, I never really succeeded. It is decades since the
jokes about them stopped. You no longer see drawings on walls
of Antony and Cleopatra mating like two dogs on a boat. For
decades now, the world's contempt has been so absolute that
there is no need to damn a man for desiring Cleopatra. Hatred
for them has lost its excitement. Curses invoking them no
longer have impact. The tall tales about Antony cravenly
submitting to an Egyptian queen have had their gaudy day. For
decades now, I have been going along with the Roman version
of things Egyptian. I keep my mouth tight shut. Disputes don't
lead to friendships. I told you, I'm only human and I need
friends. But I am not an unmitigated liar; it did not come easy
to me to fabricate lies in order to converse with my neighbors. I

struggled to alter the minutest details of my recollections, satisfying my neighbors by concocting a Cleopatra who never existed. Rome, likewise, has changed; it has recovered from the losses that attended its triumph, in particular the fall in the price of gold, made twice as bad by the loss of the substantial returns on investment Cleopatra was so adept at securing.

Many things have changed since Egypt fell. Facts have acquired a dizzying speed and I, slow as I am, have been caught up in the rhythm, with nowhere to lodge my recollections. Yes, yes, I know I have boasted of my keen memory, but I have also admitted to the ravages wrought on the records of Cleopatra. Now that I am close to death, it is better for me to die with integrity, not as a scattering of parts in some cheerless corner of the world. I need to recover some wholeness for myself.

That is why I write this. But try as I may, I cannot recapture the voice of Cleopatra. When I attempt it, I simply repeat the errors I have been compounding over the years. I started here with the intention of being utterly faithful, of cleansing my memory of the false trails I was forced to take, in order to promote the lies of Rome. I wanted to find some consolation for my solitude. But there is a wide gap between intention and achievement.

After so many decades of lies and distortions, I can find no way to set the record straight. If I begin imitating the voice of Cleopatra, within no time at all I am sounding like Propertius, who hated her, or like Cicero, who couldn't even bear to see her portrait, or like Virgil who cheapened her.

Already stiff with the approaching cold of the grave, the voice stumbles. My stylus begins to take me where it wants. The point of my stylus doesn't give a damn whether I am faithful to a woman it had neither known nor cared to know. All it wanted was to have her speak in a frantic, shrieking tone, in the way you have heard. To have her speak out of an irrational heart. But here I am beginning over. I am escaping the tyranny of my stylus, the implement that writes with fear, even when danger is distant, the fear fed to me and gobbled down from sly Roman spoons. Here I strike back against what I swallowed, here on the bed where I expect to die. And I recall exactly the words she dictated to me when she, too, was expecting to die. I jot them down here, without betrayals, just as she spoke them to me, after she had loosed herself from the rigid embrace of Antony's corpse.

Even if I could recapture in its entirety my memory of the conflagration that Rome has fanned to fury over the identity of Cleopatra, even if I were to note down word after word of what she said beside Mark Antony's corpse, I do not, however, have the skill to set before your eyes the mirror in which she might appear—motionless, so that you might contemplate her—in action, so that you might admire her. My undertaking has its necessary limits. Hence I will have no chance to bring her back to life, or of recounting in what her greatness consisted, or of communicating to you what reactions she provoked in those who witnessed her splendor. A poet, I am not. Behind me, I have no Caesar Augustus to spur me on. Before me, I have no palace to reflect the image of the queen in all her majesty. Worse still, with the same zeal employed in destroying the papers of Cleopatra, Augustus has insisted that poets celebrate his Roman self and not omit any opportunity to see to it that his memory defy the assaults of time. Always a crafty man, he set his sights on the future. If we owe Cleopatra the calendar we use today, it was Augustus who left his mark on one of the names of our months. There is no month named for Cleopatra. The Roman populace would have forgotten her long ago, were it not for the cats that invade their premises. When she left Rome on the death of Caesar, she set her cats loose in the streets. But it will not be long before they forget cats came here from Egypt; the presence of a cat in Rome shortly will summon up no more memories of Cleopatra.

Is it a concern that poets put their ink at the service of Augustus's memory? Horace showed no reluctance to do it, convinced as he was of the vileness of the woman who dared defy Rome. Propertius neither. But Virgil, far wiser—I say it without disrespect for his other virtues, since it isn't wisdom that makes a poet great—Virgil did feel an enormous regret at the end of his life. Because he gratuitously vilified Cleopatra and overpraised Octavius, he intended to burn his epic. Lying did not trouble him so long as he was blinded by the power radiating from victorious Caesar. Perhaps it was not clear to him that he was lying, for, as I said, he was blinded. But over time the blindness gave way to sight; he grasped the real size of the man, the so-called hero, creature of cunning, but he glimpsed also the man's disfiguring flaws and his degrading weaknesses. He understood finally that, in piling mud on the memory of Egypt's queen, he had extinguished a star. Remorse overwhelmed him. Like me, he did not want to go to the grave, laden with regrets, for he well knew the power of the Egyptians in the Land of the Dead. I, too, have no wish to die in regretful silence. I fear, as he did, as anyone would, to encounter in the kingdom of the dead the righteous rage of Cleopatra in all her arrogance. (Horace and Cicero were right about her on that point.)

Nobody is infallible. My queen was not. She erred considerably in not cultivating the poets of Italy. She thought them inferior men, ignorant fellows whose "hands were not fit to wash the clothes of Egyptians," to quote her words. She offered examples like that clumsy verse from Cicero:

O fortunatam natam me consule Romam

considering it a prime example of dull-witted mediocrity, and held it up as the yardstick by which to measure the poetic endeavors of Rome. She made no effort to woo the poets; in fact, she never disguised her contempt for them, confident that, back in Egypt, there were brilliant poets with scrolls enough to describe her worth, dozens of docile hands eager to eulogize her. Was she justified in her assessment of Roman poetry? Did she hit the mark when she described Julius Montanus, Macrobius, Varius Rufus, and Sulpicius of Carthage as "a bunch of plodding mediocrities"? Probably. But she missed the mark in not trying to win them over to her cause, in the hope that they might reward her by faithfully honoring her memory. Toward Cicero she behaved with unprecedented arrogance. The first time he approached her, he used the pretext of lending her a learned text in order to pursue some pettifogging lawsuit and to ingratiate himself with the wife of Caesar and the queen of Egypt. It was out of sheer disdain for Cicero that she made him a promise she had no intention of keeping. Amonius tells us so.

What was that promise? To take him back to Egypt as her guest so that, in a series of letters, he could describe the country for a Roman audience. The conditions he laid down for his trip were such as to guarantee him enough drachmas to buy himself yet another palace. Of the letters themselves, little could be expected, for he had added a provision to the contract: "Whatever I may write will be at the service of freedom and truth alone, and no one will be permitted to assess it before I have it circulated and placed in the hands of the copyists, for I submit to no censorship . . ." The deal he requested was that Cleopatra make him rich twice over and in return he would write whatever he pleased, most probably to satisfy an enemy of Cleopatra, who would reward him by doubling his riches yet again. He had inherited considerable wealth and added to it by marrying well. He further augmented it by his cleverness and his well-chosen friendships. My advice to Cleopatra would have been: "What does it matter? Give him enough to buy a palace. You lose nothing." But either I would not have dared to say it or it simply did not occur to me to say it back in those palmy days. Neither I nor anyone else of the court spoke up. Sarapion, a member of the royal cabinet since the days of Ptolemy Auletes, only worsened relations between her and Cicero. One afternoon, they say, Serapion was looking for Atticus, who was staying at Cicero's palace, when he bumped into Cicero himself. Deferentially, Cicero asked if he could be of service. Insolently Sarapion snapped back: "I'm looking for Atticus!" Not one word of greeting. No courteous conversation. It's no wonder that Cleopatra and her court received such sour commentary in all the writings of Cicero.

Thanks to these oversights, Cleopatra is doomed to be remembered in Roman letters as a general's whore, as a "book-monger" (as they term the mean female slaves here who assign work to even meaner slaves), or a cruel stepmother bent on murdering the previous sons of her husband—calumny stops at nothing! But it is too late now for these facile regrets. She should have thought twice before making such enemies. But even then she might have failed to win them over, not simply because of the loyalty of the poets to Rome and to Augustus, but because "who can tolerate a woman with all the virtues?"

I have taken so much time in getting back to her genuine voice that you may think I am dodging the issue. It isn't so. And even if it were, I have a duty to gather my forces in order to recapture freely, without fear of the consequences, that rich, complex voice in all its nuances, before I take my final steps into the world beyond. And now here they are. The exact words of Cleopatra, as dictated to me in the last hours of her life:

On the Run

Damn the day I left my refuge with the pirate band in Cilicia!
Damn the day I returned to Alexandria, those days when I studied and grew into a woman! Damn you too, Demetrius! I always respected you as my teacher, for it was you who initiated me into the mysteries of womanhood that made me what I was and what I was to become after my defeat. Damn you, because before I learned your lessons, I was invulnerable. At eleven years old, nothing could harm me. I was whole and entire, my own possession, untouched by knowledge. My life would have turned out better, if I had remained by the side of my pirates, if I had stayed as I was, if I had stopped my heart from learning the feelings of a woman. I wish I could start over on my journey to earth and remain there in beautiful Tarsus, living among but aloof from its sailors and warriors, defending myself against the knowledge of its sages. Damn those who brought me to this idiotic defeat! Damn myself for wanting to be queen of the world. Damn Rome! And above all, damn the legs of every Roman male, the handsome as well as the ugly, damn the lot of them! Note, Diomedes, this is the history of my time with the Cilician pirates, with whom I should have stayed, to whom I really belonged. This is the story of how I ran away to be with them, and I want to focus on that

runaway child. I want the name of Cleopatra to be preserved in her, in that jewel case of vitality and joy.

That self-seeking tribune, Publius Clodius Pulcer! His nick-name among gossipers was "the Sacrilegious." At a ritual in honor of the Bona Dea, which only women were allowed to attend, at the time when Caesar was the urban proctor, Clodius dressed as a woman and slipped into the meeting, hoping to satisfy his lust for Caesar's wife. He was detected but, thanks to a young slave girl called Habra, he escaped. Anyway, he used to claim, this glory-grabbing tribune, that he had made a proposal in the Sen-ate to dole out wheat to the mob, legally and at no cost to them, with the idea of winning their adoration. The measure had no precedent. The economy of Rome could not support such a subsidy. So he came up with a shortcut to bolster Rome's finances. He asked the Senate to approve the annexation of Cyprus. His main pretext, among a dozen others, was that King Ptolemy, the brother of Auletes, was in league with the pirates of Cilicia and was allowing them to use his territory as a sanctuary. "I have been a victim of the pirates of Cilicia," he began his harangue (and here he was telling the truth, because years before they had ran-sacked some of his property). "I consider the repeated mockery from Cyprus to be an insult to Rome." And so on. The Senate approved the measure, the army was dispatched, and Cyprus fell into Roman hands. Auletes did nothing to help his brother. The Egyptians, already resentful of their king because of his earlier concessions to Rome, exploded in rebellion. Before we knew it, my father was toppled from his throne and we had to flee in haste from Alexandria.

We arrived at Rhodes. There we found the virtuous Cato en route for Cyprus. Clodius had put the conservative Cato, his bitterest enemy, in personal charge of the annexation. He claimed Rome had no more honorable man, but he understood it was a splendid way to sideline Cato once and for all.

Cato treated us with contempt. He sent a message that he could not accept an invitation to visit us because he was suffering the effects of laxatives and that Auletes would have to visit him. When my father went to see him, Cato did not even rise from his seat. Even before my father could open his mouth, he called out in an unmannerly style, "What you need to do is turn round and get control of Egypt again. There is no point"—the stink had filled the room—"in your going on to Rome. Now, if you'll permit me—" He crowned the unfinished sentence with a burst of flatulence.

Once the long fart had subsided, he gestured my father to leave. Worse still, he snapped his fingers to tell him to hurry. He had treated Auletes like a dog! Not much better was the treatment he gave my uncle. Disembarking at Cyprus, he offered to put the captured king in charge of the cult of Aphrodite in Paphos. My uncle was outraged at the proposal. A Ptolemy is descended from the gods himself; he cannot serve them as their submissive priest. He chose suicide.

How much honesty was in this spotless, virtuous, shitting Cato becomes clear when I tell you that his despatches to the Roman Senate were lost in transit. Some 7,000 talents in coin and metals, plates and dining utensils, jewels and exquisite tapestries from the Cypriot treasury, never made it to Rome. He alleged pirates had seized them. We shall see.

We left Rhodes and took up residence in Athens. There one of my maids had the misfortune to die. We carried out the funeral rites and left her buried in Athenian soil.

We had hardly arrived in Rome before Auletes was rushing around, stuffing presents into the hands of senators, consuls, and other notables. He had dreams of returning to Alexandria and regaining his throne. It now belonged, not to Cleopatra Tryphaena, but to his oldest daughter Berenice, after her mother had resigned for her own eccentric reasons. Other people's pockets were bulging with his cash, while he was forced to move on to Ephesus.

By this time, I was twelve years old. I saw nothing I could clearly count on in my situation. Not that I wanted anything particular for myself; after all, I'd grown up used to instability. But I was stranded in Rome. I knew what I did not want to happen but I had no clear idea how to get what I did want. But I did come up with a plan. It was a guileless one, daringly imaginative in a childish way, and the members of the court supported it, without reservation.

I had fully resolved to leave Rome, where the moneylenders battened on my father, flattering him, offering to get him further loans, preying on his reserves, voraciously devouring the last of his riches, without the least interest in restoring him to his past greatness. My body now began to take on a woman's lines and gave me the illusion that I was capable of controlling my own destiny, that I was the mistress of my fate. I could not get to Alexandria, nor did I want to. There the woman who bounced around on the throne with no concept of royal dignity would have had me put to death without a second thought, if I had shown up. She was still fiercely jealous of my mother, though my mother, in fact, detested me as much as she did. This was an open secret. And the source of many jokes throughout Egypt.

It was necessary to leave at nightfall, to take advantage of the hours of darkness, before Auletes noticed our absence. The streets of Rome never stopped being busy and we could lose ourselves easily in the throng, once we got inside the city. But we needed to cross from the Via Flavinia to the Appian Way. It was unfortunate that we were not already living inside the walls of Rome. The palace that Pompey had lent my father as a residence was located on the outskirts of the city, not far from the Flavinian Gate. We could not have used a chariot in our escape, for undoubtedly some busybody would have scurried off to tell

Auletes, if he'd seen my highly visible retainers on the move. Then we would not even have had time to reach the coast road.

My plan was to leave without attracting attention, but we needed some sort of cover before we could reach Rome. Pompey's palace had a large balcony overlooking the street. I used to spend hours there to avoid the scenes made by the rattled Auletes as one misfortune after another shook his self-esteem. Even I, a child, was frankly embarrassed by him. From the balcony I had noticed that every morning and evening there passed in front of our house the group of gladiators that belonged to our neighbor, Cato. They came up daily from their lodgings in the city to entertain the many visitors who frequented his dining room. They were nine brawny men. Some were dressed in leather breeches, others were clad in rough, woolen coats, typical of the city's athletes. One always carried in his hands the helmet he wore in his fights; another, dressed like a Gaul, walked with the top of his shield pressed hard against his stomach in a rather laughable way. There was third who invariably kept his face covered with one sort of mask or another. And there was a very young boy, obviously Greek. I had no idea what he was doing in Rome, working at a job his obvious intelligence did not suit him for.

Morning and evening, in hiding, unseen by them, I watched the gladiators from my balcony. Then one day, I showered petals on them, laughing. Other days I tossed them candies and bread-buns. One day, when the heat was oppressive, I sprinkled them with cool water. As I watched them, they watched me, looking curiously at this bored Egyptian princess who wanted to befriend them. We exchanged an endless number of smiles that made us friends, even though not a word had passed between us. That particular afternoon, as soon as I heard their steps approaching our doors, I made an agreed-upon sign to my maids and we all set out to walk in front of the gladiators, slowly enough to be soon overtaken by them. There had been no question of informing Auletes, who was too sunk in his personal problems, anyway, to worry about Egypt, let alone about those of one of his daughters, a cocky little creature who he thought equal to every challenge, at least when protected by her own men. I had already bribed my father's guards. Accomplices in my daring, Charmian and two faithful maidservants left with me. My personal bodyguard, a handful of men, had gone ahead, to avoid arousing suspicion, along with half a dozen slaves carrying our clothes and other necessaries. And three musicians.

The following day my father would get the following message that I had left for him:

"Sole and legitimate lord of the Macedonian throne of the Lagids in Alexandria: it hurts me to see that our affairs are going so badly in Rome. I am going to seek help and allies on the rebel coasts of Cilicia. I promise you, father, that I will get to Alexandria, safe and sound, and that the troops I will engage will restore to you all that rightly belongs to you.

Your faithful daughter who loves and adores you,

Cleopatra."

Unimaginable the effect it would have on him when one of his secretaries read it aloud to him. Would he topple over the wine containers in his fury and grief? Or would he simply sleep long hours, consuming his days in endless dreams? Would he summon his friends to search for me? Or would he settle for dispatching a couple of trustworthy servants to follow my tracks and buy information? Or would he erupt in repeated outbursts of rage? Or would he punish the informants, cursing them furiously, calling them liars, till the wretches changed their story to save their skins and line their pockets? It was unlikely that any of our people would lie to him. Or would some sly Roman guarantee to find me and wheedle more gold out of him for the favor? As long as it wasn't Robirius! I was full of questions but my companions assured me he was bound to send after me, that a good number of his men would come chasing after us.

Before I could reconsider the matter, we were overtaken by the burly gladiators. Their three guards didn't dare to object, as we squeezed our way in among them, and the fighting men seemed to grasp intuitively that we were sneaking away, all as if we had rehearsed the thing.

The gladiator with the mask was the first to speak. "Hey, is it true you're Egyptians?"

The only reply was the laughter of my maids.

Then I said, "Well, one day I'm going to be queen of Egypt. But really, I'm a Lagid. I'm heir to the throne of Alexander the Great."

"Then that means you're Greeks! I knew it. You don't look Egyptian, any of you," he said. "So it's safe for me to tell you that the reason I have to wear a mask is because of the damned Egyptians!"

"There goes Telephron again!" exclaimed one of the gladiators. "Fabricating another version of his old story."

"It's old stuff for you, Cleophas, but it's my face I'm talking about."

"Don't get miffed, Telephron," replied Cleophas placatingly. "Tell the story, tell it."

Telephron began. "As luck—bad luck—would have it, I traveled to Larissa, during my student days.

"I've lived in Larissa," I interposed. "That's where Achilles came from."

"Well, it looked very Egyptian to me, whether Achilles came from there or not. You see, I'm a Greek and—"

"Get on with it!" insisted Cleophas. "Stick to the point!"

"I was a typical student and liked to wander around, exploring things for myself. One day, I saw this old man, perched on a big boulder. He was advertising for somebody to watch over a corpse. The pay was really good—at least to a student like me. I was poor and naive, you see. And I was amused by the idea as well. 'Hey, you mean the dead around here get up and walk, so they need supervision?' I shouted to the old man. 'Here in Larissa,' he said, 'same as in the rest of Thebes, the dead neither run nor breathe. But we do have a problem with wizards. They seize any chance to tear off pieces of the face, even teeth and eyes, to use in their spells. So we need to keep a careful watch on corpses all night long.'

"'What does it involve?'

"'You've got to stay awake all night. Keep your eyes on the body. Not looking away. Staring straight at it, all the time. That's all. The catch is that the wizards know how to change their shapes. They can transform themselves into flies. Or elephants.'

"I roared with laughter. 'Flies and elephants!'

"'Correct, young man. Flies and elephants. Or birds or snakes. Anything they like.'

"'I'll take the job,' I said. Not just because I needed the money, but because the whole thing seemed so ludicrous.

"'You're taking it? Then everybody here should witness it.'

"'Right. I take it. The job is mine.'

"'I only want to warn you about two things. First, the wizards will do everything in their power to make you fall asleep. You'll have your work cut out to stay awake.'

"'No problem. I accept. On my honor. And you'll pay full price?'

"'There's one more thing. If the corpse is fully intact the next morning, you get the lot. But listen carefully to this. If you fall asleep and the wizards steal part of the face—the nose, a tooth, an ear or an eye—you'll have to replace with one of your own, because we're paying you to ensure our relative goes complete to the Kingdom of the Dead. Is that clear? You must guard Telephron's body as if it were your own."

"I nodded my head in agreement. But with a little less enthusiasm than before. The dead man, it turned out, was also called Telephron, my name. That coincidence, combined with the risk, made me doubly uneasy; it undermined my courage.

"The old man took me to the house where Telephron was going to watch over Telephron. The dead man and I were alone in the room. I shut the doors and the windows as tightly as I could. Night had just fallen and the full moon appeared. Before long I had to scare away a rat and then a spider. After that, a beetle appeared, then a snake and a strange blue bird that refused to fly and hopped on one leg. These animals kept on appearing with extraordinary rapidity. I had no doubt that they were wizards in other shapes and fear overcame my heart. I was determined to remain fully alert, afraid that they might approach me in the form of a flea or a fluttering moth. There I was, unnerved because of the nonstop intrusions but tensely on guard, because of the horrendous risk I was running. Then I can't explain how—but standing erect, with one hand on my ear, bending it forward to catch the least sound—I fell fast asleep!

"The next morning trumpets awoke me. My fingers were stiff, still bent in position round my ear. Immediately the widow came in, followed by a notary who had come to testify legally as to the condition of the corpse. After a scrupulous examination, he signed a statement that Telephron, the corpse, was completely intact. The widow thanked me and said she would pay me at once. Naturally, I thanked her as any Greek would, by wishing her a long life. But in the eyes of an Egyptian widow these were the words of a curse. Totally offensive to the deceased, since I seemed eager to condemn him to spending a long period in the other world without his beloved wife.

"The servants beat me up, shouting at me 'Insolent pig! Worshipper of animals!' They pulled out my hair and tossed me into the street. They gave me no time to state my case and, of course, they gave me no money. There I was, in the middle of the street, as poor as ever and bruised all over. I started to weep with rage. As if my tears had attracted him, there arrived another man, also in tears. He was so visibly upset that I put aside my rage. I asked him what his problem was. Because of his deep, uncontrollable sobbing, it was hard to understand what he was saying. So much weeping had swollen his eyes and reminded me of the poet's words:

> *Lo, all the tears we shed today*
> *Wash not one single grief away.*

"'They killed my son,' he finally blurted out amid sobs, hiccups, sighs, and other sounds of grief I won't bother to detail for you. He pointed to the house I'd just been thrown out of. 'His wife poisoned him, so she could get all his property and marry her lover.'

"My selfish tears had stopped. I saw a way of getting even. I called out, 'This good man says the grieving widow in there is a fake. She killed his son!'

"The old man gathered strength from my shouts and started to shout himself. 'She did it! She did it! To steal his inheritance and to enrich her lover with the fruits of my labors and those of my father and my son.'

"The young widow, who was far from ugly, came out with her retainers to rebut the charge. She swore her innocence, but the people put more faith in the old man's accusation and began to stone her. But her pleas sounded so heartfelt that in the end the father of the victim himself cried out, 'Stop, that's enough for now! I'll fetch a wizard who will confirm my suspicions. I couldn't live with myself if I had the least doubt I'd acted improperly.'

"Hardly had the words left his mouth when a man with a shaven head, typical of Egyptian priests, came forward and without a word touched the mouth of the dead man with both his hands.

"The corpse suddenly breathed. In a strong deep voice it cried out, 'Let me sleep!'

"'No, I will not let you sleep,' said the priest, 'and if you do not answer my questions, I will curse you all the way to the land of the dead. What caused your death?'

"The corpse uttered an ominous shriek. 'The woman I had the misfortune to marry introduced, little by little, drops of poison into my drink. Even as she was faking smiles, she was murdering me.'

"The dead man lowered his voice and went on, 'There is something else I must tell you. The young man to whom they offered money to watch over me fell into a sleep induced by the wizards. Almost at once they started to summon me: 'Telephron, Telephron!' I felt compelled to obey them. But as the young man and I share the same name, and as he is young and nimble and I was rigid with cold, he got up first and went over to them. I saw them steal his nose and ears. I gave a shriek of horror and leapt backwards. When they realized their mistake, they stuck a false nose and ears on his face. By that time dawn was already breaking, and they had no darkness left to cover any theft from me. If I am complete, it is no credit to the rascal who shares my name. Don't give him a single drachma. He deserves nothing.'

"He let out another horrifying scream and fell down, an inanimate corpse once again.

"I felt my nose and one ear. There was no feeling in them; they were not mine. I ripped them off in my panic. I had no wish to carry around for the rest of my days replacements that were the work of vile wizards."

The gladiators broke into howls of laughter.

"Magnificent!" bellowed Cleophas. "Totally magnificent! Well done, Telephron."

The young Greek came over to me and said, "Actually, he lost them in the arena. That's why he wears a mask. Every day he invents a different story to explain it. Knowing you're Egyptians, he took the opportunity to lay the blame on Egypt. He was teasing you all along!"

Behind the mask gleamed two rascally eyes, full of life.

"Telephron, you were lucky those damned wizards didn't steal your eyes," I said. "Thanks for your story. It was truly magnificent."

"Story? What story?" the rascal replied. "I hate Egypt, and with good reason."

"I'd swear you are Egyptian yourself."

"And how would the future queen of Egypt know a thing like that?"

"By the gleam in your eyes. By your story. You know very well, Telephron, that it's a story often told in the streets of Alexandria."

I took the hand of the slave and planted a kiss on his fingers. But my eyes were fixed on the Greek boy, Apollodorus, and they said to him, "These kisses are for you."

Telephron mumbled something, humbly grateful to receive recognition from a princess. He cast his gleaming eyes to the ground and scurried off among his companions, but Apollodorus wasted no time in boldly coming closer.

I was equally quick to make him an offer. "Wouldn't you like to come with us? I have two ships waiting at Brundisium, ready to sail. I'll get you out of Rome. We'll travel together to the harbor, and if you want, you can come aboard the ship."

"Aren't you coming back?"

"One day. When I'm queen of Egypt. When they place a gold statue of me in the Temple of Venus here. But not before then."

"When you come back, Cleopatra, I'll be waiting. By that time I'll be a free man. I'll be rich and I'll marry you."

One of my maids pinched him and said, "Don't even dream of it! Cleopatra will only marry the man who is master of the world."

"That'll be me. I will be master of the world. Right now I'm only a gladiator. And before this I was merely a shepherd. I lived in a hut with a straw roof, beside a creek whose name means nothing in Rome. If I've achieved so much already in my fourteen years, how much will I have achieved by the time I'm twenty?"

Fourteen! How could he be only fourteen? So tall! He looked far older to my eyes. A thick beard covered a good part of his face. He was so, so handsome!

"Always supposing you don't die first!" put in one of the other gladiators. "Go on, Apollodorus. Escape with her. Grab your chance!" The hair of this gladiator shone in the light of the setting sun. His eyes were bright. He spoke perfect Greek. "Take advantage of the generous offer. Run off with these women. Only death awaits you here. Go on! Go back to your parents. Or try your luck in Alexandria. Anywhere but here. Why do you want to be master of the world? You know the old rhyme? 'The city is the site of dole and dearth; the country is the very soul of mirth.' Go back there."

"You obviously never were a shepherd or smelled sheep shit!"

"It's just as obvious that you know nothing about the world. Nothing of the political intrigues that control the Empire. Master of the world? You don't even know who makes the decisions that count. I was a senator once. You know that well enough. I had a name that meant something back then. I was respected and rich. Now I'm like a slave. A mere gladiator. And all because I didn't know how to bow my head before the power of gold and all the other filthy shit. I know what I'm talking about."

Then he continued:

> *Happy the man who far from commerce thrives,*
> *Where cruel usury exerts no sway;*
> *The Golden Age still rules his carefree day,*
> *His sturdy oxen plow his father's fields,*
> *And ocean storms betray no sailors' lives.*

"Your bitterness blinds you. You can't see that grass and alfalfa can never match the grandeur of a city."

"And you! You must have overlooked the cool shade of leafy beech trees. You must have been insensitive to the lush, deep grass, to the soft ears of wheat. Deaf to the song of the nightingale, blind to the lovely flowers and the ripe, luxuriant crops. In the poet's words, 'Thin was your bull amid the bounteous pastures.'"

"Thin bulls? What are you talking about? I was forever treading on snakes, dodging poisonous plants, and scratching my legs on thistles!"

"The juice of freshly ripened grapes must have pleased you, Apollodorus."

"Never tasted it! Never saw an oak struck by lightning, either. There was no chance there of ever becoming a real man, of leaving a lasting mark on the world."

"But listen to what the poet is saying, boy!

> *Here sons of soldiers till the fertile soil.*
> *Obedient to their austere mothers' call,*

They fell the forest, load up logs for home,
While evening's shadows climb the mountain tops
And lowing kine draw carts across the lea.
So all enjoy sweet hours of repose.

You see? It was men like these who earned Rome its reputation. Not the ones who've grown up amid luxury and vice. They're not a patch on the vigorous souls who once lived on the banks of the Tiber."

In the genial quarrel between the two were sprinkled lines from the Roman poets. They gave us a pleasure far different from the ones afforded by the arena.

By this time we had covered a fair stretch of the way. The walls of Rome were already in sight. A dense crowd was massed around the gates. It seemed impossible to penetrate it. The gladiators had closed ranks around us. One of my maids gave women's clothing to the Greek boy, so that he could disguise himself, saying, "If you want to come with us, better get these on you right away!"

Protected by the first shadows of the night and the confusion of the crowd, Apollodorus slipped over his cheap clothing the fine robes of an oriental princess. With an ingenuity I cannot explain, Charmian pulled out a wig from one of the bags she was carrying and rapidly fitted it on the head of the young Greek, using a veil to conceal the hairy lower half of his face.

The change of clothing only served to heighten his charms. And his own excitement produced an unfortunate result. Under the fine linens, it did not take much effort to see, bulged his erect penis. Erect from what? Panic or passion? I had never seen the like of it before as a reaction to the unexpected. Could it be that he had felt his manhood threatened by the woman's clothing and this was a kind of masculine protest? In their nervousness my maids had noticed nothing. But I was not at all nervous. In fact, I was enjoying the ease with which our escape was proceeding.

But on spying this danger of betrayal, I acted swiftly. I stood close in front of him and jammed my back against him, so that nobody else could see what I had seen. The effect was instantaneous. The body of the girlish princess, so long caressed on the balcony by his longing eyes, extinguished the erection totally. He placed his hand on my shoulder and I turned around, walking backwards. We looked each other in the eye, and his glance said to me, "Everything's under control. Relax!"

At that moment we passed through the gate of the Flaminian Way, and I swung around to check our route. A few steps more and alleyways opened on all sides before us like a labyrinth. Without the gladiators to guide us, we would have been lost at this junction. We could not have crossed the city alone or found the road to Brundisium, for the layout of Rome had none of the planning of Alexandria, precise, harmonious, and clear-cut. The Romans had had no Dinocrates to follow the planning tradition of Hippodamus. The milk of the wolf that nursed Romulus and Remus flowed capriciously and left a record of its twisting path in the tangled alleyways of the city.

Where in Rome could one enjoy the beautiful views available in Alexandria? From the Gate of the Sun to the Gate of the Moon, the guardian deities of the entrances, passes a double line of columns. Round about the midpoint stand the houses of the populace. A little farther along lies a neighborhood named in honor of Alexander the Great. Beside it is a second settlement, magnificently laid out, another line of columns crossing the first, in a series of right angles. However hard one tries, it is impossible to encompass the beauty of the city in a single glance. And none of this includes the palaces. No Roman palace can compare to the gorgeous magnificence of those in Egypt.

But why am I describing Alexandria when we were still in Rome? Let me get back to Rome. The chatter of the gladiators continued nonstop, and we came to the run-down district of

Subura, crowded with commonplace people. The rabble swarm-
ing the streets were not the only surprise; there was the over-
powering stink of the place, a revolting mixture of rotting garbage,
excrement, food, and cooking oils—a plague of odors that Alexandria would never have allowed. I had not traversed these
streets before or if I had, I had done it fast asleep on my litter
with its curtains closed, something that always makes me sleepy.
But this time I was not passing in style. The waves of people
crashed against us from in front, and the press of the people from
behind put a strain on my kidneys. There was always somebody
jabbing me with an elbow, with the pole of a litter, or a wine
vase. If I hadn't avoided it, the spike of a soldier would have
stabbed my fingers. Loaded carriages charged by without the least
concern for pedestrians. Groups of people cooked in the streets
and ate standing, talking freely as if nobody could see or hear
them, as if, instead of standing, they were lounging on well-stuffed
cushions. Others were eating on the move, surrounded by smoke
and sweating servants, followed by a mobile kitchen, the poor
slaves tottering under enormous vessels carried on the heads, their
hasty progress fanning the burning coals into life.

By now night was falling, and we were close to the multi-
story dwelling where the gladiators slept. They shared the space
with the horses of dear old Cato, plus the mob of slaves he kept
on hand. He retained them as an investment against hard times,
since he had little faith in treasures that could not defend themselves with their fingernails. The red-haired gladiator told us to
blend in with a group of obviously foreign travelers we had bumped
into. Merchants with beasts of burden and their drivers now separated us from our gladiators, if I may call them that, and left us
unprotected. I should make it clear that our guardians were quite
negligent, occupied with their own concerns, teasing each other
and joking the whole time, flirting with each other with fascinated
interest, forming their own private group, generally indifferent to

us. On reaching a corner, where the driver of a cart had problems turning and was interrupting the flow of traffic, the gladiators pushed their way out of our group altogether and blended into the group of foreigners. We were left just with Apollodorus. He was passing as a woman quite nicely, less and less like a gladiator habituated to dicing with death, while rich spectators munched away at their meals. So here ended the conversation between the ex-senator turned gladiator and a philosopher of excrement and that newly made Egyptian maiden, Apollodorus.

The crowd hustled us along and Apollodorus led the way. My maids were not at all embarrassed to chat with a man dressed as a woman and began to give him details of our journey. We had planned it carefully on those long evenings when we slunk away from the humiliations that Roman greed and corruption were inflicting on Auletes as he tried to uphold the cause of the Lagids. My maids had remained silent in the presence of the gladiators, deeming them unworthy of their conversation. But Apollodorus looked so much the part of an Egyptian woman that it was hard to call him by his real name. Even though he was risking his hide to a far greater degree than we were, he spoke at ease, with an impeccable diction and an extensive vocabulary that clearly belied his past as a humble shepherd. He asked for the details of our plan. Then, instead of correcting or upbraiding me, he combined his astuteness with mine, adding things I had overlooked, suggesting shortcuts, and in general matching my audacity with his own. Hence from our joint discussions, a naively simple plan was converted into a practical scheme of redemption, as cunning as anyone could hope for.

From that moment on, we were accomplices. He led our way as fast as the density of the crowd allowed. At the house of a cheap mask-maker he brought us to a halt. As we went inside, he told us that this was where the gladiators bought adornments for their contests.

First we crossed a patio where a mass of children were working at low tables supported variously by hooks, columns, and sticks. They were banging away at leather and brass with primitive tools, shaping articles for their master. We stepped into a small, dark room where the hammering was deafening. Apollodorus faked a woman's voice, speaking in perfect Roman Latin with no trace of a foreign accent, and talked to the owner, inventing a story to explain our presence in this place. The owner—I could hardly see a thing till my eyes adjusted to the gloom—showed no sign of believing a word of it, but he did not question it, either. He simply wanted our business, to sell us something and then get back to bullying the children.

On a large table lay a remarkable variety of masks. The majority were showy, finished in garish colors. On the far left I spotted some that brought a laugh to my lips. They could have been designed expressly for us; a good part of the Egyptian pantheon was facing us, eyeless and bodiless, with caricatured features, all in bright colors. There was Sehmet, Anubis, Horus, Thoth, and Ammon Ra.

"Those are the ones!" I cried out, unable to contain my excitement. "We want those. Exactly what we're looking for."

"You mean them animal ones?" asked the owner. He might have known his craft to perfection but in other matters he was a typical Roman ignoramus.

"That is the Egyptian pantheon," I corrected him sternly. "And the head of Horus is missing the sun and moon."

Apollodorus shot me a disapproving look and I cut short my theological lecture. He was right. Why bother to argue with this nobody?

One of the children quickly packed the masks we chose. Charmian paid. With womanly grace Apollodorus hoisted the package onto his shoulder and in the twinkling of an eye we were back outside, in the muddy alleyway. From here on our progress speeded up. The streets were less congested. Prostitutes offered their services, sitting on tall chairs in illuminated windows that lent a little light to our progress.

After we passed Porta Capena, above which an aqueduct ran, we found a cart awaiting us on the Appian Way. It belonged to the seamen who were to carry us from the port of Brundisium over the waters of the Mediterranean. It was a rough, rustic vehicle, and was still partly loaded with sacks of sand or soil. It had obviously been organized by these barbaric Romans, for they had yoked four bulls to it, sacred animals in Egypt. There was barely room for us, what with all our baggage and the slaves who had been sent ahead. My personal mounted guard would protect us but we had agreed they would follow at some distance in order not to attract attention. Never before had Cleopatra traveled in such mean circumstances, in an unroofed cart, without dignity or comfort, like a piece of cargo, and certainly not by night, the last time Auletes would choose for traveling.

Perched awkwardly there on one of the sacks of soil, I could hear, as we exited the city, the buzz of voices and noises that accompanied the smells of Rome. My excitement had left me deaf to the noise until now. My eyes had been overwhelmed by the confusion of sights and occupied all my attention. But now the light of the sun was extinguished and only the torches of our guides illuminated our route, and finally I could hear again. Our cart traveled slowly, hardly faster than a couple of women who walked along, complaining loudly about the rise in the price of barley. Along with them came the voices of workmen chatting about their day's problems:

"And now if he tells me it's no good, I'm gonna feel like yelling, and why not, eh?"

"All he said to me was they're gonna give you a set of rules and you gotta follow 'em. So I did it, as far as I understood 'em, but it's not what I'm used to, you gotta do two jobs in one day, and then figure out when to fit in this one and that one . . ."

To these voices were added those of our servants that started up again after they had fallen into silent astonishment at seeing their princess sprawled on sacks, right there in their midst. By now they had decided not to see me, and, under the pretense of chatting among themselves, were using the opportunity to pass me messages they had been wanting me to hear for some time. Things like, "That rascal Lampon, you know we paid him eight drachmas to get rid of the rats down in Toka, because there's nothing worse than rats in the vineyards, when the grapes are ripening. But instead of catching them, he just lounged around, stuffing his face with fruit and scratching his belly."

And, "Archibius, the banker, he refused to lend my parents money. Know why? Not that they were asking for too much—but for too little! Just fifty-two drachmas. He said it wasn't worth his while wasting his ink for a piddling amount like that! But we know he lends even less to some folk!"

And, "Do you know that Lucius Bellenus Gemellus asked his son Sabinus to please send Pindarus over to Dionysias, because Hermonax had asked him to take him to Keresoucha to check out his olive grove, because . . ."

The voices around me, the hoofs of the oxen, the clattering of horses, the smell of the earth, the curses of my faithful Charmian, the unconcealed excitement of Apollodorus dressed as an Egyptian woman—he was singing falsetto, in keeping with his long-haired wig—all these things combined to make this trip one of the most enjoyable of my life.

Although our pace matched only a slow walk, I felt myself soaring. I shut my eyes as I heard the lapping waters of the lake. I picked up a sharp-pointed stone that protruded from one of the sacks and, on the planks of the cart's siding, against which I was resting my back, I scratched "Queen of Kings," working in the dark, using my fingers to measure the spaces between the letters. I could see nothing. My fingers did all the work. As I scratched away, I fell asleep. I have no idea if my fingers kept on working as I slept, but the following morning, as I awoke, my eyes confirmed what I had written in the dark, as if in a dream: "Queen of Kings."

That first night, accompanied by the voices of my fellow-travelers and the sailors, we passed down the road built between the Alban and Nemi lakes. As the night got darker, the voices got fewer, even the boisterous banter of the sailors dwindled away, but the lapping of the waves and the sputtering of our guide's torch attended us all the way.

Our first stop, at dawn, was at Aricia. Afraid we might be being followed, we were quick to resume our journey, replacing the bulls with four stout horses, since we aimed to reach the Appian Forum by nightfall and immediately cross the Pontine canal by barge. Once we were on our way, Apollodorus changed back into men's clothes, and this time the gladiator was dressed as a sailor. By the fourth hour, we had arrived at the sanctuary and the spring of Juno. At Anxur, where the road passes along the coast, we quickly bought a fine tunic for Apollodorus, and around Terracina we arranged a change of horses. There, the view was impressive. We traveled along the edge of a cliff, with the sea far below. Charmian ordered a halt. We got down from the creaking, rickety cart to stretch our legs and breathe the dry air. Charmian pointed to the Mediterranean, saying, "All this is yours, Cleopatra, as far as your eyes can see, and beyond that, all these great lands that border these wide waters." With tears in her kindly eyes, she hugged me warmly.

Apollodorus and I laughed. "What's come over you, Charmian? All this bouncing around in the cart and traveling over bad roads has affected your noodle!"

Yet even though we teased her, we turned back to the humble cart and, taking out the sacks in search of sharp stones, we were fired by the desire to leave the planks covered with the inscription "Queen of Kings" in letters large and small, broad and narrow, according to what stones we used, till every surface was covered. Apollodorus, determined to please me to the fullest, left no corner untouched.

The days flew by, as crammed with jokes and games as we had left the planks of the cart.

Rumor told us it would be unwise to linger in Fundos, because the one-eyed aedile, Aufidius Lusco, a humorless lout, would have half-killed us with his unwanted attentions. He would have burnt incense in our honor, while all we wanted was to escape. So we crossed Fundos without halting, and as we left, we changed horses and spent the night in clean beds.

At the close of the following day's journey, we reached luxurious Formion. Its wide streets were jammed with pedestrians. The sight of our broken-down cart, an eyesore among so much elegance, brought us scornful attention. I sank down out of sight, ashamed of my appearance, my clothes, and the vehicle, all so inappropriate for a future queen.

Apollodorus, crouched beside me, said, "Don't worry, Cleopatra. Even if some friend of your father is here, he won't notice us. We're invisible."

Invisible! The notion aroused me! I stopped hiding and raised my head to survey the city, convinced that nobody would recognize me. Charmian had got down from the cart to arrange our lodgings. There was a great demand for accommodation, from palaces down to establishments with dancing girls and young male whores. Charmian send somebody to find us. She had arranged for us to dine and sleep like royalty that night, but she forbade me and Apollodorus to visit any of the entertainment sites. But we managed to elude her, when she fell asleep early, worn out by the journey.

As we turned the first corner, we came across a place with music floating out of its doors. We craned our necks to see the walls of its tiny rooms covered by frescos from floor to ceiling, depicting the pleasures of the flesh. The crude appearance of these clumsily painted figures involved in graceless varieties of sexual activity took away our appetite to go any farther. We returned to our rooms unenlightened as to what other forms of entertainment Formion might offer by night.

As soon as dawn broke, we made our way to Sinuesa and, once again, to poverty-stricken existence. At Sinuesa, the Appian Way left the coast and headed inland. Now my excitement died away and was superseded by boredom. I felt thoroughly fed up. At our first halt, Charmian hired me a good horse. I invited Apollodorus to climb up behind me and we set off at a gallop, leaving the cart behind.

"Now we can get serious about being invisible, Cleopatra."

"Invisible? On horseback?"

"Totally invisible, here, there, and everywhere. Wherever you like. But to do it, you have to count one hundred white goats and a hundred dappled cows. Once you've counted them, you'll be invisible."

My bodyguards were following closely. The cart was long out of sight. But there were no cows, not a single one. We came across flock after flock of goats chewing insatiably, like good Romans. But cows or anything like them, very few. There were three at the creek of a small village, one here at a house, two over there, but a hundred? It was unlikely that there were a hundred cows in the length and breadth of Italy.

The soil was changing from white to gray, to red, to black, to pink, to brown, but Apollodorus did not change. His mood was elated, his energy tireless. Everything seemed to excite him.

The sands, the rocks, the grass—all were an occasion for recalling some story, each one an opportunity for laughter.

Unfortunately, at the next changing post there were no mounts for us, and we went back to riding in the cart. In it we crossed the Campanus Bridge, over the River Savus, which divides Lacium, founded by the Homeric hero, Diomedes, from Campania, Capua, Caudius, and Beneventus.

In Beneventus, the road split in two. One led to Venusia along the Appian Way, going to the heel of Italy and to Brundisium, our destination. The other went along the Trajan Way, shorter but in worse condition, to Bari and the coast. We chose the second, because we were in such a hurry. There were so many potholes in it that we soon regretted not having taken the first route. We passed through Ordona, where people pay for water and, incredibly, swallow dust, but where the bread is the best in the world. Then came Canusius, on the banks of the Aufidius; Petreus, a place with less water than a puddle; Rubos; Bari; Gnatia, built without the blessing of the nymphs; and finally, our destination, Brundisium, where we arrived, more dead than alive, sick of all the jolting on the hard soil, but only to confront a more severe hardness, that of the sea.

Brundisium—I have already mentioned it twice, and each time I mention it, I realize, Antony, how much I have come to hate it, all these years later, for you went there to sign your treaty with Octavius. I was about to deliver your children, your twins, while you were agreeing with that puny creature to marry his sister, Octavia, now that Fulvia had died . . .

We arrived at first nightfall. Without delay, for we were still worried my father might have sent men in pursuit of us, we went aboard the three quinqueremes, taking with us my jewels and a certain amount of money that my father had agreed to give me, thanks to the wheeling and dealing of my crafty mother, on condition that I would keep it for her, something I had not the least intention of doing, because, for one thing, it was funding our escape. And also the masks that Apollodorus had got for us, plus a small mountain of clothing. We cast off and anchored a little off the coast, awaiting the first light before we sailed in earnest. I had thought it best to sail away immediately but Apollodorus and the sailors told me that the Mediterranean was not to be trusted.

The ships were hardly more comfortable than the ox-carts. Curling up, maybe in terror, my maids fell asleep. Two of my men were assigned to stand watch, and the crew settled down under their cloaks. I've no idea where Apollodorus snuggled down, for I gave myself up to dreaming and staring up at the stars, fantasizing about the triumphs and glories that life might hold for me, successes that surpassed all I ever actually gained later in my life, for they were achieved with a purity of spirit, unstained by corruption, bestowed on me like gifts at a festival, effortlessly, void of struggle and strife.

That night I saw myself attired in extraordinary garments, the darling of all Egypt. I stood at the top of a staircase and a gazing multitude acclaimed me. I saw myself in the same garments, parading with a cortege of elephants, tigers, and lions across the Campus Martius, and the crowds cheered, calling out, "Hail, Queen! You will reign over us and over our children, and your blood will reign over our descendants!" I imagined myself riding in a chariot drawn by a dozen beasts, covered in gold, as I traversed the three parts of Gaul, clad in my fabulous clothing. The beasts that drew my chariot were gilded crocodiles, chosen to stun the mob who, of course, simply adored me! All this under the cloak of night, under the blazing stars, rocked like a baby by a sea at peace. But what I did not foresee was the one thing that would lift me to the heights of glory: the arms of Mark Antony.

Let me get back to the boat anchored off Brundisium. We set sail and spent the days in a variety of recreations. Our favorite was to perform a tableau of worship to Isis. All the passengers took part in it. When we were one day out from the port of Tarsus, two speedy ships, typical of the lightweight vessels favored by pirates, drew close. I asked my men to offer no resistance and ordered them to take up the formation we had spent days practicing. It wasn't exactly a military one but we called it that out of whimsy. The crew had mastered it and the process had amused us in the deadly dull hours of the trip and it had boosted the morale of my maidens. Apollodorus and I knew all along it would serve as a defensive maneuver.

When the pirates were on the point of boarding our ship, they found us motionless, except for our fans, that on my orders were keeping time with the motion of the sea. I carried a scepter and a whip, the two symbols of royalty, and had dressed in Egyptian style, mimicking Isis. The crew and my guards were wearing masks, a lion to represent Sehmet, a jackal for Anubis, an eagle for Horus, a mandril for Toth, a ram for Ammon Ra. In their fists were javelins, set against Neptune, Venus, and Athena herself, for others among my servants were dressed as Roman gods. One of my maids held above my head rods plated with gold to suggest the rays of the sun. One of the servants in an eagle's mask, concealed his body behind the fake leaves of a banana tree and shook his two hands among them. Another displayed his hands to form the claws of the eagle, the rest of his body hidden. By the head of the jackal hung the naked body of an old woman, my beloved nanny Eter, her large, flaccid breasts dangling. Over these gods of the Empire triumphed Egypt's Isis.

When I saw the pirates moving from astonishment to action, I took one step forward and told them in my penetrating voice that I needed to speak to the captain of their flotilla, because I was heading for Cilicia and, being a princess with claims to the throne of Egypt, I required an escort for myself and my court. I said it in Greek, Egyptian, and Latin, plus a couple of barbarian languages, not knowing what they would understand. At a gesture from me, the two musicians beside me began to play the most cheerful of their dance tunes. The amazement of the pirates—at the scene, the discourse I delivered in the most solemn tone, the music that invited them to dance and laugh— worked totally in my favor. The pirates smiled, one and all. They asked for proof of my claims.

"I would have liked to bring you the golden crown that my father Auletes bestowed on Pompey," I explained in koine. "But we Lagids never take back by force what we once have given. Take me to your king. Before we begin to sail, take this. It belongs to you." I translated my words into half a dozen languages and handed over a purple bag that contained a mass of gleaming trinkets that I had brought for exactly such an occasion as this, bright baubles to dazzle the eye. "The future queen of Egypt wishes to share her treasures with the men of Cilicia." Their answer was to adore me with a divine fervor.

They burst into chatter, asking me questions in various languages, for our intended assailants came from several nations. Some of their questions I answered with a felicity that brought effusive signs of enthusiasm from them.

From that moment on, the two pirate ships watched over us. For the rest of the journey, we applied ourselves to our work with diligence, stitching veils and cloaks. Several times a day we received a visit from the leader of these allegedly cruel pirates. On each occasion he dressed differently, showing off the flashy plunder of an attack on a fishing community that he had stripped bare of what little it had. Less than looters, he and his associates were more like toothpicks scratching away the last remnants of a petty wealth.

I wondered how old he was. And if he had a brother among those crucified by my Caesar. With my limited years I found it hard to assess the age of others, but the age of this pirate was particularly elusive. Two long scars cut across his face, his wrestler's body was dismayingly strong, and his thick, bushy beard seemed a stranger to a comb. I was not the only one. None of us could guess his age. From childhood on, he had been nurtured on violence; the measure of his years was not ours.

On one of his visits I said to him, "You're a fish. You've been hooked by those you planned to hook."

My comment unnerved him. He responded by running his knife blade over the tip of his tongue and drawing blood.

"Me, a fish?" he said, widening the wound in his tongue as he spoke. "Nobody hooks me except me."

I was on the point of rebuking him. What was the idea behind hurting himself? But I caught his eye and his violent mood checked me. It was obvious that he had stuck the point of knife into his tongue to calm himself down. My words had touch a nerve I could not imagine.

"I didn't intend to upset you; it was just a—" I swallowed the word "joke."

The ageless pirate jumped back aboard his own ship with a cheetah's agility.

Apart from that one incident, the pirates labored to make our trip a pleasant one. They even pitched in with goodwill to help ready us for our arrival.

In less time than we had calculated, we skirted the danger-ous shoals ahead and the beautiful harbor of Cilicia, Tarsus, lay in sight, its quayside crowded with speedy vessels. Seen from the sea, Tarsus was a stirring sight. For a moment I credited the leg-end that here had landed a feather from the wing of Pegasus, after it was broken by Perseus.

Once more I requested the treatment proper to an heir apparent, and once more I received it.

As the governor of Cilicia came toward my ship on board his small vessel, our guards, I mean the pirates, covered us with an enormous cloth that we had sewn together from our own garments. When he was within feet of us, they suddenly pulled aside the cloth and astonished him with the same scene that had dazzled them. The musicians played, this time not dance tunes, but music that accorded with the solemnity of our *tableau vivant*. Then the pirates pulled the cloth over their own bodies and one after the other, they popped up their heads to represent the many-headed hydra.

After listening to the speech Apollodorus and I had prepared for the occasion, the governor invited the child Isis to his palace, unaware it was a child, reverencing her like Isis herself. I saw my maids beaming with delight, and my noble and faithful Charmian happy as could be.

The Cilicians were going through a serious crisis. Not long before, they had been masters of the Mediterranean, so much so that both merchant ships and those of the Roman state preferred to travel in stormy weather, storms being less perilous than pirates. To combat them, Caesar had given Pompey unprecedented resources. The Senate designated him sole general, selected from the consuls, with supreme command from the pillars of Hercules to Syria and the Pontus, and all territories twenty leagues inland. He had an army of a size never seen before. He had the authority to appoint twenty-five lieutenants, all with praetorial rank and powers, and two treasurers with the rights of quaestors, and under them he had marshaled 120,000 infantry, 7,000 cavalry, and 500 ships. It stands to reason that he had already routed a great number of the Cilicians' allies. The Cilicians themselves were untouched; on perceiving the threat of the Roman attack, they had lived up to their reputation as formidable adversaries and shut up their women, children, and treasures in the castles of the Taurus.

I arrived at a court where there was not a single woman, and I ate my meals from wooden plates. The court was composed of adventurers and desperadoes from all nations, of licensed mercenaries, citizens exiled from the destroyed cities of Italy, Spain, and Asia, soldiers and officers from the armies of Fimbria and Sertorius, runaways and outlaws from towns everywhere. They had holed up here originally because the magnificent forests of Cilicia afforded them excellent timber to construct ships, but over the course of time the governor of Cilicia proved himself the best kind of governor pirates could hope for, by his dash, his cunning, his bravery, his astonishing strategic ability, his coolness in crisis, his sense of justice, and his inveterate hatred of Romans. I should never have left that place. If I hadn't, I wouldn't be here on the brink of death, trapped where I don't deserve to be, before a mean-spirited and graceless enemy. If Caesar had defeated me! If Antony had! If Pompey had! That I could take. But this, never. I cannot continue with my story. Cleopatra's time has come.

Diomedes the Informer

Almost, almost, almost . . . she almost spoke the way I have
written, those were almost her words, or they would have
been if Cleopatra had not spoken very different ones. They
are not exactly out of tune with her. At least they approximate
her tone, and if maybe I shifted them around, if I tossed them
into a saucepan and stirred them, as though concocting a
potion, they would not be too far from the ones Cleopatra
uttered that day. But this is not the time for saucepans and
these were not her actual words. I have to confess it. If I acted
like a Roman slave in my first effort, in this second I have
only my own defects to lay the blame on: my mental laziness,
my pettiness, my clumsy tongue that forces me to make her
speak in this misleading fashion . . . Face the truth and call me
what I am, lazy, insignificant, gauche, but also add that I am
pigheaded, because I am going to try for yet a third time. This
will be my final attempt. I tense my bow. My arrow cannot
miss its target. This time there will be no mistakes, though I
am a veritable seedbed of errors. Because here I am not going
to leave evidence of my own imaginings. I simply want to

reproduce her words. I do not wish to die in the condition of a liar. Come on, Diomedes! Stop dithering! Concentrate, remember! So listen now: thus spake Cleopatra, bathed in the blood of Antony, to give testimony of her passage through life:

The Queen Dismounts with a Single Leap

The queen dismounts with a single leap. All her company does the same. They glide to the ground, abandoning their mounts.
—Virgil

We reached the gates of Pelusium before nightfall. We did not rein in our mounts even when the fortress came in sight. Still faithful, the city embraced us, set there, well-weaponed and flying its blood-red flags, in the desert zone that acted as a second wall of defense.

It was ten months since the intrigues of my husband's and brother's Ruling Council had driven me to lay my traps, devices that had won me the popular voice of Egypt. Like all good weapons, it was two-edged; I used it both to promote myself and to expel the troops of Gabirius and the rest of the Roman leeches. Regardless of the veracity of the propaganda I spread far and wide, I managed to gain the favor of the fickle mob but at the same time brought on myself the enraged displeasure of my brother's minions, who clung to him to suck out the riches of the Nile, for as long as they could avoid my eagle-eyed supervision and the enmity of Gabirius's men.

The legionaries that Aulus Gabirius had left in Egypt to protect the throne of the reinstated Auletes had enjoyed five years of the easy life of Egypt. My lasting seduction of Upper Egypt and my momentary and partial appeasement of Alexandria sat badly with their airy pretensions to imperial status. It was the visit of Gnaius Pompey that broke the spell I had cast over the city. He had come to ask for help in the civil war against Caesar. Along with Ptolemy's Ruling Council, we sat down behind closed doors and deliberated on whether to help him or not. While we were meeting, the young Ptolemy fell asleep from all the wine they had poured into him, polluting my air with all kinds of gastric discharges. As had happened with Auletes my father under different circumstances, the wretches had bloated the boy-king physically and mentally, flattering and corrupting him, poisoning his mind with frequent stories of how I was refusing to let him exercise his powers as commander in chief and husband.

Despite our deliberations we reached no easy accord. The only thing that passed off with moderate ease was Ptolemy's falling asleep, but finally we reached the conclusion it would be wise to help Pompey. We would send out with all speed sixty ships and the soldiers of Gabirius. But exactly how many of them? Potinus and Achilles, the boy-king's key advisors, wanted to keep the number laughably small. Given a choice, they would have sent none. They had secret links with the restless legionaries, by now half-Roman, half-Alexandrian, and counted on their support, based as it was on their joint hatred of Cleopatra. Protarcus, my chief minister, handled the matter adroitly. We sent ships and food supplies, along with five hundred of the finest men of Gabirius, those who would obey Achilles without discussion.

The Ruling Council and the Court of Ptolemy broadcast this support to the four winds, attributing it solely to me, inflating the numbers and setting the people of Alexandria against me. Their slanders painted me as a Rome-loving traitor to Egypt, terming me a liar because, they claimed, I said one thing and did another. My earlier wooing of Alexandria was made to work against me.

The remaining soldiers of Gabirius greedily stoked the fires of revolt. This was exactly what they had been waiting for. If their Roman leanings had predisposed them against me when I preached against the scandalous bloodletting of their fellow countrymen, they had declared themselves my open enemies since the first days of my mandate, over their bitter dispute with Marcus Calpurnius Bibulus. It occurred at the time the Parthians routed the troops of Crassus, who had then been assassinated. Marcus Calpurnius Bibulus had just been appointed governor of Syria. The Parthians were poised to swoop down over the frontier and he had only a handful of men to defend it. There were no reinforcements in Syria. Bibulus sent his two sons to Egypt, to recruit, in the name of Imperial Rome, the urgently needed soldiers of Gabirius.

They were two remarkable youngsters, only a couple of years older than Ptolemy. What a difference! Ptolemy was incapable of deciding between two figs. I don't exaggerate. One day he hurled himself to the floor in a tantrum of despair after his servants had removed the tray of figs he had been unable to select from, despite a whole morning's pondering. But the sons of Bibulus were as decisive as lightning. While Ptolemy was prematurely jaded, these boys with their avid curiosity were interested in whatever was happening. If Ptolemy had difficulty in marshaling his thoughts on the simplest of topics, the boys applied their minds to any problem with astonishing effectiveness. Where Ptolemy was fat, they were needle-thin. If Ptolemy chortled with laughter at the scurrilous jokes of the eunuchs, the boys controlled themselves and brought smiles to the faces of others with their tales of life in Syria that poked fun at Romans and Seleucids alike. They confided to Olympus, my doctor, that their father's surgeon was such a medical genius that he applied poultices to the humps of the first camels he saw. One of my cats, they nicknamed "Syrian-slayer" and when I asked why, they answered, "Syrians are so chickenhearted that even the mildest-mannered cat is enough to scare them all to death."

I was happy to let them have Gabirius's men, for they were only a nuisance to me. I acted alone at this point, because the Ruling Council of Ptolemy had not yet started to function, or rather dysfunction. It suited me to put distance between me and those soldiers. After staying with me and reaching this favorable conclusion, the sons of Bibulus went over to the barracks of the soldiers to give them their marching orders.

These troops of Gabirius, once legionaries but now mercenaries, felt no urge to go chasing Parthians. Married to Alexandrian women and made affluent by the outlandish generosity of my father, they had become habituated to a life of ease, to the facile, gossipy, unrivaled pleasures of Alexandria. Instead of being willing to appreciate the true caliber of Bibulus's sons, and carrying out orders duly given them in the name of Rome, they turned treasonously on the two boys and without giving them a chance to defend themselves, murdered them.

That act was not merely military disobedience. It was a slap in the face of Cleopatra. I could not let it pass. The queen of Egypt herself had sent them the sons of Bibulus. The order was tantamount to a decree from me; the young men were my personal friends. The murder demanded that the throne of the Lagids pay them back in full for their cruelty and insubordination. I imprisoned the killers of the boys, two Romans rapidly gone to seed in easygoing Alexandria, as fat as Ptolemy himself, continually drunk, stinking of rotten meat, rendered so impotent by food and drink that the best they could do was to molest little girls, or fall asleep before they were buggered by handsome male dancers, the *kinaidos*. Egypt's life of luxury and self-indulgence had returned these Romans to their cradles. These depraved creatures, sucking on alcohol instead of mother's milk, had grown enraged at the fine spirits of these two youngsters and somewhere

in their greasy softness had found enough energy to kill them.
Pale from sleeping day and night, they grasped daggers in their
puffy fists and slaughtered the two birdlike boys. In the words of
Cleisthenes, the court poet:

> *Two baby birds were sleeping.*
> *Two drunken thugs came creeping*
> *And stabbed them in their nest.*
> *Two daggers without feeling*
> *Two guileless fates were sealing.*
> *The worst had slain the best.*
>
> *Tell me why, ye gods above,*
> *Such metals felt no hint of love,*
> *Though forged at Hate's behest?*
> *Alas! how could that cruel steel*
> *No touch of tender mercy feel*
> *For two such chicks at rest?*

It was not up to Egypt to judge them. To do so would be
to admit such scum belonged with us. To remove any doubt that
they were Romans, I had them sent to Bibulus. Then the legionaries, I need hardly say, exploded with rage and accused me
of being a "Roman lackey" because of my actions.

But I have wandered off topic again, led astray by the mention of Gabirius and his soldiers. Let me get back to the fury that
was felt in Alexandria when the Ruling Council broadcast my
support of Pompey. I had hoped to find a chance to ingratiate
myself with Egypt when the sacred bull, Bakis, adored as the living
soul of Ammon Ra, died in Hermonthis. I intended to take the
new Bakis to the temple, to accompany it in person down the
Nile, to attend the ceremony, and thereby win for myself some
popularity with the people.

"The Queen, mistress of the Two Lands, the goddess who loves her father, rowed the boat of Ammon and took it to Hermonthis to place the bull, Bakis, in its temple." So said the inscription in the chapel of Bakis. "The Queen Cleopatra is our monarch, she is our absolute sovereign, she holds dominion over Upper and Lower Egypt. The bull Bakis accompanied Isis as she rowed the Nile."

My plan at first silenced the hostile talk against Cleopatra. The impressive royal barge traversed the Nile, inspiring confidence with its show of gold and purple. Ahead lay Thebes where the people adored me. But behind my back, Alexandria, spurred on by the Ruling Council, deposed me.

I ruled from Upper Egypt, preparing my land army with the same zeal and care I had earlier bestowed on my fleet. Alexandria had robbed me of the name of queen; now we would force it back into their mouths by a pincer-movement from land and sea.

The Ruling Council sent an ambassador to my court to sue for peace. Ptolemy, they claimed, wanted to fulfill the wishes of our father. They invited me to return to Alexandria, offering me a share of the throne they themselves had stolen from me, and protested their undying loyalty, complaining about the instability of the mob, as if they had not stoked the fires of its rage.

We were divided in our opinions about how to react. It was an act of treasonous perfidy, a plan to lure me back and assassinate me, said the High Priest Psheneriptah, the Master of the Hunt, the Lord High Steward, and my doctor Olympus. My chief minister Protarcus and I thought otherwise. The fact was that the Ruling Council was scared; it had lost control of Egypt. For the second year in a row the harvest had been disastrous, hunger was fomenting rebellion in Alexandria, but not against Cleopatra—against the Lagids, the court, the merchants, the landowners, the craftsmen, and the Jews. Now they were faced with my pincer attack.

My decision overruled the High Priest. We undertook the return to Alexandria. On the royal boats would travel my court and my bodyguards. (These were not the four hundred Gauls that Antony would one day present me with.) The army would follow us by land to protect us against possible betrayal. With three hundred men, we figured, we could hold out until the rest of my troops reinforced us.

When our boats arrived at Heliopolis, at the delta of the Nile, spies informed me that we were walking into a trap, that the royal army was readying itself to attack us as we landed. The High Priest had been right. They intended to block any retreat to Pelusium, for the numerous cavalry of Ptolemy was on the point of attacking ours, while its rearguard was waiting for our boats. We landed safely and immediately fled on horseback, galloping through the night without sleeping, stopping only to change mounts and grab a mouthful of food, on toward Ascalon, the Philistine city we had protected from the ravenous greed of the king of Judaea. In its recent issue of coins, it declared its allegiance to me, placing the image of Cleopatra on both faces. Messenger pigeons flew off to warn my army of the impending arrival of Ptolemy's troops and of our change of destination, and to advise our allies in Ascalon of our arrival.

The garrison from Pelusium joined up with us in the desert. They could protect us from a surprise attack, though the risk of one was minimal, since we had spent two full days in the saddle. Even so, I refused to relax. It was midnight and royal tents had been prepared to receive me, with a banquet on the point of being served. But I rejected any rest. I wanted, before all else, to get behind the walls of Pelusium or, better still, sail for Ascalon.

We left behind the musicians and the steaming plates. In no time at all, with fresh horses pulling our light, open chariots, we saw the torches and the enormous campfires of our army vanish into the distant night. The darkness was not total; the sky was unclouded and the enormous full moon of September lit our path. The earth, empty apart from us, flew beneath our feet, and the moon followed us. We had not slept a wink when dawn broke. In the green patch of an oasis, there in the white desert, stood four small towers, protecting it. Under its green cover fresh horses, water, wine, and food awaited us. My maids and I freshened up, and the priests chanted prayers for the gods' blessings. The scribes left messages in the care of pigeons. I half-heard the murmur of the prayers but attended to nothing fully. Palm trees shaded us and a damp coolness wrapped us round. But I was obsessed by the acid, grating breath of the desert. The desert breeze rustled incessantly, a menacing, dizzying restlessness. Ignorant of trees and flowers, it threatened the green and blue silence of the oasis with its low moanings. Nothing in the desert stayed in place. The desert knew nothing of roots and foundations. The desert was only motion. The sand danced by day and by night, tirelessly. At first glance, the sky seemed to refract only the light of the sun and stars, but a more careful scrutiny revealed it shone with sand as well, a sand of light, fine blue sand, of black, white, and golden sands.

With renewed vigor we resumed our flight in the speedy chariots. In my chariot, its fine fittings removed to make it faster for the last lap of our race, I now traveled with the Jewish general, Aristarchus, the head of the garrison in Pelusium. I intended that the city see us together. In the wink of an eye—compared to the long stretch of territory we had already covered—we were at Pelusium. The company of Aristarchus was a delight for that one particular feature of his person, the rose-like odor emanating from his mouth, so intense that even the air stirred up by our speed did not disperse it. Thanks to it, I did not need to fake a smile to persuade the citizens of Pelusium that we were allies. I shook off any trace of weariness, enlivened by that perfume from his mouth. On the road were gathering witnesses of our passing. Those roses made a visible bond between me and Aristarchus. If the presence of onlookers had not deterred me, I would have yielded to that perfume and plucked a rose from his mouth in the form of a kiss.

As I told you earlier, night still had not fallen when we reached the city gates. The sun, round and enormous, seemed to support itself on the horizon. The main thoroughfare had been cleared for our passing. The caravans had been shifted aside and a carpet of flower petals had been laid on the stones of the road. At the foot of the high gates, a reception committee greeted us with standards, and musicians and dancers, exquisitely adorned, celebrated our arrival.

This port is the key to Egypt, with its nonstop handling of all kinds of merchandise. Pelusium never experienced hunger and the scarcity common throughout the rest of Egypt, even in those dark days. The approach to the city was cluttered with travelers, mostly merchants, loaded with many kinds of goods, the typical exports of Egypt: papyrus, linen, perfumes, ivory, and stones for building or sculpting.

A storm in the Mediterranean, common in the region, had confined a multitude of merchants to the city, along with their endless variety of goods. This was the first day of good weather, after two weeks of storms. Fed up with delays, they had improvised a market at the gates to the city. There were exhibited loads of precious emeralds, metal tools, many of them of silver, imported into Egypt for our craftsmen to form into finely designed pieces. There were vessels of glass decorated with gilding or watercolors, blown glass being a recent invention that had caught the fancy of Rome, along with grotesque figurines from Alexandria, an extensive selection of ceramic ware. There, too, was the merchandise of Quintus Ovinius, which came from my wool workshops.

On both sides of the road rolled carts crammed with hens, pigs, and sheep. Wild beasts in cages growled and roared above the squeaking wheels, lions and panthers among them. A recalcitrant elephant was giving its handlers trouble. The music with which we were received was mingled with the hubbub of the travelers and the cries of animals. If Egypt were to be judged by Pelusium, it was the richest country on earth. Here were slaves, black ones from Nubia, white ones from cities fallen on bad times, there goats, over there donkeys, horses of all sorts, and camels adorned with fine trappings topped by a seat.

One thing seized my attention mightily. I commanded the chariot come to a halt. A few yards back I had seen a cart with a yoke of four robust bulls, a rare sight in Egypt, and for a second I thought it was only the effect of my tiredness. For one thing, on this side of the Mediterranean we did not see such carts, and certainly never drawn by sacred animals. But additionally, I had observed from the corner of my eye that it was identical to the one in which I had made my escape from Rome to Brundisium all those years before.

Deciding to clear up the matter, I got down from the chariot and hurried back to the cart. The vision was real enough. There stood the cart with its four strong oxen. I checked it over. "Identical!" I kept saying over and over, more shocked by the likeness than by the profane use of the animals. I got up onto it and was suddenly flooded with memories. On the planks were hundreds of scratchings: Queen of Kings. I was flabbergasted. I had to sit down. The sacks of soil were just like those we had rested on years before, as we had accommodated ourselves to the narrow spaces. The memories of that journey blinded me. I was speechless. What was it doing on this side of the waters, close by the seven mouths of the Nile, the cart the sailors had hired to help the child-princess escape from her shameful condition? I was too overwhelmed to seek an answer to the question, swamped by dreams of other times. Traitors had lured me out of Upper Egypt, where the people were loyal to me. After snatching my throne, they were now on my heels. I could not afford to lose an instant. Yet there I was, still not having received the welcome of the dignitaries, snubbing my key allies, staring at an old cart. The sight of it had reduced me to just another of its sacks of earth. A strange odor roused me from my daydreams. It was truly sublime. I leaned halfway out of the back of the cart; the odor did not come from there. But from the front. I jumped down hurriedly to trace its source. Behind my back, as if coming from a great distance, I heard the voice of my loyal Apollodorus: "It's the cart that got us away from Rome!" If it was a vision, it wasn't exclusive to Cleopatra.

I followed my nose. The bulls! It was the bulls that were giving off that odor, wholly out of character with animals. It was not hard for me to decide which of the four it was; one had a tawny hide and in the middle of its forehead gleamed a silver circle, and its light blue eyes burned with desire, while its horns curved on its head like a crescent moon on its back. The bull was breathing out an intense, divine odor that I could not pull myself away from. Its shiny hide was soft to my touch. It bent its legs without withdrawing its eyes from mine. It was offering me its broad back. Fascinated by the sight, I got up on the animal. As soon as I was mounted, it stood up abruptly, slipping out of the traces that fastened it to the cart. I could not save myself by grabbing hold of the traces, for it carried me off, as agile as a rapacious feline, as rapid as lightning. As we passed under the gate of the city, I turned my head and I saw my company and the reception committee charging after me, yelling and gesticulating. In an instant we left them behind. We raced down the streets of Pelusium. Our passage created an uproar. At one corner they tried to halt us. The bull flew over a barrier and crossed the square faster than the sound of the cries that had been reaching us: "It's carrying off the queen! The bull is stealing our Cleopatra!"

They lowered ropes from balconies, but the bull sidestepped them and charged on. It passed through the gate that gave onto the sea just as a group of men were struggling with all their strength to close its heavy weight. It slipped through without a moment to spare. It started to run along the wharf. Fishermen and soldiers were paralyzed with astonishment. Their nets remained motionless in their hands, their arrows and spears frozen in place. The only sound was the thudding of hoofs on the planks of the wharf. Seeing those mariners petrified, I breathed the cool air of the Mediterranean and felt the excitement of having a bull beneath me, clasping it between my thighs, as if I were the one urging it on. I enjoyed the thrill of it all. And not just in my legs. Shivers of delight rippled through my whole body. I thought, "This bull has carried me off, as its prisoner, and to what strange pleasures!" That thought made even more delicious the feel of its hide, the sweetness of its odor, the excitement of its gallop. As we reached the end of the wharf, the bull jumped. "I am bound to die!" I should have been thinking. But I couldn't think at all. When we fell into the sea, my eyes were bathed in tears. And they were not tears of grief!

I am prepared to swear that right there, as we smashed hard into the water, the bull turned toward me, exposing its underside. I'd swear that even though its muzzle was animal, it knew how to kiss me, and that it possessed me physically, giving me a pleasure that nothing can rival, not even a dream or the imagination, much less gold or power or war. But I can't swear that it was literally true, only that I wanted it to be true. My memory blurs now just as my eyes blurred back then. I saw nothing; my eyes were blinded with pleasure.

The indisputable fact is that, whether or not I was being serviced by it, we both came to the surface groaning and we continued our progress. Its hairy body, the back between my legs, moved over the waves. The breeze was stirred by our motion, the water splashed my feet, the sun blazed on the back of the sea that looked almost metallic under its fire; all these combined to heighten the ecstasy that its smell and the movement of its body had induced in me. We were bound together in one giant heart that pounded with the blood of the universe. I moaned, the bull moaned. Its swimming hoofs skimmed the sea. The water barely touched its extremities; the traveler of the waves carried me along without the water wetting me. We left behind us a wake of white hoof prints. Who controlled the reins of our watery charge? Since when did a country bull cut its way through the waves of the unharvested sea?

The bull's bellows turned into words. Behind the animal sounds that my own body forced from my mouth, I heard it say: Kymothoe, Spio, Glauconome, Halie, Erato, Sao, Amphitrite, Eunice, Thetis, Eulymene, Agave, Eudora, Doto, Pherousa, Galataea, Actaie, Pontomedusa, Hippotoe, Lysianasa, Kymo, Eione, Haimede, Plexausre, Aucrante, Proto . . .

"Oh bull!" I wanted to say, interrupting its listing. "Shut up! Your catalog of names is ruining my delirium. Shut up! You're ruining things. Don't ruin them! Give me more of the pleasure with which you transported Cleopatra to another side of the world. Shut up, please, my bull, my little bull, shut up!"

But the divine bull did not shut up. Its silky hide changed its feel and the water of the sea splashed salt on my skin. Without stopping it continued its listing, droning on in a hoarse voice like a bronchitic clergyman's, drawing out the vowels, almost intoning: "Calypso, Panope, Cranto, Neomeris, Hyponoe, Ianira, Polynome, Autonoe, Melite Dione, Nesea, Dero, Euagore, Psamathae, Eumolpe . . ."

I ceased to plead with it; the voice of the bull had left me cold. Its hide, hardened by the sea and sun, pricked me here and there. The wind now battered me with a cold fist; the galloping jarred my weary bones. The bull concluded its pedantic listing: "Ione, Dynamene, Keto, and Limnoria!"

The Nereids suddenly emerged from the waves, responding to the invocation of the divine bull, to accompany our journey. The arrival of these beautiful guardians broke the spell that had bound us. I thought, "Now we are approaching Scylla and Charybdis. I suspect my bull called on them to negotiate our safe passage between the dangerous rocks and the deadly whirlpool."

But I knew immediately, as if in answer to my suspicion, that the bull and I had ourselves been the fearful whirlpool across from the rocks. We ourselves were a twofold threat to ships. Behind our lustful pleasures lay the menace we fear and cannot avoid on our trip through life: the dangerous love for another and for that other's body. The invocation of the sea-nymphs and their answering presence had drawn us away from the island where the rocks lay shrouded in smoke and fire.

The beautiful nymphs with their green hair were like sisters, different in feature but with some traits in common. There were some fifty in number. They followed us along, perched on the backs of whales. After them appeared the Tritons, swirling around us. We all moved along at a furious speed, the Greek garments of the females blown open like sails by the wind. My bull proved to be the swiftest of ships. The sun, round and enormous, like an orangey peach, pursued us relentlessly, blazing continually from the line of the horizon. One after another, the nymphs swerved from their tracks to introduce themselves to me.

"Cleopatra, my name is Galatea. I am as white as milk." Really she was as white as the sea-foam left by our passage. On her green hair lay a spattering of white foam, and on her white breasts too.

"I am Actaea, she who shifts the restless sands. Greetings, royal queen!" Her skin was the color of sand. Her gleaming eyes were gold-tinted.

Each one was as enviably beautiful as the other. Beautiful! The evening sun was covering them with its velvety light and made them even more beautiful. How was it possible that these delightful bodies had ventured to interrupt the infinite pleasure the bull had been giving me? Compared with them, the bull was now nothing but a brute animal. The waters had darkened its coloring, dulling its appeal.

"I'm Euagore, my queen, she who murmurs softly."

The Nereids did not crowd me or come all at once in a discourteous rush. First one and then another, giving me time to enjoy studying the shapes of the clouds or bathing in the foam raised by the dances of the chubby Tritons who performed the most unexpected moves, accompanied by their shoals of fish. I'd laugh, laugh with gusto, in admiration for the way their human-looking arms cut through the air like fins through water, forceful, elegant, swift. I'd listen to them trumpeting on their immense seashells. Then along would come another nymph, waving a branch of coral. Then another Triton, this one bearing an iron trident rusted and crusted by its long contact with salt water.

Though this scene was fascinating, it did not make the lasting impression that the simple act of crouching to get into the Roman cart had made on me. Nor did it thrill me the way my contact with the bull's body had done. My brain started spinning from the rush of sensations. "Let's begin at the beginning, Cleopatra," I told myself, in an effort to compose myself mentally. "To begin, the bull repeats the myth of Europa's journey, undertaken after her dreaming that two continents were fighting over her beauty. Why did you come for me, dear bull? So that Cleopatra will wage a struggle over two continents?" As I thought the words, Jupiter let out a howl, as if he'd been transfixed by a spear, and all the nymphs disappeared from sight. The Tritons fell silent, swallowed by the sea. The sun skulked behind a cloud. Slowly the bull sank into the water, which climbed up above my feet, covering my legs, thighs, and waist. "Cleopatra, you've misread things," I told myself. "Think again!" And the sinking ceased.

I cried aloud, "The truth is that the number of the continents is not two but three, and they cannot belong to any queen, even though she were the darling of the gods and the living incarnation of Egypt's Isis. Yet if the gods gave her their vote and set her astride the bull's back to send her across the sea, the queen is able to unite the continents in loving friendship, arranging from Africa's shore a marriage between the two, to form one single territory."

The words were barely out of my mouth, when Selene appeared above the sea, her moonlight glistening on the white horns of the bull, on its head, its neck, its broad back. The nymphs reappeared, as beautiful as before, and the Tritons returned from their golden palace beneath the waves and sounded their horns, trumpeting vigorously but without the terrible violence they employ to rout the enemies of the gods.

"A single Earth!" I repeated. The Tritons raised themselves farther above the surface to reveal their majestic tails, and the whales and the nymphs turned into waterspouts. "A single continent that is two in one, one in two, each at peace with the other. With neither trying to impose itself on the other, their gods will dine together in convivial ease."

I raised myself by grasping one of the wet horns and with the other pressed back down the floating folds of my purple robe, for the bull had picked up speed again, swimming like a dolphin. My broad cloak rippled gaily on my shoulders; I would create a single continent, where gods and animals walked side by side in harmony.

Here the bull addressed me, while my thighs navigated its course: "Cleopatra, there is only one way to hold on to power. Not to harangue, not to bribe, not to chastise, not to fail in your administration, not to make gold out of stones—all these are sound guidelines for a ruler. But your only way to preserve your throne is to be Isis incarnate and make yourself a queen of kings. Be Isis! Be the glory of womankind!"

The Tritons approached me and, each fondling in his fist something that could have been an erect penis, they sang to me in fluting tones that imitated women's voices.

> *I am the sovereign mistress of the earth.*
> *Hermes himself first taught me writing's worth*
> *To scribe all things, both sacred and profane.*
> *My laws control mankind, where'er I reign.*
> *Cronos, my father, rules in Heaven's house;*
> *Osiris is my brother and my spouse.*
> *I bring the earth's best fruits to mortal men.*
> *Each night I make the stars shine bright again.*

Then the vastness of the sea rumbled thunderously, as if its profound and enormous tongue were playing tricks, and there on the ruffled surface appeared an opening from which arose Neptune, god of the seas, a huge, bearded giant, as white as marble, with purple eyes and red lips. He turned his head to stare at me. He was grasping in his right hand his erect penis, extraordinary, beautiful, and his arm jerked up and down and he spattered the sea with drops of his silvery jism.

Then he spoke:

> *Be thou the goddess dear to women all.*
> *For thee they built Bubastis' mighty wall.*
> *'Twas thou who marked off earth from heaven's height*
> *And thou who taught the stars to shine their light*
> *And Sun and Moon to course through day and night.*

Thou guide of ocean's ever-restless tides,
Thou teacher of where human good abides,
Bringing to men the partners that they need
That in nine months may come forth love's ripe seed.
Thou taught to offspring how to pay due heed
To parents and before thy rod have quailed
All those who in their pious duty failed;
Then aided by Osiris, limits set
To ills that fragile human lives beget.

Turning toward me, he showed me the lowest part of his belly, opened like a vaginal eye. "You have, O goddess, the eye that sees all things from the flesh. You gave it to women and closed it in men, so that women might find in them the pleasure that heals the pain that comes from seeing all. Between their legs men carry the organ women need to make the pain of being bearable."

Neptune placed his erect penis into the red eye of his lower belly, to seal it. The rest of his penis remained in the place where males have it. Then he sank back down below the surface, slowly. While the Tritons blew their horns, silvery sperm was scattered around. When only his head was visible, he spoke his last words, "You will reign in a palace made for daylight. I return to mine, the male palace, which lives out by night all the hours of the day."

The sea settled back to calm, the opening of the god closed over. The Nereids continued with their introductions.

"I am Nesaie, lady queen, she who surrounds islands," said one.

When another of these beauties said to me, "I am Kymo, the wave," an immense wave lifted up the bull and me. One after another, without seeing any of them, I heard them calling, "I am Pontoporeia; I lead the seas to places beyond the sea . . . I am Protho, she who drives the waters forward . . . I am Eulimene; I guide sailors to safe harbors . . ." The wave burst and a mass of foam abruptly deposited us on the sandy shore, close to the mouth of a river.

The bull shook off the water. It no longer emitted the divine odor. It did not transform itself into a man and loose my girdle to have intercourse with me. Instead, it half-turned away. It now had a fish's tail. It ran back to the sea and again began to swim like a dolphin, its feet moving like oars. Its desire had been to fertilize me with a dream.

The round, enormous sun, still a peachy orange, rested on the horizon. I turned my eyes from the sea and surveyed our landing spot. At first glance I thought it was Themiskira, on the banks of the Thermidon River, for there to receive me were the Amazons, mounted on splendid steeds, drawn up in military formation, a strap of viper's skin holding in place the bow and quiver, the only covering for their chests, long hair disheveled, discolored by sun and salt, in the most barbaric disarray. They wore strange-looking boots, tied by gleaming laces. On foot, on both sides of the queen and her captains, stood two dozen stately old men as her guardians.

The sight of the army, illuminated by the setting sun that covered it with a velvety peachy fuzz, as if turning these warriors into fruits, was impressive. How many women there were, and how handsome! I walked toward them. On the fine horses and on the women's attractive bodies glittered lines of precious stones. The horses' heads were decorated with purple tassels and their reins were gilded. The foreheads of the Amazons were decorated with a stiff curl. Each one was a Venus, but an earthy, savage Venus. I could imagine them emerging from the earth the way Venus emerged from the sea!

My clothes were wet and most likely my hair looked as messy as theirs. I ran my hands through it and realized that it had come loose, dropping down to my shoulders and onto my back.

Then I fiddled with my forehead trying to arrange a curl like theirs. As if responding to a silent order, one of the long-bearded elders, dressed in Greek style like the other elders, hurried forward and with a tiny gold knife clipped a lock of my hair. Officiously, with an ointment one of his fellows brought him, he arranged a curl that clung to my forehead. It must have resembled the Amazons' lock, a small twist of bright hair, the start of a spiral, shining on my temples like a breaking smile.

He said to me, "It's called the curl of Aphrodite."

The sound of his voice brought to mind his identity, despite the years that had passed and aged him. He was Acusilaus, the poet exiled by Caesar.

"Give them a sign of friendship, your Majesty," he whispered in my ear. "Take off your cloak or something."

I pulled off my clothing and dropped it on the sand. The formation of Amazons approached. They rode with incomparable elegance, combining ease with energy, their two bare legs bent over the dark, shiny hide of their mounts, their torsos erect, knees forward, the pale-colored reins loose in their hands. They were of many different races. The queen had an olive skin and was as tall and thin as a stalk of wheat. The arrangement or disarrangement of her hair was slightly different from that of the others. She wore it like Rodogun, the Persian queen, who, according to legend, was washing her hair when she was informed that a subject tribe had risen in revolt. She hurriedly arranged her hair as best she could, swearing that she would not finish washing it or even comb it until the rebellion had been quashed. With that, she leapt onto her horse, a magnificent mare called Niseana, and galloped off to war. One half of her hair was modestly arranged, as befitted her self-control; the other floated wild, like a Bacchant's, and bespoke her furious energy. Also, like Rodogun, the way in which her eyebrows arched upward from the point where they met above her nose delighted me with their strong curve. Her eyes were a mixture of black and gray, cheerful eyes, naturally handsome, as haughty as a leader's ought to be. Her mouth was delicately formed, as if the work of love and loving, and its very shape seemed to speak of kisses. The captain to her right was short and chubby, white-skinned, her light-colored nipples barely visible on her tiny breasts. Her hair was almost gray; at least it looked gray in this light, tossed back and, like that of the others, falling down between her shoulderblades. There were other women with eyes as light as honey or as dark and fiery as a horse's back—all the horses were virtually identical as if bred from one original pair—or as blue as the sky or the sea or as wild as waving wheat. Other eyes flashed between huge rims, others were elongated and small, still others rounded. Some had rosy faces, some were pale, and others yellowish; there were all shades of dark, and one was as white as the foam of the sea-nymph Galataiera. Women tall and short, women robust and delicate. All the races of the world welcomed me, offering me their finest specimens.

The queen dismounted with a single leap. The masses of Amazons did likewise. The majority sat down by the horses' feet, but the queen and her captains came forward.

Behind them, musicians began to play uncanny music but stopped the second that the queen and her captains reached me. Even now, without horses under them, they retained something of the air of centaurs about them, indomitable, elegant, glowing with beauty, with a freedom and confidence in their movements, found only among the most privileged males. But there was nothing masculine about them. Strands of semiprecious stones crossed the edges of their breasts, their groins, and their ankles. The latter were used to fasten their high footwear, which resembled Phrygian boots except that they were made of wild

animal skins. These women literally glowed; they had no cause
to be envious of the Nereids. One of them crowned me with a
wreath of flowers.

"Welcome, Cleopatra," said the queen, before I could say
a word myself. "It is written: It is not recorded that any flock
rebelled against its shepherd, either to thwart him or to prevent
him using their products, but all the same, these flocks are un-
friendly to all strangers, more so than to those who control and
exploit them. Men, however . . ."

She paused. Her troops rose to their feet and followed the
footsteps of their queen toward me, approaching extremely close
and bringing their saddleless horses with them, so close that the
tassels dangled before my face.

"Men," the queen repeated in a disgusted tone. Her followers hissed with intenser disgust. "Men!" said the queen a third
time and her followers hissed again, louder this time, some boo-
ing and others bursting into scornful laughter. "Human beings,"
continued the queen, in a change of tone that quietened the
expressions of contempt, "human beings, female and male—"
She said "male" too fast for the others to react to it with hostility, "rebel against only those in whom they detect an intention
to rule them wisely. Let a governor prove an egoistic tyrant, who
robs their wealth, abuses them, exploits them, and corrupts them
with bribes and violence, and they will adore his stupidity and
misrule. Let his government be just and prudent, they will pay
him back with insurrections and defiance. Today we welcome a
queen, who, like Ciro, used her wisdom to subdue the haughty
Egyptians. Her subjects were many, her mighty cities benefited
from her good government. Your Majesty, Queen Cleopatra,
queen of kings, we, the Amazons, declare ourselves your subjects. The queen will return to her throne. She will increase the
riches and widen the boundaries of Egypt. She will subjugate cities
without number and we shall be her allies, her friends, her right

arm in war, subjects of unquestioned loyalty. The pause in the rule of Cleopatra is only temporary; it is the result of her father's poor choice, because a woman does not need the aid of a weakling brother to authorize her possession of a throne."

The elders had worked their way through the Amazons and their horses in order to hear the queen from close at hand. On hearing the mention of the weakling brother, they interrupted in chorus: "Down with the filthy institution of marriage! Let women take charge of governing!"

Behind the shouts of the men, an Amazon was shrieking, "Death before a husband's bed!"

"A quotation from Aeschylus," I muttered to myself, recognizing the famous phrase. I was upset and put out. "What a petty thing is human will," I continued. "Instead of giving me as an ally the garrison commanded by the Jew of Pelusium and Ascalon, the gods have brought me here to seal an alliance with these creatures, the last thing I wanted . . . I'm finished. This is ridiculous, totally absurd!" I regretted removing my cloak as a sign of friendship.

The old men stopped chanting their slogans and the queen went on. "Cleopatra will return to Egypt, to queen it over kings. Her subjects will be the Medes, the Hyrcanians, who feed their dead to the dogs, the Syrians, Assyrians, Cappadocians, Phrygians, Lydians, Carians, Phoenicians, Babylonians, Bactrians, Indians, Cilicians, Scythians, Paphlagonians, Magadians, Cypriots, and her reign shall be free of terror. She will be adored like a goddess, she will instill into the masses a desire to worship her, they will call her 'generous of heart,' and her glory will exceed that of the son of Cambyses. Her subjects will include Pasagardians, Maraphians, Maspians, Germans, Pantialians, and Derusians, as well as nomads, the Daians, Mardians, Dropicans, and Sargacians—all the tribes of Persia! Her subjects will be Gauls, Spaniards, Jews, and all the kingdoms that look on the Mediterranean and the great

Ocean. Thus speaks Hippolyta the Third, Queen of the Amazons, in welcome of Cleopatra the Seventh, declaring herself and
her troops the foremost of her loyal subjects."

After the enumeration of possible future subjects, I felt safer
and more comfortable, now that government by women and the
hatred for marriage had been left behind. As soon as the queen
stopped talking, the musicians started up, producing a merry chaos
on their instruments, filling the air with sounds like the voices
of eunuchs. The queen bade me good-bye with a gesture, and
off she went, followed by the rest of the Amazons. I lifted my
cloak off the ground, shook it clean, and put it back on.

Once fully dressed, I turned away from the sea and the slop-
ing beach. At first I had assumed because of the presence of the
Amazons that I had landed in Themiskira at the mouth of the
River Thermidon. Now, with a chance to look around, I saw it
was the Isle of Evening, in the swamp of Tritonis, for the place
was exactly as the poets describe it. To one side there was an
abundance of fruit trees, uncountable flocks of goats and sheep,
and magnificent dogs. Between them and the river extended a
plain as far as the sea. There two gigantic palm trees, like two
pillars, flanked an enormous black stone. I was soon to learn that
this was the Temple of Demeter. The sun still remained fixed to
the horizon, motionless, and I realized that on this island sunset
was everlasting.

As I already told you, by my side a powerful river debouched
into the sea, protecting the Amazons from any flank attacks. Their
land defense was a range of irregular escarpments, partly bare of
vegetation, where the flat top was crowned by dense woodland.
I soon discovered that on the far side of the range were sheer
cliffs but right then I felt it was a weak point. Between the range,
which the evening sun was staining blue, and the sea was a stretch
of level land, free from undergrowth, and on it stood the gigantic palms and the black stone, the one feature that dominated all

others. On the other side, the fruit trees, the herds of livestock and the mangers of the horses, marked off by bales of fodder, along with stakes and stones that functioned as corrals, acted as a complicated defensive wall for what I may call the nest of the Amazons.

The impression the place gave me was a disturbing one. Though the fruit trees and the livestock evoked a sense of peace, the absence of buildings, the force of the river, the ceaseless crashing of the waves, the movement of the mounted army like so many ants in the distance—if there were three hundred Amazons, there had to be two or three times that number of horses— all spoke of restless motion. Though the range of hills was not far from the sea, the open plain in the middle and the proximity of the sea created a sense of broad, generous space. The home of the Amazons was spacious, everything was in motion there. The island was the very opposite of a desert but it had something in common with one. I felt the desert on my skin, because it was still caked with salt, and the damp atmosphere did not dispel it. "When all is said and done," I thought, "everything outside Alexandria is desert." I added the words of the poet:

> *Alexandria is all of Earth.*
> *All Earth is Alexandria.*

The great city came back into my mind, its columned arcades, the temple of Serapis, the innumerable streets crisscrossing . . . I had to get back there as fast as possible.

While I was surveying the place and sighing for my city, the elders had readied themselves to serve me. Some of them came carrying a triclinium that they set down on the sand. They placed me in it, cloak and all. Others brought over trays of fresh figs and nuts, olives, pomegranates, cheeses, bread, and dried fish from Lake Mareotis, brought here perhaps by land, perhaps by sea.

They resettled the crown on my disheveled locks and served me wine. They placed a garland of wheat ears on me. The hundreds of Amazons paid us no attention, absorbed by I-don't-know-what. The queen had disappeared from sight.

The gathering now consisted of the old men and me. I thought I recognized, under all the wrinkles, Philo, the Roman poet who frequented the palace of Pompey. I was almost certain that the first one I had identified was Acusilaus but not being wholly certain, I addressed him as "poet."

To my astonishment, all the old men answered my call.

"Acusilaus?" I asked and he nodded. "You're all poets?"

They nodded their heads, all except one, who came close and said in sorry voice, "I am a false poet. I am Castor, the historian. I married the daughter of King Deiotarus, whom Cicero defended. My father-in-law killed my wife and planned to assassinate me too. I escaped by leaving in my marriage bed a substitute for me. In return for my life, I offered him a night of love with my darling wife. Since I fled from my city, I have been writing verses. But I am no poet."

"Yes, you are a poet, Castor," another old man assured him warmly.

"No, I'm not. I sold my life in order to save it, Your Majesty. I can't be a poet. I am what remains when all of Castor has gone. I am . . ."

Another poet put his arms round his shoulders and Castor fell quiet in his grief.

"You recognized me," Acusilaus said, interrupting the awkward moment, "though the last time you saw me you were a child."

"And are you Philo?" I asked the other.

Philo nodded.

"What brings you here, Cleopatra?" Acusilaus asked.

"I was brought here over the seas. But not by my own choice. I was with my entourage at the gates of Pelusium when a god in the shape of a bull seduced me. My plan is to go to Ascalon. There men await me to form an army and to restore me to my throne. Surely my people are already on their way. It is suicide to remain in Pelusium without gathering reinforcements."

"The god did not err, Cleopatra. The truth is that the Amazons do not have inspectors of public works or guardians of the State's treasures. There are no officials charged with maintaining food supplies, no collectors of taxes, no garbage-disposal staff. There is no court. There are no nobles. There is just the queen with her warriors."

"Well," put in another poet, "the walls of Ascalon are something to be reckoned with. It is magnificently fortified. Its garrison consists of a cohort of infantry and a squadron of cavalry. It is not a bad refuge."

"Thank you for your opinions, but to stick to the point, why would I choose to come to the land of the Amazons in order to restore order in Alexandria? Nobody has the right to act as he pleases, unless everything is organized in the best interests of improvement. I have two questions: Can I really ally myself with the Amazons? And what would I get out of that alliance?"

Instead of answering my questions, an aged poet, full of wrinkles, with hair as red as fire, put a question to the others. "Pardon my ignorance, but where is Ascalon?"

"Five hundred and twenty stadia from Jerusalem, which is all too short a distance, if you realize how much hatred the Jews have for its inhabitants," Castor replied.

"It's a lovely city. They've recently built an aqueduct from Laodice in the direction of the sea. The baths there are famous. There are springs and colonnades, admirable for both their architecture and their proportions."

"Yes, it is lovely," said Acusilaus. "But an alliance with these ferocious women warriors is better for Cleopatra."

"They're a bunch of bandits," said Philo. "A roving band of female thugs who survive on what they can steal."

"It's also true," said Acusilaus, "that theirs is a city without ovens. Fire is kindled here only to illuminate the night with torches or to make a bonfire to spur on tales and intimacies. They're probably the only human beings who do not use fire for cooking or melting metals. It serves them only to flutter around, like moths."

"That's just silly talk," said another. "They were the first people to use iron, and that's why initially they won all their battles."

"True, true, but that was centuries ago. Nowadays . . ."

"Their camps have no buildings, no tents even," said Philo. "They sleep out in the open. For a temple they have a big black rock to which they offer worship. Do you call this—" he pointed to the sky and the four cardinal points where there was no sign of a building, "a city?"

"It's a city for Amazons. This is the way they live. They dress without proper clothing and they live without walls and roofs."

"What about you?" I asked.

Acusilaus was the one to answer. "We live on the other side of the hill. Craftsmen from nearby towns have cobbled together something rustic for us. We pass our time there."

"We have some palaces," Philo made clear. "Anybody who wants treasures or sculptures has them. If Acusilaus wants his palace austere, that's his choice."

"Yes. Right enough."

"The rest," added another who until then had not opened his mouth, "stand on pillars of Tenarus marble, for they quarry it in the Peloponnese. They have coffered ceilings of ivory be-

tween gilded beams, and as for our fruit trees, they are a match
for those of Phaeacia."

"Why did you come here, you poets?" I asked. "For inspiration, I bet!"

The poets laughed.

"We didn't 'come,' Cleopatra, any more than you did. We
were brought here, snatched away. We are the booty of the
Amazons—"

Somebody interrupted this remark from Philo: "Nobody
leaves Egypt out of choice. I am Peteosochus, also known as
Peteuris, son of Selebous Persa from Epigonus. Did I need to
leave Egypt to find inspiration?"

"Well, I for one would have come here for inspiration,"
said Acusilaus, "if I'd been young and I could have come freely,
not being driven into exile. I'd have been interested in knowing how these women lived. Do you know, Your Majesty, that
they supply their needs from plunder? The ribbon that they wear
across their breasts, the quiver, the bow, the arrows, the golden
shields in the shape of half-moons, their silver axes, their bread
and olives—they got it all by violence. And why are their
possessions so different? Because there's more than one town
that will buy off their attacks by fabricating for them special
objects designed to please them. Since they love poetry and
music, they kidnap musicians and poets, musical instruments
and rolls of paper. They picked us for our advanced years, as
you can see. They believe that the older the poet, the better
his poetry. Unlike certain rulers who have turned against some
of us, the Amazons don't request us to write poems in their
praise."

"They hate laudatory verses," asserted another. I hadn't seen
him until then and as if he read my mind, he added, "I'm
Tegogolo, Queen of Kings, it's a pleasure to hear your voice and
an even greater one to converse with you."

"They hate any verses written to get favors," said another old man, who had had the nerve to sit on the edge of my litter. "For them, we write the poems we want to write."

"We really say what we mean," said a third.

"And do you really want government by women?" I asked. "Do you really hate the institution of marriage?"

All except Philo said yes.

"Among themselves, Cleopatra, there is no stealing and plundering. They don't hit each other, they don't disobey orders, they live in exemplary harmony. Of course, there's no question of adultery. Not one of them is capable of a vile or shameful action."

"But they don't bother about trade or agriculture," said Philo.

Acusilaus said, "Cleopatra, the *maat,* as you Egyptians call harmony, justice, order, truth, the ideal condition of the universe that only a good monarch can bestow—the maat is a real possibility for the Amazons."

"I think you've gone blind, Acusilaus," said my companion on the litter, in a resigned voice. "They don't know anything but war. And even that, in the Roman style. They have no hoplites, no code of honor. Their war consists of—how can I describe it—trickery and deceit."

Here, everybody chimed in, one remark overlaying another:

"There's no word for their kind of warfare."

"It's a war of women."

"Obviously it's a war of women. They learned to fight like that when they fought against Heracles. It took eight of them to die fighting one man, for them to work out their special type of warfare."

"They are anti-hoplites. They use only light weapons. They act by night. They use cunning. Their shields are shaped like half-moons. They can't use them in military formations."

"Nobody can beat them in combat, except the hero."

"Pisiannassa used a shield made of wicker."

"How can you believe such nonsense? What good is a wicker shield?"

"Of course not. That's one of Estoa's lies."

"No bigger lie than those of bad artists who paint them in checkered breeches and boots!"

"Heracles was wearing the skin of a lion and it made him invulnerable. As a reminder, they wear a ribbon on their chests and use it to invoke the protection of the gods."

"His came from a lion, theirs from a viper."

"They're both wild animals."

"And those panther cloaks, why do they wear those?"

"Eight of them fought against Heracles, one after the other."

"Marpe was the seventh to die, Asteria the sixth."

"Aello was the first to attack him and the first to die."

"Deianeira was his fifth victim, fighting in single combat against the invincible hero."

"Eriobea was the fourth."

"Alcipe was number nine, and the last Amazon to die in single combat. After her, they attacked him as a group."

"But even several at a time could not defeat the man in the lion skin. Eurybe, Celaneo, and Phoebe, shoulder to shoulder with their shields, had been unbeaten in battle till they encountered him. He killed them, all three with one swipe of his sword."

"In the next encounter, they did see victory. Areto was their captain. She went with Pantariste to kill Heracles's captains, in order to avenge the death of Hippolyta. The Amazons won that battle because they fought in their own special style."

"Cunning replaced force."

"That's an understatement. It was more than mere cunning . . ."

"You're not going to deny that the speed of their defenses makes a contribution to defeating a strong enemy."

"Not to mention their tactic of doing the unexpected."

"Sometimes their battles resemble dances more than warfare. They even take musicians along and . . ."

". . . Hipo, Marpesia, and Lampado, the sister generals, went into battle dancing with their shields, shaking their quivers and jingling the bells on them, stamping on the ground, playing their flageolets in unison, producing a savage music that incited them to war."

"While they're fighting, they dance on their horses' backs, even while galloping, and they leap from one horse to another, without a saddle to land on, and they jump through fire."

"Their capes of panther skin . . . I need an answer."

"Personally, I've never seen them use them."

"You haven't? Don't you have eyes in your head?"

"When Mirina, the first Amazon queen in Lybia, invaded Atlantis . . ."

"That was wholesale slaughter! There were thirty thousand of them. Three thousand infantry, the rest on horseback!"

"Omphale, the Amazon, bought Heracles as a slave. She set him to weaving, spinning, and carding wool, among other things. Every time he made a mistake, she spanked him with a golden sandal. His incompetence finally exasperated her and she sent him back to his home."

"And what about Pantasaite? When Heracles's captains fled, she led the chase after them. Two Greek infantrymen attacked her, but she killed them both. She suffocated one and chopped off the head of the other with her two-headed axe."

"Philippis was the second of the nine to fight hand to hand with the unbeatable Heracles."

"Prothoe was the third."

"It's a long time now since Valasca was queen. She cut off the thumbs and pulled out the right eye of all her prisoners, to make them useless in battle—"

Philo interrupted, "Filthy tricksters. Tell it like it is. They're filthy tricksters!"

They responded to his cry with silence, shaking their heads in disagreement and sighing.

"Oh, Philo," Acusilaus said wearily. He was the only one to speak.

Then another broke the silence with a change of subject. "They hunt by night, using nets and other contraptions. Sometimes in groups, sometimes alone. They take dogs with them."

"The dogs here are vicious."

"They sure scare me."

"They train them, the way they do their horses."

"They've got the finest horses. Only horses from Norerathea, the best of the best. Branded with a triangle on the side of the head."

"It's the breed that went down to drink at Lake Neyef."

"And get one thing clear, Cleopatra: they don't hate men."

"Well, not exactly," said the rascally old man perched on my litter.

"If that's detesting, the prettiest of them can come and detest me!"

"It'd be hard to pick the prettiest. They are all stunning. And they don't show their age, Cleopatra. The years don't seem to leave a mark on them."

The poets gabbled on, interrupting each other. I caught a phrase here and there, but I was forming my own notions of these remarkable women.

I asked them, "And everyone who comes to the Isle of Evening stays here?"

"Evening? What are you talking about?"

"This isn't the Isle of Evening, Cleopatra. We are west of Alexandria, on the mainland, not far from from the border with Cyrenaica."

"We don't all stay here. Almost all, but not all. Tigelius . . ."

"The Sardian."

"He was a rum one!"

"If he got it into his head, he couldn't stop humming the song of Bacchus, from the highest chord to the lowest, from the beginning of a meal right to the end. He'd do this in our palaces, but when the Amazons asked him to sing, he wouldn't utter a peep!"

"Definitely a weird fellow! Sometimes he'd run around as if an enemy were chasing him, then at other times he'd walk so slow and solemn you'd think he was carrying the layettes of Juno."

"He'd be awake all night right until daybreak and then he'd sleep through the day, like a dormouse."

"There was no predicting his mood, any more than the wind."

"We threw him out. With the permission of the Amazons. And not just with their permission. With their full agreement."

"We did the right thing. There was no living with him."

Suddenly the earth rumbled. It quaked. The unseen sinews of rock and fire that hold shut the jaws of earth so that they don't open and devour us, started to creak. They threatened to open wide. We were suddenly surrounded by an impressive number of Amazons.

"Relax, Cleopatra. It is a fold in time, one more that Chronos is bringing you. Wait a moment."

The words were barely out of his mouth when the quaking stopped. The powerful army of Amazons around us melted away. Quietly, I stayed on my litter and the poets resumed their heated conversation.

A single Amazon appeared and interrupted our group, singing in koine, a language she pronounced with the same accent as her queen.

Now is the hour to retire
And give fond welcome to desire.
Here burns the Amazonian fire.
Earth, air, and water all aspire . . .

I did not catch all her words. She was clapping her hands and each time she brought them together, a tongue of fire seemed to blaze between them.

The old men got up, taking away the trays of the food we had been nibbling. The Amazons would let the men write whatever they chose and reward them with palaces and treasures, but effectively they were the Amazons' servants. The poets bade me a friendly goodbye.

"Will I see you all again?" I asked somewhat anxiously. With them, I felt on familiar ground. I couldn't say the same for the Amazons.

"Perhaps," said Philo.

"Count on it!" corrected Acusilaus. "Tomorrow. At least in a few days." He took Philo by the arm and dragged him off, at the same time using him as a support. He rebuked him as they went, "You always have to look on the black side, Philo. Maybe your pessimism is the source of your first-rate stories, but it makes you hard to get along with. You see the negative in everything, always what's wrong. Of course we're going to see Cleopatra again! Were you joking? What kind of dark clouds fill your head? What were you thinking about?"

The orangey sun was still there, as if rooted to the spot, as if leaning on the horizon were the only position it knew.

With the poets had departed most of the musicians, along with the slaves that carried their instruments. The Amazons waited until the males were out of sight before they began their preparations. Only three interpreters remained behind and they were blind. I realized this when they approached my litter. Two had no eyes at all. The eyes of the third were covered with whitish scales. What were the Amazons planning to do that couldn't be seen by men's eyes? To tell you the truth, I was scared of these women. They removed my cloak and robe, they washed away the salt from my body with a water perfumed with petals, and, laying me down once again on the litter, covered my breasts, belly, and pubic hair with a reddish, oily paste, thick and transparent, that they called "Aphrodite's cream." On my hair, which they left loose, they spread another, earthier paste. They fixed again the curl on my forehead with the ointment of Aphrodite, rapidly bandaged my body and head, even my eyes, with long, broad strips of linen, raised up the litter on their shoulders, and set off walking, accompanied by musicians, who went off at a faster pace than we, their music disappearing into the distance. Everyone was singing this chant:

> *Prepare me to be raped by gods of lust,*
> *Display my limbs to men no one can trust,*
> *Who pass their aching nights with open eyes.*
> *Let slaves sing out the beauty of my thighs.*
> *Let boys beat drums and ring out chiming bells*
> *And touch my woman's body where it swells,*
> *Desiring to consume me with their lips—*
> *But let them know for gods alone my hips*
> *And thighs are meant, for them alone.*
> *So let men weep and make their fruitless moan!*

They walked for a long stretch, carrying me on their shoulders, still singing. A good part of the way I had to lean back, because we were going uphill. Then they halted and stopped singing. The music was long gone. They uncovered my eyes and removed the bandages from the rest of my body. They lowered my feet to the ground on what appeared to be the final section of a steep, muddy road. Stars were blinking bright as if extremely close to my face, hurting my eyes with their brightness. The dusk that had been prolonged since the bull ran off with me had finally ended. The sun's disc had been swallowed by the earth. Once again I closed my eyes, afraid that my stare might fix them immovably in place, but I had to open them again when the Amazons whispered to me to walk at their pace.

The air, full of cool dampness, was pleasant to my skin. It was night and I had no clothes on, but I wasn't cold. The air smelled of greenery, as if thick vegetation were nearby. It wrapped me round with its strong smell. I was dressed in green air, my naked skin clad in airy greenness.

With a few steps we reached the crown of the hill. The path gave onto a level surface that, as far as I could determine, was circular. In its center stood a grove, its trees silhouetted against the sky. As I approached, its branches bathed me in moist aromas, as if they were stretching their buds out toward me, and their the leaves were sticking to my skin. Perhaps this sensation was the result of the Amazons' hypnotic songs. Cleopatra was absorbed by the trees. My veins were the trees' veins, the channels of their leaves. I was Spring, wreathed in flowers. I was Summer, naked and carrying a garland of wheat. I was Autumn, with dirtied feet—though not with grape juice but with the mud of the path—and I was Winter with my hair tousled, whitened here and there by the starlight. I was possessed by the spirit of the wood. I wanted to halt there amid the trees and wait till I sent out roots. A madness overwhelmed me, an arboreal fever. On my tongue I felt small leaves sprouting, their tips playfully tickling my lips.

I wanted to run through the trees but my fever held me in place, motionless, transformed into tree. I let the Amazons carry me a few steps more along the hilltop. Then down a slope, then through the foothills, where they ended in a precipice. Here was no more mud, only rock. They lowered me to a low ledge and I clung there to a projection of rock. They followed and we entered the mouth of an almost inaccessible cave in the sheer cliff face. Inside were three steps lit by flickering torches. Above lay a long, broad gallery with a low smooth ceiling. There were gathered about three hundred women and the blind musicians. The queen of the Amazons, stretched out on an enormous polished stone, as black as river rock, was singing as follows:

> *Through my mouth will pass your words.*
> *Listen, Cleopatra, and repeat them.*

But it was she who repeated them to a hypnotic melody, reinforced by the chords of the blind musicians. They had covered her upper body with a thick layer of clay and grass that by now was practically dry. The mud hid her feminine curves. Her torso was rounded like an egg with her arms inside the covering. She fell silent, and the musicians beat on resonant drums.

They placed me on a rock similar to Hippolyta's, but less shiny. The gray stone was cold but it was as smooth as a jewel. Hippolyta started her song again, first in a low key and with a stately rhythm. Then, after a few phrases, the tone harshened and its piercing notes nearly deafened me. She sang rapidly like a woman possessed or disturbed, and she made me uneasy. While she was singing, they bathed me in aromatic water and with the palms of their hands beat on the dry clay over her chest, one after another, not violently but as on a drum, each one giving it a couple of beats, then turning aside to make way for the next. Then after touching her, they began to dance with feverish frenzy.

Hippolyta was singing,

> *I am the mouth of my dead.*
> *I am the mouth of the bodies.*

I am the body of the mouth of their bodies.
I am the lips of their dead.
I am the body of their dead.
I am the life of their dead in my body.
I am the vulva that the bull failed to penetrate,
the vulva that gives life to the voices of their dead
through a channel of shining semen from the handsomest youth.
My two legs are the two lips of the mouth of my dead.
My torso is the tongue of the dead.
My two arms are the thousand words the dead speak.
My hair is the laughter of the dead.

Behind her, a chorus of Amazons was speaking words that I could hear because they were repeated over and over.

You have placenta in your center,
You have placenta in your center.
I forbid you fear, hear me, O hear!
You have placenta in your center.

At the same time Hippolyta was going on with her song:

My curl is the loving kiss of the dead.
My nipples are the coughing of the dead.
My knees are the folds in the lips of my dead.
My mouth is the mouth of the living, the mouth of the dead.
In my vulva is an eye . . .

When she said, "In my vulva is an eye," the mud that covered her broke into two pieces. The mud was dark, but inside it were visible streaks of lighter soils with which it had been mixed. The handsome torso of Hippolyta was perfectly clean. Left naked in this way, the ever-youthful Amazon, stretched on the black stone between the two pieces of her shell of clay, was dazzling, the most lovely of lovely women. Imprinted on the underside of the clay, the dazzle of her beauty was echoed there, as she continued:

In my vulva is the eye that looks into the well of life.

Her long, dark, thick hair slid in a tangle over her shoulders. Her cheeks were burning, her expression was entirely detached from those of us who surrounded her. She responded to nothing going on around her. Her face showed no trace of her knowing where she was. She was speaking into the ear of the gods, she was present among them, we were invisible to her, she had detached herself, gone to the furthest extreme, and was singing from a city of shadows. Her olive skin seemed light in comparison to her dark, enormous nipples which were of the same color as her fleshy lips, her scanty, black pubic hair and her deeply dark vulva which she left visible by keeping her legs apart and bent. Of the same dark color was the hair in her armpits, as dark as the mane of the horse who was her daily companion.

I am the mouth of my dead.
I am the mouth of their bodies.

She had taken up again her disturbing song, this time in a trance from its beginning. Dozens of Amazons were dancing by now, performing graceful but feverish movements. As they danced, they were going off, perhaps, to the same city where their queen was singing. They were the drop of oil that turns the iron to gold, the firewood to gold, the ashes to gold, the water of the sea into coins minted from gold. A dance of gold. Those dance movements were the drop that transforms the flesh into gold. They beat their heels on the floor; they were beatings of the winds. They swirled their arms; they were flashes of brightness, scales of the fish that the fisherman's knife scrapes off. Their thighs were pealing bells, they were metals clashing, they were water and tide, the gold of the bone, the blood that kindles the color in gold.

Hippolyta's expression changed, as if she were suddenly back with us. Her voice lowered its volume and the musicians responded by falling silent. A gesture from her let us know that she had heard something; it had broken in on her flight, forcing its way into her delirium. Then the galloping of horses resounded in the cave. The sound came from all corners, even from the roof. Hooves were racing, getting closer to us. Nearer and nearer every moment. Shouts in the ears, drops of orange splashed on their eyes, darts hurled into their chests.

The delirious dance of the Amazons ended, stopped by the beating hooves.

They lit more torches, bathing the roof of the cave in light. It was solid rock, without cracks, a huge, unbroken block of stone, on which sounded the rapid passage of numerous horses. The sound became deafening. They were now right above us. Then it stopped. Silence. A moment of total silence, followed by pawing of hooves, loud and close.

By this time my body was free of all the oils. The Amazons were paying me no attention whatsoever. We were all listening intently to the sound of the hooves on the earth above. Underneath them, there in the echoing cave, we were vibrating like a drumskin, an echo of the echo.

Then came a storm with a different sound, a beating of gigantic wings. The sound thundered above our heads. We had all been frozen in place from the moment we heard the hooves. Now menaced by the new sound, we dashed about, terrified. But nothing happened close to us. The wings kept beating, heavily, slowly, frighteningly. But they were not present among

us. We turned aside our bodies to avoid being hit, crouching or
darting from side to side, dodging a blow that never came.

We were grotesquely disconcerted, like clappers without
bells. Then we heard a voice. Of what? A bird? A man? A croak-
ing speech, an eagle's word or a leopard's? What did it say? I
couldn't understand. Yet it bordered on the comprehensible. It
came from the mouth of the cave. The beautiful face of a bird,
with a blunt, rounded beak edged with blood-red band, its round,
lidless eyes gleaming intensely, was lit up by the lamp it was carrying. The hand had a human shape, but it still remained an eagle's
claw. The face was both a bird's and a man's, though it had no
skin on it. It came into the cave. Surrounding its face were masses
of dark plumes that were mingled with the thick, well-combed
hair of a man, falling to his shoulders. Across its chest hung ten
strings of pearly and golden beads. The hips were clad in a linen
skirt. It bent its body to move into the low gallery. The cave
seemed too small to accommodate the enormous god. It sat down
on the second stair and once again pronounced the disturbing
words. I wanted to understand them. It was saying something I
ought to understand. What was it reciting? Out from the beak
came polished words, carefully enunciated by the tongue. Were
they words? They were the articulations of a man-eagle, a
woman-lion. They sounded like Ethiopian, then Hebrew. Now
they were Syrian, now every language I knew in one. It was a
troglodyte language, both none and every one simultaneously,
the roar of a beast, the song of a nightingale, the voice of the
wind and sea. The language of the gods! Is this what poets strive
to express?

The words had a strange effect on me. They drove me to
shift position; up became down, right became left. I danced,
whirling my soul and mind around.

It finished speaking and put the lamp on the ground, lighting up bare feet, enormous handsome legs, and the skirt embroi-

dered with a series of figures carrying the solar disc on the head, supported on the horn of the moon, and then it got up. There was no room for it to stand fully upright. It raised its arms and lifted up the roof of the cave, detaching it from the hilltop with an over-powering sound! The god of the rising sun raised his arms even higher, stretching his body to the full. The stars became visible beside us. The god seemed to grow even more. The roof of the cave moved upwards again, supported by the hands of this terrify-ing giant, and started to glow red. The stars disappeared from sight, and the centaurs—it was they whose hooves we had heard—started to tumble from the cavetop, all at the same time, down onto the edge of the hill, crowding together as they fought for a foothold. Magnificent, mounts without equal, torsos unparalleled, faces of unrivaled character! Gathered there, they formed a living frieze, so perfect in shape that only their movements proved they were not the finest of stone sculptures! Seeing the Amazons, whose beauty was enhanced by the light of the torches, they hurled them-selves upon them, their penises erect, in a rush mad enough to shame Chiron, lascivious, drunken, the long hair of their armpits soaked with sweat, their eyes glittering, panting to gorge on this banquet of women! The Amazons had left their bows and quiv-ers, lances and maces, axes and shields down by the sea, to attend my welcoming ceremony without the least sign of bellicosity, and now they clung to each other, racing around, as their only form of defense. The enormous god, infuriated by the behavior of the lubricious centaurs who were grabbing at any woman who came within reach, blew on them in his rage. His freezing breath put out the torches on the walls and made the centaurs recoil. The Amazons, the musicians, and I, though we were hugging one another, shivered with cold. The god stamped his heel on the ground, making it quiver like a drumskin. He stamped a second time, driving us away from him with the force of the blow. The earth shook and we were sent in the direction of the lusting centaurs, who defied the earth tremors in their desperate desire. From the point where his heel had hit, there burst out a stream of fire, a fountain of steepling flames, and from the depths of the earth we heard the voice of Vulcan complaining: "Who is stealing fire from my forge?"

The flames shot up vertically and the heat warmed the circle we had formed around them. The god blew again toward the centaurs, four times, once into each of the four points of the compass. The centaurs fled, but the four slowest he froze into stone where they stood. The god was ice and fire. Ice his breath. Fire in his extended hands, turning the rock to glowing red. There was fire in his staff, fire in the stamping of his heel, fire in his angry breast, but his breath was freezing. The four petrified centaurs were fixed at the cardinal points and their heads supported the rock. The god lowered his arms and with a gesture invited an Amazon to bring him his extinguished lamp. He lit it in the fountain of fire. Following his example, the Amazons lit their torches in it. Once again, from under the earth, Vulcan protested, "Give back the fire of my forge!"

The bird-headed god with his extraordinary hair stamped again on the ground. The fountain vanished, swallowed by the ground. The four centaurs remained there, turned to illuminated pillars, their stony penises still erect. The rock turned a whitish hue. The Amazons clustered around me.

We left the cave in a hurry. It was now open on all sides, ripped open by the god. I thought to myself, "If the god could violate a vaginal gallery like this, which seemed to defy all attack and whose location was known only to the initiated, how could he fail to inspire in the centaurs a desire to mount the Amazons?" But immediately I rejected my idea. It was an unworthy notion, conceived in darkness, stupid. Though the centaurs were divinely handsome in body, and under other circumstances the Amazons would have been impressed by their beauty, their violent onset had been idiotic. Their misunderstanding of women transformed carnal intercourse into a slapstick farce. They had discerned in the women what was truly alive in them, the alivest part of their living, their desire. And they wanted to steal it, cut it out, snatch it away in order to satisfy their thirst for violence and cruelty. To violate! How repulsive! Through my head there passed the beauty of the centaurs, now tainted with a need to vomit. They were flesh at its most rotten. They were rotten with decay even though they had not yet died. And to think that the poets had described the warring of the Amazons as something ignoble and unworthy. The Amazons commit no rape when the battle is over. They do not inflict violation on women.

By now there was not the slightest trace of the other centaurs. Apart from the four frozen into rock, they had vanished into the night.

The hill trembled again as a good number of Amazons trod on it. The air was thick with dust. I and the Amazons around me walked back over the level ground to where they lived. We turned and saw the hill in convulsions. The god was lifting the ripped-apart rock up into the sky. He was standing upright on Hippolyta's stone. His arms were high and in them was the single piece of rock that formed the blunted top of the hill. We kept moving toward the sea, turning to look at him now and then, illuminated by his lamp and the torches which were still burning.

Even at this distance, my heart leapt when I looked at him. It is one thing to see a painting of a god, a very different thing to see the hair on his birdlike head. And to hear the words coming from his hard beak! The Amazon who had stayed with him climbed up on a petrified centaur beside the god. She touched his head, caressing it and passing a comb through the feathery locks. She was singing,

O handsome god, whose breath is cold as frost,
Your skin burns up my touch, and I am lost.
To you as god I offer sweet adorings,
But as a man I bring you fierce implorings.
Return, my god, up from the watery deep
And in your arms my quivering body keep,
Till love returned for love transforms me twice,
To freezing vapor and to scalding ice!

Could this Amazon be in love with the god? How ridiculous! His skin was fire and his breath freezing snow. How could he satisfy a woman, constituted so?

The scene was grotesque. It made me sullenly angry.

"Why the hell are all the gods giants?" I mused.

"All of them?" asked Hippolyta.

"Why does it have to be that way?"

"What are you talking about?"

"Hippolyta, in the sea Neptune presented himself to me. He was enormous. A giant. Now this Egyptian deity . . ."

"Nonsense! It isn't always so. They're not always giants, Cleopatra. Today this god—the one Orthea loves—appeared this way because he wanted to destroy our cave. Sometimes he shows up the size of a hare. Orthea crouches down and sings to him in a very soft voice and chats to him."

"That's grotesque!"

"What's grotesque about it? You must be over-tired! It's not at all grotesque. Yes, he's a god, and yes, his breath is ice, and yes, he can steal Vulcan's fire when he wants to, but so what? What is really grotesque is men's idea that you can make one being out of two bodies. Love, Cleopatra, is the consciousness of the exciting differences between two people. Or do you think that love is the union of two souls, a melding of two into one, the unity that obliterates the pain of being alive? Or worse—

do you think the institution of marriage consolidates the dream of love?"

At that point, I wasn't thinking at all. But her words calmed me. I was only aware of my exhaustion, if I may call it that. Hippolyta was quite right. I was worn out. I could hardly stand. I wanted to lie down and sleep.

"We'll go to bed shortly," said Hippolyta. "We'll give you some wine to make sure you sleep well. But you'll hear our stories first, so that your curiosity doesn't wake you before sunrise."

The Amazons had dispersed. I wondered if they had gone night-hunting, for I heard dogs barking. Just a small group remained huddled round a blazing fire. The queen signaled me to sit down. Not on a stately throne, but on the ground. I obeyed. But before my rear touched the ground, one of the Amazons slipped a comfy but firm cushion under me. Another did the same for Hippolyta.

Still, with total clarity, the song or lament of the lovesick Orthea could be heard. The blind musicians hadn't come back with us. Doubtless, they would sleep with the poets.

The women gave me a flavorful wine to drink and spread in front of me an impressive array of desserts.

"I'm Melanippe," said the Amazon to my left. She was white-skinned, as if the sun had never touched her. In her smooth movements was a gentleness that denied any acquaintance with galloping horses. She seemed created to snuggle down on soft cushions. Around her waist were three rolls of fat that gave a sort of kindly smile to her waist. She continued, "I'm not going to tell you the story about men declaring war on all the Amazons from Themiskira to Tripoli, from darkest Lybia to Thermidon, because they were convinced—probably by Athena—that if they made war on us, they would overcome the curse that afflicts the human race for its being born of women. None of that."

Beside Melanippe, so gentle, soft and satiny, so domestic and bright, sat another Amazon, sun-burned, rough and muscular, as hard as a statue. She was munching noisily on fresh, green, fibrous peapods, extracting with her teeth some flavor or nourishment.

From the other side of the fire spoke another Amazon that I could not see clearly because of the brightness of the blaze. She was saying, "My name is Atalanta. I was born when my father sold in distant lands the cords my countrywomen produced, in exchange for jewels and coins that had no effigies stamped on them. My mother concealed my birth from him. Every time he asked for his son, she'd reply, 'You'll see him when you get back. He'll be here then. You'll see your boy with your own eyes when you return.' Throughout his long trip he would fondle the idea of his baby boy, probably sick of the numerous women in his town, without stopping to think that it was the work of the women on those cords that was making him a rich man. By the time he returned I was two years old. He came home with a sumptuous retinue of elephants, a load of gold, and dozens of new slaves. He exploded with rage when he saw I was female. Without recovering from his long trip, without changing his soiled clothes, he just grabbed another horse, picked me up, and took me into the dark forest, where he dropped me among brambles and said, 'I never saw you. I never saw you and I never knew your mother had you. I want a son, a boy.' And there he left blonde little Atalanta, and her only companions were fear, hunger, and cold. A wild boar looked after me, the biggest one in the vicinity. One afternoon a cunning hunter tracked it right to its lair. The boar bellowed at seeing itself in a death trap, not concerned about its life—for animals have no fear of death—but grieved at the idea of leaving me, its child, to grow up alone.

"The hunter noticed me, understood what had happened and said to the boar: 'I won't kill you, boar, for you have protected this orphan child. But now I will rear her and I will come hunting you every afternoon.'

"And that's the way it was, exactly as he said.

"As I grew up, I retained my virginity, being constantly armed to ward off men. Two centaurs once tried to rape me, but I killed them both. My appetite was stimulated by the taste for flesh. So I took part in all sorts of battles, and once I beat Peleus, the father of Achilles, in a fight."

Next to the fire, I was sipping wine, eating candies, and feeling drowsy, when two handsome dogs appeared among us. A strange sensation of peace came over me. The other Amazons had now returned. We went on chatting in small groups, but we all paid attention when one Amazon raised her voice and launched into her story, sprinkling it with brief commentaries that I won't bother you with here.

Sitting in front of the blazing fire which had never been used to roast meat or cook fruit and vegetables, to prepare iron for the forge, to harden clay into pots or tenderize hard grains into soft foods, the Amazons somehow read my thoughts. I was wondering how it was that so many different races could live together in a uniform style, in a harmonious community, without a trace of conflict. Some told their story in beautifully polished hexameters, which I could not memorize because of their length, while others made contributions in clumsier rhythms.

"Once I had flaxen curls, though born a Roman maid . . ." began Melanippe.

Our men had slaughtered German soldiers in a raid.
They sacked the city, robbed the granaries of wheat,
And with a blaze that brought an early dawn
Burnt to gray ashes houses built of wood,
Poisoned the wells, and spattered earth with children's blood.
They raped the women . . .

Unsatisfied and drunk, at break of day,
They raped the sour-willed serving girl, so oft

Raped by her master, then two little girls,
While women screamed, and next a pretty widow
Digging her husband's grave. A dozen men

Forced her body, and left her bleeding there,
Ripping away her clitoris, thrusting wide
Her blood-stained thighs. She tried to creep away,
Crippled by painful loins, but down she dropped
In vineyards trampled underfoot, and mute
She lay until a midwife came with sacred shears,
Used to cut the newborn's cord, to clip away
Her final glory, long and flaxen locks . . .

While soldiers burned the ripening crops
And stacked up treasure in their carts,
The ravished widow checked her tears
And to the midwife said, "My hair
Is of no count. You must preserve my tongue
To speak against the cruelty of Rome
To ages yet to come."

The hair was bound in sacred cords
And carted off to conquering Rome.
But in the hands of Romans weaving it
The sacred cords to serpents turned,
Biting the victors with the conquered's spleen
And bringing Death where Beauty should be seen . . .

The dying widow lay there, torn and bruised,
A pool of blood between her ravished thighs,
Heart broken, like a creature sacrificed,
Barely alive and shorn of flaxen hair.
Again she said, "Preserve my tongue to speak

Of how the Roman penis makes a sword
That maims and kills . . ."

The midwife was a witch and with her shears
Cut off the widow's tongue and washed it clean
And placed it in a cart that went to Rome.

My hair was flaxen, though I came from Rome.
I wore a wig of German captives' hair
And lived a life of thoughtless vanity,
Until I heard that tongue. It spoke to me
Of Romans using women with contempt,
Defenseless women, treated worse than beasts,
Without an axe or spear to fend off foes.
I saw the rape of women, old and young,
I smelled the smoke of noble houses burned
And knew the harshness of a winter's night
Without an axe to chop the wood, a fire
To cook the food, a knife to cut the meat,
For all had been transported back to Rome.

I saw the milkless breasts of German wives
And in my heart I breathed the ash-filled air,
I smelled spilled German blood and Roman piss.
I fled with twenty horses and my gold
Toward the south . . .

                                    Toward the south
Where sunlight would reduce my hate, and joy
My soul with love for Aphrodite,
Isis, Demeter, goddesses who bring
To Amazons the best of earthly things."

Here Melanippe said to me, "Cleopatra, I must tell you what all the rest know. That I'm the only one of the Amazons who doesn't enjoy warfare. I don't take part in combat, but I do hunt by night and I spread my nets . . ."

She sat down and behind me somebody was singing in a sweet voice: "The story of Camilla dresses the Amazon as an arrow." The enigmatic words were repeated several times but their meaning became no clearer. The song was so beautiful in itself that I did not fret about understanding the significance of its lyrics.

Another Amazon who did not mention her name interrupted the song. She rose to her feet, saying in a musical voice, "Cleopatra, hail! Queen of queens and of kings! I've always refused to handle coins. The only ones I accept are those with your face stamped on them, for I admire you. Now listen to my reason for joining the Amazons."

She began:

> I am not here because I hate all men
> Or fear the thoughtless violence of their ways.
> I detest the spinning wheel and carded wool.
> To be a wife appalls my sense of pride
> As much as giving pleasures paid by coin.
> I hate the housebound life as I hate jails,
> The chatter with the servants, and the waste
> Of time in smearing oils and creams
> And listening to the babble of small babes.
> I love my carnal pleasures with a man
> But have no wish to guard his worldly goods,
> Clashing with slaves and bankers all the day.
>
> The pathlesss sky delights me, and the earth
> Where manmade roads have never dared to go.

I map the source of rivers still unnamed
And give them mine. I ride a camel's back
And train a cheetah for the hunt, and stay
Awake all night or sleep until I choose
To wake. I love this sweet disorder best.
With stars above I joy in love's delights.
I squander gold and melt my trinkets down
To fashion arms. I dance unclothed. I choose
The man I most desire; and when he comes,
We laugh away our lusty nights of love.
I speak with gods and goddesses as friends
And never once renounce my woman's soul.

"She's not speaking personally, Cleopatra," someone said from the dark. "That's our hymn."

"It may well be the hymn of the Amazons. But it's mine as well. That's why I'm here. I agree with its outlook completely."

The woman clapped her hands and flames flashed between them. She warbled out an eery song and danced. How beautiful she was! How extraordinarily beautiful, twirling her body in a way I'd never seen, like a wave of the sea, an unhoped-for joy. Then several got up to dance together, all graceful, while others sang, adapting to music the poem I had just heard recited:

I speak with gods and goddesses as friends
And never once renounce my woman's soul.

A red-haired Amazon placed her hand on the reciter's shoulder and said, "That hymn belongs to all of us. You can't claim it as your own."

"Of course I can. And so can you. And so you ought to do. So everybody ought to do. That's why its ours."

"I mean it. I'm not playing the game of 'It isn't true.'"

"It isn't true!" sang out a handsome voice behind me.

"It isn't true!" chorused the Amazons.

They began to play their game. They sang the phrase "It isn't true," and one of them would reply by trotting out some traditional wisdom, so that they could all chorus again, "It isn't true!" At other times, they would chant, "But, this is true." Then a voice had to make a comment they all considered true and they would round it off by chorusing again "Yes, that is true!" The whole procedure was accompanied by dances and bizarre melodies, charming but outlandish. Dogs barked, disturbed by the clapping, and jumped up panting against the dancers.

"It isn't true."

We lived in kitchens, cooking, baking bread,
Till younger women claimed our husband's bed.

Once again I recognized an allusion to Aeschylus.

"It isn't true!"

"It isn't true!"

We joined the band of Amazons because
Vile men had raped our sister and we knew
That what one suffers all must suffer too.

"It isn't true!"

"It isn't true!"

We joined the band of Amazons because
The mighty goddess Pallas forced us to,
When Zeus's bolt had scattered far and wide
The Argive fleet and battered Ajax' pride,
For raping wise Cassandra while Troy burned.
Hence we to fiery Amazons were turned.

"It isn't true!"

"But this is true!"

We are the children of the God of War
As wolf-raised Romulus and Remus were.

"Yes, that is true!"

"It isn't true!"
"*When young, we burned one nipple off our chest*
To leave the right side with no trace of breast."
"It isn't true!"
"But this is true."
"*Each god and goddess treats us like a friend*
And to our arms grants power without end."
"Yes, that is true!"
"It isn't true!"
"*We broke male children's legbones, cutting short*
Their speed, to cripple them in war and sport."
"It isn't true!"
"But this is true."
"Yes this is true!"
"*We went to Troy and forced our foes to flee,*
Wielding the arms that bring us victory!"
"Yes, that is true!"
"It isn't true."
"*All that we keep of lost Atlantis' pride*
Is songs the victims sang the day they died."
"It isn't true!"

Here, as if in contradiction, someone sang what might have
been a song from Atlantis:

> *Beat loudly on your turquoise drum,*
> *O child of flowery passion, come!*
> *Come with heron's feathers dressed*
> *And stripes of paint across your chest!*
> *And here to leave you satisfied*
> *Are shields made from a tiger's hide.*

"It isn't true," called half of the Amazon chorus.
"But it is true," challenged the other. "It is. It is!"
"Neither the song nor Atlantis is real."

"Atlantis is as real as you and I are. Thirty thousand Amazons once invaded it. There were innumerable prisoners. Nobody ever saw booty like it!"

"Pure gossip!"

"It's true."

"It's a falsehood."

"It's true, I tell you."

With an imperious gesture Hippolyta brought the dance to an end; it had grown feverish and the quarrel over the reality of Atlantis was on the point of developing into a pitched battle. She walked away and everyone followed her.

All together we arrived at the communal bed of the Amazons. On one side of the two palm trees that guarded the giant black stone, somebody had spread a thick, soft covering of cool grass. Hippolyta took me to where the covering looked thickest and there we halted. All the Amazons settled down to sleep, without another word. The only sound was the tuneful weeping of the lovesick Orthea; all else was still, until Hippolyta resumed the conversation we had begun around the fire.

"Orthea. Did you really mean she's grotesque? What's wrong with her? Thalestris made love all night, for three consecutive nights, with Alexander the Great. She wanted a son by him. 'There's nothing better than a son of Alexander,' she said. But Love's arrows were infected and she died shortly afterwards, without having borne a child. Penthesilea was defeated by Achilles, because she allowed herself to love him. Do you think Penthesilea and Thalestris fell for that old canard, that one's mate is one's other half and together the two compose one unity? But I see you don't want to discuss this. You can hardly keep your eyes open. Let night fall on the Amazons!"

She fell quiet. Where she and I lay down, they had spread a layer of rose petals over the cool grass. All the Amazons, stretched out on their soft collective bed, were listening to the lamentations of Orthea over her passion for the god. One or two repeated her words out of sympathy for her. Others were weeping, distressed. A somewhat chubby Amazon, lying near me, kept clutching her hand to her chest to check an impulse to sob. But the sobs emerged and between them she was saying, "Poor little thing, just listen to her, poor little Orthea." A small woman, smiling and rosy-cheeked, replied, "But if you've got us, dummy, what else do you want?" Cackles broke out in unmitigated ridicule. Some laughed with a certain tenderness, as if they noticed in the lamentations a childlike quality that stirred them, but most were mercilessly contemptuous. Orthea's song simply enraged others and they put their hands to their ears to blot it out.

Hippolyta's attitude surprised me most. In an intimate tone, inviting sleep, she sang us all a lullaby, as she crouched on the bed of petals, resting one knee on it.

> *Demeter, grieving friend to grieving friends,*
> *Who guide your chariot with fell snakes for reins,*
> *Tracing great paths of woe that never ends,*
> *Now grant us peace, bring comfort to our pains.*
>
> *Artemis, titanic archer, almost male,*
> *Nursing the young of beast and humankind!*
> *As long as dogs hunt deer o'er hill and dale,*
> *Cherish us all with loving heart and mind.*
>
> *Now come, soft Sleep, and all our sorrows take,*
> *That we may gently sleep and gently wake.*

A wave of serenity passed over the Amazons. They had all cuddled up to each other, their bodies bent, arms laid across the next body, as if when standing they had been separate pieces of a huge, broken dish, which the act of lying down had reassembled.

They composed one huge body, contradicting the false image of the tirelessly conflictive Amazon portrayed by artists. Nobody here brandished a sword, drew a bow, waved an axe or drove home a dagger! Nobody was beaten, nobody stabbed, nobody hauled away by the hair. The foot of one was hooked in the armpit of another, here a head lay on a breast, there a bottom was up against a belly, and there again an arm across a thigh. It was like a thread passing through the eye of a needle. Or a button through a buttonhole. Lying there together, they melded into each other, both mold and model, unified, united. Hippolyta and I were the only ones who did not form part of this necklace of bodies. She was leaning one knee to the ground, the rest of her body tilted toward the sky. I watched her crouched there.

Then she said to me, "When Antiope was our queen, she fell in love with Solon, the youngest of the three Athenian brothers who accompanied Theseus. Antiope never showed her love for him, though she was always pleasant and friendly toward him. Her refusal to respond drove him to throw himself in the river. We drink the blood that flows from love's slavery. We eat raw the flesh of those whom Aphrodite, Eros, and Venus cannot enflame! We restore strength to human weakness with the marrow of the beast! The Amazons, a poet will say it, are the closest likeness of the soul. Our name means 'women of the moon,' because we keep watch on the darkness of hearts and control what no one else even dare touch. Those who hate us vilify us by saying we lack one breast, as if eating raw meat, sleeping outside, and being skilled in weapons made us less than women. We all have two beautiful breasts. We are body, body, body!"

Her harsh words grated through the air. As if to protect themselves from them, the Amazons huddled closer together.

Once again the queen began to sing:

"O Hestia, patron of the family hearth,
Daughter of Cronos, shield us from life's storms,
Refuge of blessed gods and mortal kind,
Welcoming fire that burns in shifting forms!

With Hestia's blessings round our warm hearth shed,
Let's love the day that's here, the day ahead,
But fear cold death less than a husband's bed."

The songs and words of Hippolyta, the lamentations of the Amazon in love with the god, the soft grass, and the presence of night had left the Amazons in an amatory mood. The majority were masturbating, some working on others, some on themselves. The stink they were giving off was intolerable. Their aroused vulvas smelled abominably. There were hundred of vulvas emitting odors, and thousands of fingers repeating it.

A woman's smell is a woman's smell. Imagine the effect of hundreds of them all in panting masturbation. Their mild caresses had now become rapid rubbings. Hit by the repugnant odor, I thought: "This smell is what gives these warriors their indomitable spirit. It's stronger than iron! And it lasts longer!"

The assembled bodies stretched on the soft grass were raising a limb or two here and there to facilitate their pleasures of this ceremony of the flesh. The period of their lassitude had been brief. The caresses, daring and intimate, had given way to kisses. The mouth that was not kissing another mouth was kissing a breast, a thigh, a back.

The queen ceased her singing. She grabbed me in her arms, but without rubbing against me like the others. She planted a kiss on my mouth. A quick kiss, a surprise that I must admit disconcerted me. "I want you to see," she said, and to satisfy her will, she laid me down, my back against her chest, her two hands placed on my two naked breasts. This also disconcerted me but she imposed her will on mine. All the Amazons were having excited fun, groaning or kissing, kissing or groaning. Maybe some had taken on male shape or male gods had appeared among the interlocked bodies, but the fact is that hard phalluses were penetrating female bodies. The phalluses gleamed in the night, glistening from the vulvas. "Here nobody's scared of getting pregnant," Hippolyta whispered to me.

Orthea, who had been shrilling her complaints to the god with breath of ice and skin of fire, now arrived among us, running agitatedly. Only embers remained of the blazing fire. Only starlight picked out the uncertain silhouettes of bodies against the sky. Orthea got onto our collective bed where all varieties of the carnal act were in heated progress. Here there were twosomes, here a solo act, there a threesome. As the groups that made up the interlocking texture on the crowded living carpet shifted unpredictably, Orthea, the weeping lover of the unattainable god, had to watch her step, while she looked for a place to lie down.

"Look, Cleopatra," said Hippolyta, "it's Orthea. Even though she loves a handsome deity, she can't say no to a bit of pleasure. That's why they say that some of us give the cold shoulder to anybody who isn't prepared to indulge our appetites. There's some truth in that."

The new arrival found a place to throw herself down on the grass, already as excited as the other women. Hardly was she down, when she started to feel herself, shutting her eyes. Out of all those I could see from my royal position, she was the only one who shut her eyes. All the rest were experiencing pleasure with their eyes wide open or at least half open, their eyes glinting like sparks, burning.

Now the intense odor no longer irritated me. I don't know if I'd stopped smelling it or if I had started to enjoy being wrapped up in it, when the queen lowered one hand to my vulva and touched me. An explosion raced through my body, an electric charge from head to toes. Now I was just one among all the others, another living nerve on the carpet of flesh. Though I did not shut my eyes, I ceased to see, lost track of who was who and how and where, of who came and who went. The undetermined presences were like sharp needles deliciously piercing my skin and we were one body, pleasured flesh united in the communal bowl that fed the long, long night. But there must have been some crack in our bowl, a weakness at some point, because imperceptibly the hours crept by until we all lay fast asleep.

Dreams came. Have you any idea what it is like to dream among Amazons? Among them, the delicate net that contains dreams so that they do not invade territories not proper to them has been torn to shreds. If not one single corner of their night-visions remained empty, if the visions lacked proportion and were all truncated, incomplete, if vibrant with intense colors, they flooded the mind with enigmatic fragments that defied any attempt to build coherence, they went further, overflowing into consciousness and rationality. These were dreams that refused to hover on the edge of wakefulness. Dreaming occurred but not like that of one who abandons himself to Morpheus, but who conquers him, knowing full well that these indomitable dreams would invade the whole of life with their mighty insanity. Wakefulness would strike here and there with its axe and brandish its shield and once again restore its network. But only so that the dreams would return to rip holes in it, gnawing at it with their teeth. The axe would be dented against the hard bodies of the dreams, the shield would be reduced to a mockery, and the dreams would creep back to gnaw again at sanity's net.

Headless dreams, running around like beheaded chickens. Thieving dreams, with their hands cut off. Dreams where limbs multiplied and bodies sprouted two heads. Dreams where everything was cruelty in motion. Dreams all woman where no man gained entrance. Dreams with placenta drenched in menstrual blood, where life itself was menace. Fertility was incarnate in them. It was flesh on the point of doubling itself. Bodies half-alive. Bodies on the verge of death. Women's bodies.

These dreams were woman. The indefinable essence of woman. Impervious to language, for language contains a masculine element beside the feminine. None of the nonsense that men impose on women to render them innocuous, isolated from their generative powers, dressing them in provocative curves to take advantage of them later, draping their souls in gold, if women have souls. Women stripped of the immunity that belongs to them as the center of being! Not needed by anyone for anything! Here, instead, was the conception that knows how to found cities and bring beings into the world! The fertility that rules. No sentimental twaddle, no chatting with the servants, no cosmetics as the sole theme of conversation. But an unflinching stare at the central power: the mystery of life.

One vision I was able to retain from the kingdom of Amazonian dreams. A female dragon, swishing its tail with nine spinal projections, was menacing an Amazon with its deadly venom. The hooves of her horse, quick to obey the tugging reins, saved her from a blow of the dragon's horns. She raised a strange weapon to its jaws. Though it gleamed with gold like other weapons of the Amazons, it was kitchen tongs. With it she nipped the snorting lips and then she smacked the creature on the back of its neck with a soup spoon. The dragon that no hero could slay collapsed at the Amazon's feet, lifeless by the hooves of her panicky mount.

This vision was visual, as the word implies. But it was also auditory. Words thundered out while it was happening. It achieved more completeness in words than it did in images, because at times the images got blurry and shrank to miniature size, as if abruptly forced into the far distance.

We slept, as you might expect, for many hours. When we opened our eyes, the sun had already crossed a fair stretch of sky. A dazzling sky filled the air with a sense of well-being. The dogs roused themselves when their owners got up. Around our bed, a flock of young eunuchs had prepared tens of gilded waterbasins, adorned with fine copperwork, set on solid tripods. Cattle were grazing peacefully among trees loaded with fruit. Horses pranced by with an invincible air. Waves of the sea broke gently on the light sand. The river seemed motionless. The evening before it had had waves. Maybe it had been a trick of the light. Now as morning began, it had a pleasantly relaxed look to it. Everything was serene.

In the center of what had been the cave that the god had forced open stood the god himself, wrapped in mist, the only thing not bright and clear in the whole scene. Unmoving, surrounded by light shadow, he avoided our scrutiny. Was he there alone? Had Orthea, the Amazon who loved him, returned to pass the night with him after her bout of collective lovemaking? Had they at last found a way to fuse with each other? As if in answer to my question, I saw Orthea walking not far from me. I returned my glance to the hill. On the flat top supported by the petrified centaurs, a herd of deer was feeding quietly amid trees.

By the gilded washbasins, with the help of the shaven-headed eunuchs dressed in the large Egyptian skirts of thick white linen, the Amazons removed their strings of semiprecious stones and washed themselves. They then put on short togas of fine linen.

We breakfasted on fresh figs and nuts. While we ate, various groups were preparing themselves for leaving. They readied their horses in the oddest way. Instead of putting saddles or blankets on their backs, they rubbed them with strongly perfumed oils. They themselves dressed in tunics with gathered sleeves, tied around the waist and reaching down almost to the knees.

Hippolyta asked me what plans I had in mind to recover the throne of Egypt.

I explained where my entourage was located, assuming that they must by now be on the road to Ascalon, the Philistine city where several allied kings awaited me and where part of the treasures of the Lagids was deposited safely under lock and key. There I planned to recruit an army.

"And how are you going to do that?"

"I'm starting with you and me. I know from you that nobody but the hero can defeat you. I have a handful of men in Ascalon and more in Pelusium. My ships are ready. It is a considerable fleet. The rest of my army awaits my orders in Hermonthis. Then the King of Nabatea has promised help, and the messages from Petra are all positive. But the greater part of my army will be mercenaries."

When I said "mercenaries," the Amazons, who up till then had listened respectfully, burst into open laughter, as if I had said something comically idiotic.

"You mean Persians?" asked Hippolyta, ignoring the laughter. "A bad alliance. They'll gobble up Egypt before you realize it. As for mercenaries . . ."

Once again her friends burst out laughing. "Well, for a start, what are you going to pay them with? Not all the gold in the world can inspire an army with courage, make it invincible—and that's what you need!"

Now it was my turn to laugh. How could she be so ingenuous?

"Your Majesty," I said, holding in my amusement. "Egypt's gold is exactly what makes an army brave. The people of the Nile are not made for the arts of war, but we win our battles because we pay high wages to foreigners."

"I think, Cleopatra, we think, I should say, and I don't mean to challenge you, that you've no idea what wars are made of."

"Of course I have. Wars are fought with intelligence and gold."

"Seriously?"

The other Amazons had lost interest in our conversation, being more concerned with preparing for their departure.

"Naturally you need the gods on your side," I added, thinking that was what she referred to.

"There's no human activity in which the gods don't participate, if they are summoned properly. But I'm not talking about that. Would you agree that war is an encounter between persons, that it does not resemble the struggle of a tiger to control its territory, that it isn't like the fury of a zebra or a squabble in the marketplace between uncouth thieves?"

"I'll agree to that."

"And that force, in order to be victorious force, requires intelligence, cunning and, above all, spirit."

"Agreed."

"If these qualities are present and necessary in every human activity, they are more so in war, because otherwise it wouldn't be war but just swapping blows at random, and under those conditions not even Hercules could achieve anything."

"True. I seeing what you're getting at. But you can have all that with good management and the right strategy . . . and with gold. You can get it with gold."

"Stop right there, Cleopatra! Gold is like excrement, impossible to live without, but useless."

Her words were interrupted by a sound I did not recognize. It crashed through the air, profoundly unsettling the Amazons. They all ran for their weapons and off toward their horses. The three columns hurriedly prepared for battle, as the eunuchs bustled to bring them their feathered helmets, the golden shields, and the maces, but not the axes. I struggled to understand what was happening, but I caught only fragmentary comments: "the

Sirens again" . . . "those damned singers" . . . "claws in the
throat." It made no sense to me that a sound got them battle-
ready. The more I try to describe that sound, the more its description eludes me. It was insidious, sweet to an extreme, almost
cloying, even disgusting. I had never heard it before but somehow it failed to surprise me. At moments it appalled me, it disturbed me, and yet it had the jaded quality of a song sung too
often, something chewed in the mouth by a cow, something trite.

Queen Hippolyta came over to me, dressed in the Amazon tunic, mounted on a splendid Lybian steed, and she invited
me to get up.

"Come on, Cleopatra."

"On your horse? Give me my own."

"Not now."

She reached out an arm. I grabbed it and climbed up beside her. One of the eunuchs dashed forward to give me the
banner of the Amazons to carry. Hippolyta dispatched a small
contingent under the command of Melanippe toward the far side
of the hill, while we trotted toward the river. Hippolyta explained,
"The song of the Sirens comes from underground. We have to
hold back the males. The monsters await them on the sand, where
the bull touched shore."

We galloped over the well-trodden road of white earth that
ran alongside the river racing fast a few feet below. Its waters
seemed to carry along the song of the Sirens. Somebody shouted,
"Look!" pointing to the channel. A man was already swimming
there with feeble strokes. I saw a rope fly out and it lassoed the
swimmer, dragging him back toward the bank.

"It's not one of our men," said Hippolyta, starting to gallop again. The roped man was cursing the Amazon who was
unconcernedly tying him to the trunk of a tree. "Let me go!
Your womb will wither! Your children will have clay for flesh!
Let me go, you unwomanly bitch!" The people here are so

terrified of water that they do not even fish, but when the Sirens call . . . !

The road was closed from both sides. To our right, the steep hill, its stone washed away by the years until it was almost vertical, revealed here and there the black entrances to inaccessible caves. To the left ran the river, some five feet below. A deep, muddy trench separated us from it. Stones projected from it. Trees grew out of the muddy banks. A distant cleft in the hill widened with the river, opening up a path about a hundred cubits wide. There Hippolyta ordered a halt and drew up the troops in formation, three wedgelike units to the front and one behind as rearguard. This will give you an idea of their positions:

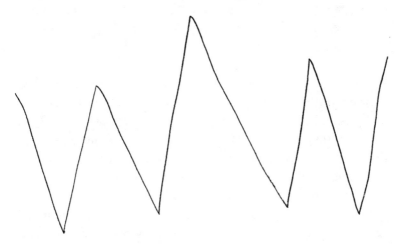

The eight lines closed the pass that led to the Sirens and exposed the greatest number of Amazons to the battlefront. To our left, down below, getting their feet wet in the flood that licked the trunks of the trees on the bank, the eunuchs were tying long ropes to the trees in readiness for their role in the fight.

The Amazons' horses, lined up alongside each other, facing the front the same as their riders, formed up perfectly according to the pattern that Hippolyta had ordered, in which the queen occupied the central position. If they had had the shields of hoplites and not the half-moon shields they did have, which did not interlock with their neighbor's, they would have composed an invincible rampart against any foe.

Then a small contingent of rebel males came into sight, racing toward us, determined to get past us, escape through the pass, and reach the Sirens. Where the bend in the hill came to an end in what I called the cut and where the cliff-face, now thickening out, again narrowed the road, Hippolyta positioned us, a reserve of armed personnel, a tight defensive wall, to be ready for a stampede of men who were approaching as fast as they could, which wasn't fast, for they were mounted on shabby beasts of burden. They themselves, in contrast, were dressed in purple caftans and wore wigs, necklaces, and bracelets. Their eyes had a garish makeup and their cheeks were rouged, like those of Lydians. Their eagerness to reach the Sirens left their ranks in disorder and blocked their lines of sight, so that they were unaware of our presence.

Hippolyta shouted, "Stop where you are, you fools!"

But they did not halt. There was a good number of them, but they were badly mounted on nags, oxen, donkeys, mules, and camels. They were advancing in total disorder.

Hippolyta repeated her order: "Stop where you are, you fools. Don't you recognize the song of the bloodthirsty Sirens? Keep on running and you will meet the worst of deaths! The creatures are waiting on the seashore to devour you. They have the breasts of women, but they have vultures' heads and lions' claws. They are monsters!"

Without halting a second, the panting men cried out haphazardly, "Get out the way! Let us through, you useless fools! Open the pass, you mannish women!"

They were without weapons. The most warlike of them carried branches broken from fruit trees as they hurried along.

Some branches still had leaves and unripe fruit dangling from them. Did they really plan to use these instead of weapons, to batter our heads with green peaches? Their war cry was as absurd as their weapons. "The sea! the sea!" But even this was a wild confusion of shouts, intermingled with the threat "Death to the Amazons!"

They approached us nervously. We gave a half-turn and quickly took up a battle formation. We watched them come on. On the broad stretch of land chosen as the battleground, they looked like a bunch of rebellious desperadoes. Their principal enemy was their own desperation to answer the Sirens' call. We received them with calculated coolness. They were distraught and suffering even before we touched them.

The collision between the two unbalanced forces was deadly for the males. The Amazons battered them with mauls, knocking them off their mounts and clouting them viciously with unmitigated rage. Eager at all costs to reach their insane goal, the men could only respond by scratching, biting, and throwing useless punches into the air or against the Amazon shields.

The contingent of men was routed and lay scattered on the ground, their caftans torn, the wigs lost, bones broken, bodies thrashed and beaten. The Amazons retired to let the eunuchs sweep the battlefield clean of the defeated. They pushed them down the slippery slope that led to the rocky river bank. In addition to the beating the Amazons had handed out, the eunuchs hustled the males down with less compassion than they'd have for animals, not caring if a leg was broken or a body crashed into the rocks below.

On the ledge of the bank where the waters of the river were rising, the prisoners were tied to the trees. They still resisted, spitting, scratching, and biting. "The sea! the sea!" they kept shouting. Half a dozen Amazons exchanged blows with the few men who still had the energy to try to move toward the pass.

Now a second contingent of men was on its way. Equally badly prepared for battle, they came puffing and panting toward us. We lined up in the same formation as before, seven lines, seven protruding wedges, and we received the attack. The result was the same again. The men went tumbling down. We fell back. The eunuchs got on with their job. A third group now appeared. These males showed the same desperation as the others, but they were dressed differently. They wore caftans of scarlet and gray made of rough wool, double tunics of the sort worn by petty kings—the outer one, the *kandys,* with long sleeves dyed a Phoenician purple, with figures on fighting falcons embroidered in gold, the inner one, the *chiton,* with white spots on it.

The Sirens had not quit singing. The noise of battle had not dimmed the appeal of their song for the men. Now the sound of steel was stilled and the frightened cattle were lowing quietly, but the bleating of the men, "The sea! the sea!" was counterpointed by the continuing song of the Sirens. The noise of battle had been only background noise to the insidiously seductive voices of these monsters. "It's the auditory equivalent," I thought to myself, "of the smell the Amazons were giving off last night." But at once I rejected the thought and put both my hands to my ears. True, I had rejected the thought but it persisted. "It sounds exactly like the smell of masturbating female bodies. That's why men can't resist it." I fought off the idea again, telling myself, "This sound is as sticky-sweet as honey, and the smell of the Amazon genitals was strong, almost rotten, a sea-smell like shell-fish." Then the idea counterattacked. "But you must realize that this song sounds the way men perceive it. Yesterday you were smelling things the way women smell them. Today you're hearing things the way men hear them. It's the same thing. If there is a difference, it's because what you perceived yesterday when you got whiff of the women is now passing through the hearing of males, but essentially it's the same thing." In answer to this

thought, I said, "Thank my lucky stars for being born a woman!"
Then I added, rebuking myself, "That will do, Cleopatra! You're
getting carried away by the combative spirit of the Amazons!"

Throughout all the fighting, I had stuck close to the fiery
Hippolyta, who used her half-moon shield to protect us both from
the scratches, bites, and feeble blows of the males. Cleopatra stood
out among our troop for various reasons, my Greek clothes, my
not having my own horse and for the standard I carried, but above
all, for my coolheadedness, my long tousled hair, and the curl
on my forehead hidden by a helmet feather. Otherwise I was one
of them. I was the standard-bearer for the defenders, until be-
deviled perhaps by the rash idea of the identity of the smell of
vulvas and the Sirens' song, I heard, for the smallest fraction of
an instant, an atom of time, exactly what the men were hearing.
To me its sound was like the most delightful sexual delirium
blown toward me on a gust of wind, without kisses but as if I
had been struck by lightning, as if tiny tingling sensations were
creeping all over my naked body, on the verge of breaking my
skin but drawing no blood in the end. I was tempted for that
fraction of a second to turn round, hurl Hippolyta off the horse,
and gallop right into the throat of the Sirens, if that would have
made the sound any more intense.

But the time was so brief that my body had no time to react
to what at that moment seemed the wisest thing in the world to
do. It vanished like a spark. Their songs enchanted me because
they were wordless, or, if they had words, I couldn't distinguish
them. They were songs laden with age-old experiences and stories of long ago. I thank the kindly gods for allowing me to hear
them. Is there a similar song for women? Will I ever hear it? Will
it come whispered to me from the halls of the dead, the last sound
I hear in my life on earth, as I breathe in a finer air? Will I hear
something like it? Or have I been hearing it for years without
allowing it to enter, a sound seeking to penetrate to my soul?

That song is what bound me to Mark Antony for fourteen years and fed my desire to meld our two stories into one. Once the sensation had passed, the song sounded to me like spilled honey, annoyingly sticky, with hairs and fluff caught in it. How could it have sounded so different a moment before?

I now became aware of the battle. More aggressive males were making for us. All had a lost look in their eyes, with no will to maintain their composure, sweating profusely. I was sick of seeing their agitated bodies hurtling toward a pointless martyrdom, boldly confronting us instead of pleading for the pity their situation deserved. I raised my eyes to the clifftop. Centaurs with lascivious eyes were watching the battle from caves in the face of the unscalable wall. Indifferent, like us and the eunuchs, to the songs of the monsters, they were enjoying the sunlit spectacle below: handsome women in short clothes pulled tight at the waist, with naked legs, battling with men.

While the centaurs were enjoying the sight of the Amazons' beauty, the men were blind to it. The deluding song made them prefer the hideous destroyers to their beautiful protectors. They struggled to free themselves from the Amazons, screaming imprecations: "May dogs eat you for having exceeded the proper limits of a woman! You should cut off both your breasts; they're good for nothing, you beardless men!" and other such ugly curses that brought howls of laughter from the centaurs. The men could not see the beauty right before their eyes, because the promise of knowing everything cast a spell on them. Their desperation brought puzzling phrases to their twisting lips: "Not even a sword could penetrate you and give you children! Wombs of stone! Skirts of scraping rock! Your milk poisons newborns!"

Eunuchs and Amazons continued their work, but the moment arrived when it wasn't possible for the eunuchs to hold so many beside the rocks. To keep the men back, we rounded up cattle and drove them at them. Some men leaped over the backs of the animals. Others were trampled underfoot or stunned by mauls. But some thrust the animals back, determined to proceed at any price. As we re-formed, we could not drive the cattle toward the rearguard, because the place was a milling throng of donkeys, camels, oxen, ostriches and men. The men had not intended it but their animals were shielding them.

The fight against the rebels was exhausting. Animals whirled around in panic. We had to find human heads to smite among biting animals. The cry "The sea! the sea!" directed us to where we could deliver a blow, after dodging the horns of an ox or the snapping teeth of a donkey. Our formation broke up. As we forced our horses through the mêlée, we left a passage open. Quoting the poet, I called out:

> *No shepherd am I from the mountain's steep*
> *Who watches over his wandering sheep!*

And I followed up with another verse:

> *No fisherman I, drawing nets from the deep.*
> *In chains the Sirens I'd like to keep.*

I received approving laughter from the Amazons for my wit. It lightened their weariness and renewed their vigor. Hippolyta was standing on the back of her horse and fighting from there. My thighs were hurting me after being squashed for so long by the nervous beasts, trapped in this whirl of violence. I did not need Hippolyta's shield, because there were no men around to hit me with their fists. But the constant collision with the animals hurt me badly.

Then I saw another contingent of men riding on ostriches. They were dressed in caftans the same color as the plumage of their mounts, but before they collided with the cattle, the singing stopped. Silence. The Sirens had stopped their song. The honeyed melody, which for a second had thrilled me to the core, by this time had left me cloyed beyond belief.

Instantly the infatuated frenzy left the men. Now they started to feel the force of the blows they had received. "Oh, my ribs!" . . . "Oh, my jaw!" . . . "Oh, my bones!" . . . "Oh, oh, oh!" The riverbank was thick with these cries from the tied-up men.

Returned to sanity, their delirium past, those who were still on the battlefield left off pushing against the cattle. Now nobody was interested in going to the sea. A fair number gave way to fear, scared that the Amazons, once aroused, would continue to fight. The bravest of these frightened men exchanged glances with the Amazons, trying to ingratiate themselves, while the cowardly ones tried to race back home, without even a word of thanks. But they found no way out, rounded up like cattle themselves. Beasts of transport and burden, panicky and disorderly, moved here and there unpredictably, even though the men no longer tried to break through. A considerable group of men, with shaven heads like eunuchs but mostly covered with turbans, now appeared on the edge of the battlefield, behind the ostriches and their riders. They were clad in long robes of rough wool, and lowly sandals. They were shepherds, who knowing their job, started to impose order on the animals, separating them out. The frightened animals calmed down under the expert management of these bald heads.

Our stress left us. Over the hard faces of the warriors was spreading a benign smile. Someone let out a cackling laugh. Three others joined in, then ten, then a hundred. In no time at all they were all hooting with laughter. Quite a number of men stopped complaining and laughed, too. Where before they had been keen to scratch and pummel us, now they wanted to hug us, still highly excited but no longer crazy. The most sensible unloosed their companions and made bandages out of the frayed ropes and improvised stretchers for the most seriously wounded. If they had looked incompetent as warriors, now they impressed us with their sense of organization and manly decorum. They exuded cool charm and good-natured courage. The youngest ones with the first growth of hair on their lips collected up from the mud bracelets, necklaces, turbans, and wigs, and formed a human chain to wash them clean in the river. At the water's edge, those who could walk were washing off the mud that they had picked up while tied to the trees.

The group of Amazons who had taken up their position on the far flank of the hill, far smaller in number than our group, commanded by the fierce and allegedly cruel Melanippe, came and joined up with us. She was accompanied by a large pack of magnificent greyhounds, all the same color, like the horses.

"Hail, Hippolyta! We failed to protect our musicians and poets to the full. We knew from the start that we wouldn't arrive in time to lock them into their palaces. So we spread a huge net to catch them like fish in the clearing between the hill and the thick clump of fruit trees. It offers the only route to the sea. One by one they blundered into it and we stopped their ears with wax. Then we tied them to the fruit trees to make sure they stayed there. We weren't aware at the time that Acusilaus had given us the slip." Melanippe's face showed her grief and dismay.

The old man had zigzagged his way to the sea. In a zig he had escaped Melanippe's nets, in a zag he fell into the claws of the monsters.

"Philo told me," she went on, "that Acusilaus had sealed his ears with wax the instant the Sirens began to sing. Once deaf, he retained enough self-control to get away safely. Once he had the Sirens in view, he unplugged his ears and handed himself over to them. Philo said he was obsessed by their song, and that he'd lie awake nights, unable to sleep, tormented by

memories of it. He'd asked the musicians to compose something resembling it. They tried but never managed to produce
anything with the same impact. Philo said he'd thought out this
stratagem weeks ago, that he'd talked about it without going
into details." The Amazon's eyes were wet with tears. "I saw
him in the distance and chased after him, but before I could
reach him, the Sirens had grabbed him. They were flapping their
heavy wings and stomping around on their terrible feet. They
held him fast. While some of them sang, others began to devour him, the hands he wrote with, the feet that had brought
him to them, then his legs and arms. He was still alive. Insen-
sible to pain because of the spell of their song, he was shouting, "Eat me! Devour me! My mouth, my lips, my tongue—take
them!" The monsters ripped off his clothing. His chest was
covered in blood from his torn-off arms and legs. But he had a
fearsome erection. In one bite they ate his lips, with another
his eyes. With another his tongue, with another his erect penis.
Then they stopped singing so that, with his pleasure at an end,
he would feel the full pain of his destruction. So that our poet
would experience what it is to turn into rotting flesh under the
hot sun! It would have been kinder to throw him to the dogs,
to let them finish him off with their slavering jaws. I drew my
bow and fired to put him out of his misery. My arrow hit his
heart. I killed him to set him free. May the gods forgive me for
killing a poet! Acusilaus was weeping, I know. With no eyes
to weep, he was weeping in his heart. He was weeping the way
I'm weeping now . . ."

"And the Sirens? Did you wound any of them?" one of the
men asked Melanippe, horrified by her terrible story.

"I emptied my quiver against them," she replied furiously.
"When they heard the sound of my arrows, they fluttered up
toward them and with their wings turned them aside. Only one

arrow got through. It landed in the eye of one Siren. But it was too late. Acusilaus was already in pieces. Tough as I am, it broke my heart to see it!"

I turned my eyes away, unable to bear her grief. The centaurs had retired into the caves in the cliff, annoyed at the good work of the shepherds and the tears of the Amazons. Following my glance, Hippolyta recited,

> *Nothing incites a centaur more to rage*
> *Than signs of harmony well displayed*
> *Like circles and hexameters, all things*
> *Composed with care. Instead, they seek*
> *Violence and fire. Laughter they hate and fear*
> *As enemies to peace and human good—*

The verses were interrupted by the arrival of a group of armed warriors. These were genuine soldiers, totally different from the vanquished males, both in their mounts and the manner of their dress. They were manly and handsome, with well-developed muscles, a crack squadron from a nearby village. When the Sirens began to sing, the gates of their barracks had been barred by prepubescent boys and the windows had been plugged with rocks and mud. They now came with the king's herald, dressed in clothes of gold and vermilion.

"The voice of Carnedes," he announced, "king of Cyrene, sends this message: 'Hail, you protectors of foolish men! I send you General Lucius Severus, to escort the queens, Cleopatra VII, daughter of Ptolomy Philopator, Queen of Egypt, and Hippolyta, Queen of the Amazons, to a banquet in celebration of their victory.'"

So they knew I was with the Amazons, but how? I was astonished at the speed with which the news had traveled.

A man's voice spoke behind me. "These women always reject such invitations. But with Cleopatra present among us, who knows what they will do?"

The herald proceeded with his message, reciting a catalog of praise, clumsy and inappropriate, in honor of the Amazons.

"The doctors of Cyrene have a fine reputation," answered Hippolyta. "If the king will receive our wounded along with ourselves, so that his surgeons may attend them . . ."

"Agreed," said the herald without hesitation. "Your request anticipated an offer I was about to make."

They gave me a splendid horse and passed the standard to a safe place. We undertook the journey to the nearby city in almost complete silence, visibly fatigued. After traveling five stades, we were covered in white dust from the road. Our exhaustion was extreme by the time we caught sight of the city perched on two hilltops. Beautifully sculpted tombs were set on the walls. Hippolyta's quiver gave a scraping sound as she pulled an arrow from it. She drew the bow so far back that its points touched. The arrow hissed through the air. It soared and came racing down between the two eyes of a deer that had been watching its hissing trajectory as keenly as we had. The knives of the Amazons that they had declined to use in the battle now flashed in the sun. Brandishing them, they raced toward the fallen animal. Their dogs remained quietly behind on the road for their owners had not given them orders to follow.

With a gesture of her head, Hippolyta told me to follow her. We did not wait for the other Amazons and we did not summon the dogs. The defeated men we had now left far behind. But at our heels followed the warriors of Cyrene, with the splendid weapons and embossed helmets, each one bearing a banner. The easternmost mount served as a citadel. There stood high walls and the white, imposing tower of the royal palace. We halted to offer prayers to the gods. By the city gate, a well-fed nomadic tribe got down from their camels and began to set up their tents, perhaps drawn from a distant land by the enchanting song of the Sirens.

Once the prayers were over, Hippolyta asked me to go into Cyrene and represent the Amazons. "We feel suffocated inside walls and ceilings. You go in and give the king our good wishes. We will camp besides the nomads, here, at the foot of the walls."

I wanted to protest, in light of my less than royal attire, but she went on. "Your dignity, Cleopatra, is all the dressing you need. Once inside the city you will reassume your courtly airs. They are bound to see you that way, coming from the ranks of the Amazons."

She hugged me fondly and kissed my cheek. After she had fixed my curl of Aphrodite, she bade me goodbye. "Cleopatra, don't forget our alliance. We will join your army, come what may. Your other allies will sneer and tell you that using us is like using a shield of fruit to ward off steel. But fruits with their fine skins defend soft flesh from the fiercest of encounters better than do the swords of torpid men. Grapes defy howling winds with their skins. Figs hoard exquisite pulp inside their velvety robes and laugh at thunder and lightning. The slender skin of an apple is enough to ward off the mold in the air. The peel of an orange guards the juice better than a silver jug. And remember this: "Fear cold death less than a husband's bed." If you forget it, sooner than you imagine, he or you and he will pay a deadly price . . ." There followed another hug. Then words whispered in my ear. "All the same, don't despise the scepter of Venus." I laughed heartily at this coy reference to the penis and answered quietly, "I won't let go of the unfailing amulet of seduction, I assure you. But tell me, Hippolyta, if I attract a husband, how do I keep him at a distance?"

Hippolyta loosed her arms and said loudly, "Cleopatra, it has happened to you once. You lost your throne because of a husband. But that was the least of it. If you allow yourself to be carried away by the desire to be the complementary half of a man, he will die, murdered by his son. And if you try it one more time after that, then he, whoever he may be, will die at his own hand. Then they will kill your children. They will make themselves masters of the people of Alexandria, of Thebes, of the two Memphises, and of the borders of the Nile. Egypt will be lost. Whatever happens, we shall remain faithful to you. When your children perish, victims of the anger of the gods for your not having fled a husband's bed, here on my naked breasts these nipples will redden as a sign of grief, as if they themselves had fed your children."

She took a step backwards and gave an order. "Convey her inside!"

The warriors of Cyrene obeyed. Surrounded by them, I passed through the gateway. The people had gathered to welcome the Amazons and as I came in, they filled the air with cheering. By my side walked the handsome general, Lucius Severus. "This is Cyrene, Your Majesty. The city takes its name from a nymph of Thessalia who was ravished by Apollo. He was dazzled when he saw her dominate a lion without using weapons. She gave birth to Aristaeus, the great hunter whose son Actaeon died in terrible fashion after seeing Artemis bathing."

They led me to the fountain of Cyre, below the Temple of Ceres, in the center of the citadel. There I drank water and listened to prayers. Priests offered propitiatory sacrifices over fires. They interpreted entrails, as the soldiers guided me along. We skirted a high wall, then passed under a narrow arch in it that allowed only one horse to pass at a time. On the capitals of the columns were beautifully sculpted reliefs representing a battle of the Amazons. The masses were not allowed to enter this august patio. It was surrounded by leafy old banana trees. In the center, on a round platform, a group of sculptures, the work of a master craftsman, dominated the space. It represented intertwined Amazons fighting invisible foes. The scene was doubly impressive because the spectator found herself in the place of the foe. It both excited and terrified at the same time. The sculpted figures competed with the living Amazons in both beauty and vitality.

And they had something extra that the living women did not possess. The stone from which they were carved seemed to defy the laws governing everday stone. Though it was hard, it had a softness that accorded with the femininity of the Amazons. This femininity acted as a corrective to their strength. It did not move but it created the impression of Amazons leaping on their enemies with warriorlike fury. When I looked at the faces, I fell silent. They seemed to be seeing me there with their eyes of stone. If the Amazons I'd met had impressed me with their beauty and boldness, these Amazons in stone were truly—and I say it without any hesitation—sacred.

Two beautiful slaves, dressed in white Greek robes and sandals—they stood out strikingly beside the stone sculptures—opened the blue, studded door into the palace.

The handsome general dismounted and said, "Queen of Kings, it was an unwarranted privilege to escort you here. It is something I will tell to my sons, and my sons to their sons, and their sons to their sons. I, Lucius Severus, son of Sempronius, I who was born from the womb of Thaesis of Oxyrhynchus, one day walked beside the great Cleopatra VII, Queen of Egypt, Isis on earth. Her horse and mine trotted side by side in the streets of Cyrene. Only a hand's distance away from me I saw her offer a prayer to the gods. I saw her moisten her lips with the water of the goddess."

He stretched out his hand to me and caught me, as I jumped down from my horse.

"This, too, I will tell my children, and my children will tell it to their children, and their children will tell it to their chil-

dren, that for an instant I held in my grasp the great Queen of
Egypt as she dismounted."

He said all this with such charm that I could not be offended
by his long-winded flummery. He was certainly very good-
looking, his proud head crowned by the thickest, darkest hair.
His lips were well-defined and there was something Italian in
his profile. Caught there in his helpful arms, I could not escape
a naughty twinge of desire. But as I moved away, I was force-
fully reminded of the pathetic deer that Hippolyta had shot.
Perhaps because he had mentioned Cyrene, the nymph, whose
son the goddess had transformed into a stag when she caught him
watching her bathe and who was devoured by his own hounds.

"Careful!" I told him. "Staghorns may appear on your forehead, and he didn't even touch the goddess . . ."

"I'd defy the fury of my merciless hounds," he murmured
suavely in my ear, "to go riding again with the queen." Then he
knelt humbly at my feet.

The herald in scarlet and gold approached and announced,
"Cleopatra, enter the palace of the king. We will not enter. Our
duty was to bring you to this door. In the upper room they await
you. There they will welcome you as a queen deserves to be
welcomed."

I crossed the threshold. They closed it behind me. I halted
to let my eyes get used to the gloom. The broad gallery with its
lofty ceiling was lit only by a light at the rear. The far wall was
crossed by a staircase with wide steps that began at the left and
ended at the far upper right. On the first step I looked upward.
After the first easy ascent, the staircase climbed steeply up into
the white tower I had seen from outside the city walls. I went
up the first flight. Each step was so broad it took me three or
four paces to cross each one. The first flight led to a splendid room.
It was empty. Its size equaled that of the gallery below and the
ceiling was equally high, but here the light was brighter. The

doors of the balcony that overlooked the outskirts of the city were ajar. I took a peek. To the left, in the direction of the sea, the four centaurs turned into stone the previous night were picked out by the evening sun as they supported the great slab of stone. The sides of the cliff were like a vertical wall, pure stone, like a quarried facade. On top of the slab there was a clump of trees, silhouetted against the fiery evening sky. The god had awoken and cast off his cloak of mist. I saw him clearly, as if he were only a few paces away. The erection that men have when they awaken was visible even at this distance. I saw it advance in profile, like a bizarre companion; it headed toward one of the stone centaurs. On its back sat an unclothed woman. The god turned his back on me as he turned his front to her. Then he extended his arms. He rubbed himself against the torso of the centaur, his hands up high so as not to touch her. "He's penetrating her!" I thought. "Once, twice, in he goes." There was no doubt that the woman was Orthea. "There he goes again!"

I lowered my gaze. I was so embarrassed! "Lucky Orthea," I was thinking, as the god continued on the job, his arms still aloft. "He doesn't want to touch her, or he'd set her skin on fire." The god's body shuddered and he lowered his arms quickly, leaning against the torso of the centaur. "He's ejaculating," I said to myself. "He's feeling wobbly with all that pleasure, and he has to hang onto something." Then I felt, I literally felt, a current of cold air sweep over me, a current so cold I felt like vomiting, but so strong it made me shudder just like he did. I stretched out my arms to support myself against the window frame and I breathed out. Then I understood. The god, too, needed to breathe out and his cold breath must be freezing his beloved to the bone. He sank down to his knees. The woman was now a white stone, the centaur a glow of red. The god let out a howl. His howl crossed the vast distance. Another charge shot through my body, piercing me like an arrow of pain. I turned my eyes away from the hill. By reciprocating her desire, he had killed her and he was in tears over it. He had had his fun, just as the Sirens had had theirs chomping on the body of Acusilaus. Now he was weeping where they had refused to weep. "Does it make much difference?" I wondered. The god groaned once more but it failed to move me. My sympathy was with Orthea.

At my feet, twenty paces from the wall, the Amazons were gathered. The well-fed pack of dogs frisked nervously around them, circling. The Amazons were gorging on raw meat. Fresh blood dribbled down their arms. They were not aware that Orthea's desire had been satisfied, with fatal consequences. They had not heard the lament of the god, too busy gobbling down the deer meat.

I turned away from the balcony. The room was as high and wide as the gallery on the ground floor, its wall bare and white, but the floor was covered with beautiful carpets. In the center stood three tables with vessels and plates of sculpted silver, surrounded by embroidered couches. In front of me was a cup of precious stones set into heavy gold. "There's no way," I thought to myself, "I can sit down at the table without getting my hair fixed and my clothes changed." I ended up walking to the far end of the room. There was another balcony, again with its doors ajar. I peeked out at the center of Cyrene. I saw the Temple of Cyrene. In it, as in the other temples, braziers were smoking. The alleyways were in uproar, crammed with a multitude of women, children, and soldiers attending the file of men injured in the battle over the Sirens as they walked slowly by. The embarrassed men were shaking their heads, resigned or ashamed. Passing through the noisy throng, they approached the temple. As I had done, they all drank from the fountain of Cyre.

I half-shut my eyes and almost fell asleep, I was so weary, and the sounds of the ground were lulling me to rest. They also brought Alexandria to mind. I saw it before me. It was me they were welcoming. The shouts were cheers. My retinue was headed by twenty elephants, followed by hundred of ostriches, loaded with jewels and fastened together with beautiful chains of silver. Behind them came tame lions, panthers, caged zebras, then I myself magnificent in a chariot of gold and purple!

"Hail, Cleopatra!"

I jumped, startled to hear my name called by a familiar voice. The king of Cyrene was approaching me, along with his well-fed retinue which was still in the process of climbing the stairs. They wore luxurious garments equal to anything in Egypt. I felt dazed, as weary as a peasant after a day of labor, so fatigued by my night of dreams and my sudden daydream visit to Alexandria that it took me a moment or two to realize that members of my own retinue were present among the courtiers of Cyrene.

The same voice spoke again. "Cleopatra, the long afternoon you spent on the back of the bull was our equivalent of seven days and nights. Your starry night with the Amazons lasted a week in our time. Since you left Pelusium, two weeks have gone by for us."

Who was talking to me, I wondered again, in that so familiar voice? But I could not see the speaker. The voice came from behind me, from somewhere beside the king. It was the voice of somebody shorter than the people standing there, a woman's voice.

The king gestured with his hand. They all threw themselves to the floor, face down on the beautiful carpets, apart from a black dwarf of a slave who placed in front of the king a purple cushion. He helped his majesty put both his knees on it, so that he, too, could throw himself face down.

"Hail, Queen of Kings," said the king. His voice sounded young, a contrast to his elderly style of clothing, but it was a voice with dignity to it.

Only one person behind him had remained standing. "When you and the bull leaped off the wharf at Pelusium, Nep-

tune picked up a pearl. He blew on it and he spoke to it in order
to give me your form, Cleopatra. Identical to you, I appeared to
the fishermen on the dock. Advised by the gods, I guided your
people. I divided them into two teams. I sent the warlike ones
on to Ascalon. But your maids, secretary, personal servants, and
bodyguards are all here. We arrived yesterday from the port of
Barca."

The pearl had my shape and my voice. I now realized why
it sounded so irritatingly familiar, like one of my sisters'. I stepped
forward and took the king by the hand, kissed his fingers, and
helped him get up off his knees. He was quite elderly. In his features I read intelligence, wisdom, and prudence, the epitome of
temperance. "He hates wine," I thought to myself, I, the daughter
of Auletes.

"Because it dissolves pearls," said my double. She came close
and took my hands. Hers were as smooth as a pearl's surface, but
in everything else she was identical to me, except that her hair
was properly coiffured, and I, after two weeks of not combing
or washing or changing my outfits, could pass for a veritable
Amazon. I was the one who didn't look like Cleopatra.

The courtiers remained with their mouths on the carpet.
Cleopatra the pearl passed her smooth hand over my weary forehead, relaxing me considerably. She was a pearl, she was water.
She let go of me and with one hand took the face of the king and
with the other his aged hand. She kissed him, saying, "I grant you
my pearly condition. If wine never touches it, you will not die."

Then she gave a half-turn and strode off with a careful grace,
avoiding the bodies still prostrated on the carpet. On the landing of the staircase she removed the veil from her shoulders and
placed it over her face. Without a word, she went downstairs. I
heard her in the gallery requesting them to open the door. Hinges
squeaked, footsteps sounded, the door banged shut, and she was
gone.

The king ordered the courtiers to stand up. Charmian and Apollodorus displayed unmistakable signs of joyful affection.

"It was terrible," said Apollodorus, "having to talk to a pearl instead of to you."

"By Jupiter, Apollodorus," Charmian reproved him. "That's no way to talk about a goddess!"

"Not even a goddess talks like Cleopatra," Apollodorus replied winningly. His brain was so alert! He never seemed to get a day older. He was still the youngster that I'd met in Rome all those years before, clad in the garments of a gladiator. "Talking to the pearl was like talking to an oyster."

My maidservants took me away to get me ready to eat. I asked them about the pearl Cleopatra.

"Your Majesty, she's with the Amazons. She went off with them. They must all have gone back to their city. Their dogs aren't barking anymore."

When we got back to the banqueting room, they were bringing in baskets of bread. Dishes of food awaited us on the tables. Musicians and dancers celebrated the now absent Amazons.

As soon as they cleared the tables, I asked to be carried to my bed. I was exhausted. On the fine bed they had prepared for me, I dropped asleep. It was like falling down a well. There in the deeps, I lost all contact with the surface of life. My dreams were nothing like those of my night before among the Amazons. The only thing I remember is a forest of leafless trees. The branches were twisted and jarringly interlocked. There were no straight lines, no circles, no patterns. I stared at them from what must have been a flying position, for I was seeing them from on high. They were a mass of tangled and tortured limbs. The branches did not scratch my skin but they disturbed my peace of mind. "Order!" I was shouting. "Geometry!" I added somewhat absurdly. Losing control, I burst into tears and kept calling out, "Parmenides! Come here, Parmenides!" I had gone crazy. My thoughts leapt about, unconnected with each other. They broke into pieces and I couldn't control them. I stopped calling for Parmenides. Then there were more branches, more unrecognized shapes, more disharmony, patternless and fragmented, heading in all directions, shapes without meaning, disfiguring the air, violating the sky, warring on life itself.

The voice of Apollodorus woke me. "Something urgent, Cleopatra. Wake up. It's already past noon. Get up!"

Charmian, seated beside me, shook me by the shoulder. With your hand, Charmian, your noble hand, you wiped out that terrible vision of leafless forest, with its branches lifeless and chaotic. Had I cried out for her in my sleep to help me like a defenseless child?

I hugged Charmian. I tried to understand the meaning of the dream with my daylight mind. It was silly to be frightened of bare branches, but I could not get rid of the uneasy feeling.

On the edge of my bed, behind the fine netting, stood the handsome Severus, the general who had accompanied me to the doors of the royal palace. He held a pigeon in his hands. With him were Diomedes my secretary, the wise Demetrius, and Josephus, the captain of my personal guard. I was still hugging Charmian. Seeing me upset, Apollodorus had sat behind me and was massaging my neck and shoulders.

Severus was eyeing Apollodorus's caress and my bare back. Then he lowered his gaze, gave the pigeon to Josephus, and went out.

Josephus took the message from the pigeon's body. Diomedes spread it out and decoded it, with these comments. "Pompey, defeated by Julius Caesar at Pharsalia, has come to Egypt seeking aid and refuge. Logical enough, if he doesn't take into account that Cleopatra is here precisely for sending him reinforcements. He disembarked and by himself, without his men, boarded a small boat that the boy-king sent to pick him up, trusting the boy-king's word. They were passing by the lighthouse when Achilles traitorously stabbed him in the back. It was the Roman sword of Septimius that beheaded him. Caesar arrived hot on the heels and was welcomed with a ring and the head of Pompey. He wept. The lictors checked the streets of Alexandria and found pockets of resistance. A good number of soldiers have been killed in skirmishes and . . . Caesar's living in your palace, Cleopatra, and asks to see you."

"There's no time to lose," I said, leaping out of bed. Charmian covered me with a tunic, fastening its ties and saying, "Calmly, child, calmly."

"Yes, it's essential," said Josephus approvingly, "that you have an interview with Caesar."

"Demetrius?"

Unlike his usual self, the wise counselor gabbled a rapid answer, as if his thoughts were tumbling over each other. "Pompey's men. Yes. Must be waiting to assassinate you. No idea what Caesar's up to. No dealings with him yet. Pompey our man. Clear to everybody. Taking both the Lagids as hostages? Could be. Then grab all Egypt. Could be. Just don't know. Ought to provoke a showdown with Pompey's men. If we can. No threats against Caesar. Not smart. Lucky for us he's set himself up in Alexandria. But Alexandria's hostile to him now. No doubt of that. Killing his men in ambushes. Now one at a time, but things will heat up. We're outside the city. Like it or not, Caesar's our man!"

"Josephus, how many men do we have at our disposal? Can we take on Cassius?"

"Cleopatra, Pelusium is already in the hands of Achilles. Right now, it'd be pure suicide."

"We could raise an army here, get the fleet to join us, and attack by sea."

"We don't have time, Cleopatra. We'd leave everything wide open for Ptolemy."

"Yes, you're right, Josephus. So let get things plain. One, we can't attack Cassius, because we don't have enough soldiers. Two, we don't have time on our side, so we can't think of raising an army. Three, it's risky but Cleopatra ought to see Caesar, because we need him as an ally. If Ptolemy gets him to take his side against us, we're done for. Four, Ptolemy's men are waiting for the queen to show so they can kill her."

"Right, Demetrius. So . . ."

"Josephus, my opinion is exactly the opposite of yours. Alexandria will be Caesar's enemy. Ptolemy won't be able to keep it calm. Time is on our side. We take our time recruiting an army, then we march against Ptolemy, and we get Caesar on our side."

"I disagree. If we wait, Caesar gets chummy with Ptolemy. Why wouldn't he? We delay in getting there and Caesar will help him against us."

"Could be but . . . I'm not a man of war and we're dealing here with a war. How do we get Cleopatra to Caesar without Ptolemy's men killing her? We can't endanger the queen."

"Cleopatra, a suggestion," put in Apollodorus. "Remember how we used to play at making you invisible? That's what we have to do now. You've got to get you to Caesar without any risk of Ptolemy's men intercepting you."

"But all entrances to the city are blocked off. They're scared of you showing up there. They know they've got to stop you seeing Caesar," said Josephus bluntly.

Guided by the methodical intelligence of Demetrius, we agreed on the following: With the army already under arms in Ascalon, we would advance toward Pelusium and engage Achilles. Meanwhile, those forces we had in place against Cassius would move against him, in the hope of dividing his superior forces.

We would embark on a merchant ship in Barca and head to Alexandria as fast as possible. We would bribe the port officials to let us anchor in the Kings' Harbor.

In the meantime, the levy would continue, to provide us with the necessary reinforcements. Josephus would stay in Cyrene.

The rest of the plan we would figure out en route to Alexandria. Now the important thing was not to waste time. As the poet says, "Time runs ahead and has no hair on the nape of its neck to hold it back." We had to be installed on that merchant ship that same day and be ready to sail at dawn. If we hurried, there would be no time for anyone to sneak a message to Ptolemy about our plans.

Josephus rushed off to Barca to arrange for our trip.

I bade good-bye to the hospitable Carneades III, without divulging my plans to him. He put his army at my service and showed every sign of joy at the news that Josephus would be staying to recruit troops locally for the army of Cleopatra.

I sent Apollodorus and Charmian ahead to finish off the preparations at the port and then I galloped off to say good-bye to the Amazons. Half a dozen men from my personal guard accompanied me. The wise Demetrius also came along as he was dying to meet Amazons.

I had no plans to neglect my alliance with the Amazons. I wanted to ask them to embark on our warships. Instead of experienced veterans, I wanted Amazons there. I knew they would be itching to attack Alexandria with the advance guard and I'd have to be very persuasive to keep them in the rear. But I was not going to change my mind. What atrocities would they not get up to in my beloved Alexandria, planned by artists and inhabited by gods, these women possessed by martial frenzy? I was trusting that there'd be no need for them to do any actual fighting, if I could meet Caesar successfully and avert a battle between my army and Ptolemy's infantry. But I would not be proposing my own idea but that of Cyrus, as documented by Xenophon. As Hippolyta honored Cyrus, I knew that she would recognize and respect his views.

Drawing near, I left my companions and went forward alone to warn the Amazons that men would be entering their camp. I was rehearsing my arguments about their place in my forces, determined to avoid offending them or leaving them feeling slighted, when suddenly, I heard curses and heart-breaking lamentations.

"I loved it so much!" one was saying.

"That's what women must feel when they lose a child," said another.

There followed more upsetting cries and I rose on my stirrups to see what the problem was.

They were gathered by the Temple of Demeter, some on horseback, others on foot, all of them naked. Their hands, faces, and breasts were covered in blood. They had sacrificed a horse, and as if in answer to my questions, they broke into a hymn:

> *The sun we worship and to him we bring*
> *This horse. To heaven's swiftest power*
> *We offer now the swiftest of our things.*
> *To heaven's most beloved power we send*
> *The most beloved of the things we own,*
> *On which we never war, our earthly sun,*
> *This horse . . .*

What I saw in Hippolyta's hands appalled me; in her left hand was a knife, in the right the enormous purple penis of the horse. She was howling at having castrated the creature. The head with its blond mane lay on the ground, the body was dismembered. Behind me, another Amazon was leaning over the dismembered parts and interpreting the intestines. Hundreds of other

Amazons, seated on horseback, were all menstruating; blood covered the horses' backs and their own thighs. I retraced my steps. Out of the corner of my eye I glimpsed another horse, a fine animal, rearing and kicking against its reins. Its back was bathed in blood as were the legs of the rider. But a river of blood was pouring down the animal's legs. It too had been castrated in readiness for sacrifice.

There was no sign of the dogs. They had all fled the abhorrent scene.

I felt sorry for my double, the pearl. She had no place in this society. As if in response to my thoughts, I saw her in the distance, slinking away toward the wooded riverbank. In her arms she carried an enormous bouquet of yellow flowers; her loosened hair drifted behind her as she fled. For a moment I considered racing toward her, calling her, snatching her up onto my horse, and rescuing her from this fearful world. Then I remembered it had been her decision to leave me and I returned to my retinue, without saying a word about what I'd seen. Not one word about the horse, nor of its penis, nor of the Amazons' bodies stained with its blood, nor of the plunging of the second castrated horse. What I did say was, "We're going back. They are in no condition to receive us. We're going straight back to Cyrene. I'm sorry, Demetrius, but there's no alternative."

Demetrius read my distraught expression and raised no objection. We retraced our steps and met with our men on the crossroads to Barca. I was deeply upset. I could not rid my mind of the sight of those women, both bleeding themselves and, as if that were not enough, splattered with animal blood.

I couldn't eat a thing for the rest of the day.

We made good time to Barca. By the time night had fallen, we were on board the merchant vessel. At all costs we wanted to forestall any rumor of the true identity of the good ship "Cyrene."

I could hardly catch a wink of sleep but before I did finally drop off, I had changed my opinion radically about the Amazons. I would not take them to Alexandria with me or even let them come in the rearguard. They would not form part of my army. Anywhere. They would not be counted among my allies. I found them repulsive. To take them with me would be to guarantee the destruction of all I held dear. They represented barbarism, disorder, the absence of self-control, death to urban life and respect for law, and they would ensure my downfall. I wanted to build an empire; they wanted to ban fire in the oven, to fracture all forms of social order, set up gods to control the city markets, and install altars in city squares, in the gymnasiums, perfumeries, exchanges, arenas, meeting places, pharmacies, barbershops, and of course in all the temples so they could practice their rites there.

The world for them was the fragmented chaos I had dreamed of before Charmian woke me. They despised everything I wanted to uphold and maintain in an orderly Alexandria. The only way to keep them as allies was to discover some land where mankind had never set foot and send them there.

This passed through my mind, as I eventually drifted off to sleep, but I was resolute in my decision, even before expressing it in words.

As we sailed, we worked on getting me in to see Caesar. Immediately after reaching Alexandria, Apollodorus and I passed a small launch, the type merchants used to furnish the palaces of Bruckheion with recently unloaded merchandise. Apollodorus would take me to my palace wrapped in a carpet that supposedly we were delivering to Caesar as a present. The palace servants recognized Apollodorus and they informed Caesar's staff that the gift was undoubtedly from me. Curious, he agreed to see the gift and hear the personal message that came with it.

Once in the presence of Caesar, it was my job to convince him of the value of an alliance with me.

The palace servants were loyal to me. But in case of any problems, this was the ideal place to rescue me from. We knew the palace inside out. Those who lived there worshiped me, but we also brought with the merchandise enough soldiers to carry out a rescue mission.

To use the words of Apollodorus, we were playing at making me invisible. Hidden inside the carpet, I escaped the vigilance of Ptolemy.

It was while on board the ship, I had learned that Josephus and the good-looking Severus had bathed the pearl Cleopatra in wine. They did not share Charmian's reverence for her. "We couldn't run the risk of having your double running around," Josephus would explain to me. "Severus's idea was to bring her as gifts from you a variety of showy presents, beautiful objects of gold, clothes, foodstuffs, along with a bath of aromatic waters. He passed it off as a special preparation from the queen to fend off fatigue and increase beauty." Then four pygmies from the court of King Carneades had bathed her, right in front of Severus. The bathwater contained a considerable quantity of wine hidden in the spices and perfumes.

"When we were planning it," Josephus told me in a whisper, "Severus told me that once there was nothing but the dissolved pearl in the bathtub, he would drink the bathtub empty, right down to the final drop. His dream was that he'd tell to his sons, and his sons would tell their sons, and their sons would tell their sons that one night Severus got drunk drinking a replica of the beautiful Cleopatra."

You all know how my plan to see Caesar worked out. I followed it exactly and I arrived in Caesar's presence on the shoulders of my loyal Apollodorus. Caesar was quite smitten with his good looks and Apollodorus used them to predispose Caesar in my favor before unwrapping the present. Then I seduced him and made him love me. It was the only way to secure him as an ally. "If the goddess thought of it," I said to myself, "so that Dido would not be tempted to betray her son, what's wrong with me trying it too?"

But now that I recall for the last time my stay with the Amazons and my return aboard a merchant ship to Alexandria, I realize that on that trip I made a decision to relinquish my status as a goddess, as Isis on earth, in order to lower myself to the level of a colt, my hooves beating the plain to the rhythm of my gallop, in the pointless race that lovers run in bed. I dismounted from the splendid horse the gods had bestowed on me, to turn myself into part of an animal. It was on board the merchant ship where I opted to switch my two goddess legs for the four legs of a lowly beast. Now I wouldn't take a step by myself. Always I had to have a lover. I became addicted to needing a partner in life; I lived in enslavement, self-abasement, and hysterical self-deception, as I became part of the animal with two backs and four legs that travels along moaning, without achievements, without getting anywhere in the world. Without progress, expending immense effort, but forever circling round the same old point, excavating its grave in the process. Good-bye to the face of the sun that strides toward the kingdom of light and sanity! Now eyes will see only another pair of eyes, like the lowest of the beasts, believing to find in them a divine insight into the reality of things!

I forgot the time I galloped on a bull. As I enjoyed my ride, as I pleasured myself on its body in my journey over the sea, I blinded myself. I failed to see Proteus, the monster who inhabits the island of Pharos, take the shape of a terrifying lizard with the mane of a dragon, curled up on its own tail. I saw nothing when he transformed into an agile tiger with a mottled coat. I didn't even see him wave good-bye to me. I was blind to such a marvel as this! The pity of it!

What happened to me was what happened to my mirror image. Didn't I too dissolve? Didn't I swig down my own throat the dream of what I was going to be? Didn't I end up like Acusilaus in the jaws of vicious Sirens? Or like the pearl Cleopatra in the mouth of the good-looking Severus? Didn't I do that to myself, when I inveigled Caesar into an alliance, in order to get back what rightfully belonged to me? To be what I am, I opted to see myself through the eyes of a man. I drank my self. But do you think I gobbled and guzzled my self without help? Apollodorus, Apollodorus, my loyal friend, my accomplice— forgive my honesty—it was you who urged me toward this act of self-devouring! While our boat was retracing the steps of the bull across the seas, thanks to you, I was undoing all the fine work that the gods had delicately planned, their scheme to endow me with a glorious place in history.

On the boat, prodded by Apollodorus, I went around destroying, ripping apart the designs of the gods. I don't know why this did not release gale-force winds or tidal waves. I turned my back on the gods; they turned theirs on me. I need to understand the consequences of my actions, but just as the Sirens' song blinded the male slaves, the complicity of Apollodorus, who had acted as my friend for all those years—don't fault my absence of sentimentality here—blinded me to understanding. Now I could never be Isis, now I would not be the one to unite two continents with a garland of flowers. I would not defend the territories of the gods. The gods who one day revealed their power in every flower, every ravine, every wave, are soon to fall silent. The trees of Elysium will lose their leaves. Their branches will display no harmony; they will form a chaotic tangle. Nature will lose its power to act, forfeit what the earth produces, the living soul of things, the breath of the World. Mankind will yearn to replace this truncated soul but will not be able to observe its own drives with joy and satisfaction. Dionysus will have to gather his belongings from the royal hall and drag them to the squalid passages of a hideout.

The gods knew that I would pay the price alone. I would lead Caesar to his death. They warned him of it, when they forced him to swim in the waters off Alexandria to save his life, in the rebellion of Ptolemy against my throne. Once he was dead, I would lead Antony, as he would lead me, into the jaws of defeat. I would destroy my design, I would end my life without having lived it. I would bring death upon Egypt. And the gods, I would drive them with me toward oblivion and deceit, to remain outside daily life, to be lost as inconsequential oddities on the verge of being forgotten.

I will achieve my final destruction by dismounting abruptly from my self, by yielding to the quadruple rhythm of that gallop that makes the heart of love resonate, two lives in one, Mark Antony and Cleopatra interlocking their destinies. I, too, hearkened to the song of the Sirens. The Amazons, natural enemies of love, did not come to protect me. My destiny was far worse than those of Acusilaus, Penthesilea, Thalestris, and Orthea. Antony dragged me toward defeat, and now the little man who claims to be my conqueror will gobble me up and murder my Apollodorus, Charmian, my faithful maidservants, and my three children born of Roman fathers, Caesarion, the legitimate heir of Julius Caesar and my twins by Antony.

I say all this, bathed in the blood of my Antony. I speak out in a loud voice to a world that in a few hours will perish with me. The Romans will not pardon me, but their chains are not for me. I will not grace their triumph; I will stain it by my absence. I hitched my star, the dream I received from heaven, first to that of Caesar and then to Antony's, Romans both. I planned to have them as allies, though their people were my enemies and would one day bring to an end the kingdom of the gods on earth, destroying me and mine. Without the governing gods, we are are nothing.

The Romans hated my accomplices, a hate in part unde-
served, for they always remained loyal to Rome and if they accepted my company, it was because they were convinced it would lead to the extension of the Empire. Let it be stated clearly: neither Caesar nor Mark Antony were unfaithful to Rome. Neither of them was an imbecile; the dream of uniting two continents would have been the guarantee of an eternity of sense, but a different future awaits them now, with Asia and Lybia abandoned, isolated on their peninsula and in the petty territory of Europe, convinced of being the center of the world. But the world is much more than you, Rome! It had another luster, it dreamed better dreams, it beat to the rhythm of the souls of various gods who were something more than statues and paintings! You assassinated Julius Caesar, for he dreamed of something bigger than your pettiness. You killed Mark Antony for the same reason, and with those two deaths you were committing long-term suicide. Your future was with me, but you chose to hate me, idiots!

From now on, men and women will be different from those I knew. Romans will dominate, reason will be in control, a cruel sort of reason, stained in men's blood. A blood different from Mark Antony's. Though he took me down roads that were not mine, he knew the tone of voice in which men used to speak to the gods and he saw their faces.

Diomedes the Informer

Those were the last words of Cleopatra and they are close to being mine as well. Diomedes can now pass through the gates of death with a clear conscience. Traitor and informer once, now I have truly been your voice, my queen. That was how you spoke before you were murdered by the Roman vipers who had so much fear of you. That poison did not come from a basket loaded with figs but from an order trembling with fear, a coward's order, for it hid the hand that cast the stone.

Now I will join you in peace. I trust that there, in the place where you await me, the gods still deign to speak with men. For here on earth, as you foresaw, they maintain a mournful silence.

Author's Note

I wrote this book hand in glove with ancient authors. Some were Cleopatra's contemporaries, most of them her enemies, like Virgil, Propertius and Cicero, all of whom despised her. I chose others, ranging from Sophocles to Anyte or Theocritus, convinced Cleopatra could have loved them.

I paid homage to these poets, whom I worship, by frequently turning their verses into adventures. One can recognize fragments of one or another poet in my narrative: Horace in the account of Cleopatra's epic journey from Rome to the coast, an ancient Greek epigram in the section about Cleopatra and the graffiti artists, etc.

Memory and betrayal: I make more mischievous use of some classical texts, inverting their intentions, as when I redeployed a passage from Menander in writing about the Amazons. In Marguerite Yourcenar's translation, Menander says:

> *Reste fidèle, femme, à ta position*
> *De femme, à l'interieur de la maison. L'infâme*
> *Seule hasarde le pied au dehors. C'est au chien*
> *Qu'est la rue, et jamais à la femme de bien.*

Both Cleopatra and the Amazons—and that's one of the reasons I paired them in this book—choose to live a life "unfaithful" to their "nature." Both, like "infamous persons," live "a dog's life," to put it in Menander's terms.

In another case, I borrowed one of Apuleius's narrations in *The Golden Ass,* which he had lifted from a popular Greek tale, and restored it to the mouth of a Greek narrator, one of Cleopatra's gladiator friends.

May these authors pardon my homages, and the readers enjoy them.

—C.B.